ELECTROCHEMISTRY
in
BIOLOGY and MEDICINE

THE ELECTROCHEMICAL SOCIETY SERIES

THE CORROSION HANDBOOK
Edited by
Herbert H. Uhlig

MODERN ELECTROPLATING
Edited by
Allen G. Gray

ELECTROCHEMISTRY IN BIOLOGY
AND MEDICINE
Edited by
Theodore Shedlovsky

VAPOR-PLATING
By
C. F. Powell, I. E. Campbell,
and B. W. Gonser

ELECTROCHEMISTRY

in

BIOLOGY and MEDICINE

Edited by
THEODORE SHEDLOVSKY
Rockefeller Institute for Medical Research

Sponsored by
THE ELECTROCHEMICAL SOCIETY, INC.
New York, N. Y.

JOHN WILEY & SONS, INC., NEW YORK
CHAPMAN & HALL, LIMITED, LONDON
1955

CHEMISTRY
addl.

COPYRIGHT, 1955

BY

JOHN WILEY & SONS, INC.

———

All Rights Reserved

Library of Congress Catalog Card Number: 55–8561

PRINTED IN THE UNITED STATES OF AMERICA

PREFACE

This book grew out of the Symposium on Electrochemistry in Biology and Medicine held in New York during the One Hundred and Third Meeting of the Electrochemical Society in April of 1953. Although some of the chapters are essentially like the papers that were presented at the Symposium, others are the result of further thought and deliberation. The subjects covered include discussions, from several points of view, of membranes, nerve and plant cells, biologically important ions, and applications of polarography, electrocardiography, and electroencephalography in medicine.

The contributing authors are active scientific investigators whose chapters in this volume are based largely on their own experimental work in the fields they discuss. Among them are physicists, chemists, biologists, and medical men, yet they all share an interest in the difficult fundamental electrochemical problems of living processes.

My thanks are due to the members of the Editorial Advisory Board for their service and to all the authors, whose contributions and helpful cooperation with the editor have made this book possible.

THEODORE SHEDLOVSKY
Editor

New York, N. Y.
April, 1955

614

CONTRIBUTORS

CONTENTS

xi

/·

Introduction

THEODORE SHEDLOVSKY *

Electrochemistry is concerned with the electrical properties and behavior of substances and with the transformation of chemical energy into electrical energy or vice versa. It is related to biology and medicine in two ways. First, it provides powerful laboratory methods and tools for the study of biologically important substances, such as viruses, hormones, enzymes and other proteins, and also for the determination in biological environments of such factors as acidity, oxidation-reduction, ionic mobility, activity and diffusion, dielectric constant and dipole moments. Second, living organisms and in fact all living cells are complicated electrochemical systems capable of transforming chemical energy and ionic transport into electrical signals. With appropriate apparatus the neurophysiologist may examine such electrical signals to learn what he can about the functions of nerve and muscle. The medical clinician, armed with a substantial background of correlated, empirical knowledge, observes the electrical signals from the heart or from the brain and thus is aided in arriving at a diagnosis.

It is appropriate, I think, to introduce this symposium by recalling briefly the early history of electrochemistry.

In the eighteenth century, frictional electricity stored in Leyden jars, an invention of von Kleist in 1745, aroused considerable interest in electrical experimentation besides providing occasional entertainment for the laity. Benjamin Franklin's well-known contributions to electrical science belong to this period; but it remained for Luigi Galvani of Bologna, the anatomist, surgeon, and obstetrician who experimented with the effect of Leyden jar discharges upon frogs, to discover the intimate relationship between physiology and electricity. He reported this discovery in 1791 in his two classic papers on the subject. Its importance in the history of electrochemistry and biology warrants the following quotation from his first paper in the *Transactions of the Science Institute of Bologna*.[1]

* From the Rockefeller Institute for Medical Research, New York, N. Y.

1

I had dissected a frog . . . and had placed it upon a table on which there was an electric machine, while I set about doing certain other things. The frog was entirely separated from the conductor of the machine and indeed was at no small distance away from it. While one of those who were assisting me touched lightly and by chance the point of his scalpel to the internal crural nerves of the frog, suddenly all the muscles of its limbs were seen to be so contracted that they seemed to have fallen into tonic convulsions. Another of my assistants, who was making ready to take up certain experiments in electricity with me, seemed to notice that this happened only at the moment when a spark came from the conductor of the machine. He was struck with the novelty of the phenomenon, and immediately spoke to me about it, for I was at the moment occupied with other things and mentally preoccupied. I was at once tempted to repeat the experiment so as to make clear whatever might be obscure in it. For this purpose I took up the scalpel and moved its point close to one or the other of the crural nerves of the frog while at the same time one of my assistants elicited sparks from the electric machine. The phenomenon happened exactly as before. Strong contractions took place in every muscle of the limb, and at the very moment when the sparks appeared the animal was seized as it were with tetanus.

During the next 5 years Galvani occupied himself with other experiments that provided the basis for his theory of "animal electricity," which he formulated into the five following postulated principles. (1) Animals have an electricity peculiar to themselves. (2) The organs to which this animal electricity has the greatest affinity, and in which it is distributed, are the nerves, and the most important organ of its secretion is the brain. (3) The inner substance of the nerve is specialized for conducting electricity, whereas the outer oily layer prevents its dispersal and permits its accumulation. (4) The receivers of the animal electricity are the muscles, and they are, like a Leyden jar, negative on the outside and positive on the inside. (5) The mechanism of the motion consists in the discharge of the electric fluid from the inside of the muscle by way of the nerve to the outside, and this discharge of the muscular Leyden jar furnishes an electrical stimulus to the irritable muscle fibers, which therefore contract. In formulating these principles Galvani was, of course, influenced by the current ideas of his time, which held that animal spirits arose from the blood in the brain.

Galvani's work soon attracted the attention of Alessandro Volta, professor of Natural Philosophy at the University of Pavia. In 1800, two years after Galvani's death, he wrote a memorandum to Sir Joseph Banks in England, "On the Electricity Excited by the Mere Contact of Conducting Substances of Different Kinds." It was read before the Royal Society and published in the *Philosophical Magazine* within a few months. The fact that Volta was completely aware of a profound

relationship between electricity and biology is evident in the following
quotation from the first and last part of his paper.[2]

I have the pleasure of communicating to you, and through you to the Royal
Society, some striking results I have obtained in pursuing my experiments on
electricity excited by the mere mutual contact of different kinds of metal, and
even by that of other conductors, also different from each other, either liquid
or containing some liquid, to which they are properly indebted for their conducting power. The principle of these results is the construction of an apparatus having a resemblance in its effects to the Leyden flask. The apparatus
to which I allude, and which will, no doubt, astonish you, is only the assem-
blage of a number of good conductors of different kinds arranged in a certain
manner. Thirty or more pieces of copper, or, better, silver, applied each to
a piece of tin or zinc, which is much better, and as many strata of salt water
or any other conducting liquid, or pasteboard, skin, etc., well soaked in these
liquids; such strata interposed between every pair of two different metals and
always in the same order are all that is necessary for constructing my new
instrument.

To this apparatus, much more similar to the natural electric organ of the
torpedo or the electric eel, etc., than to the Leyden flask, I would wish to
give the name of the "Artificial Electric Organ." . . .

All the facts which I have related in this long paper in regard to the action
which the electric fluid excited and, when moved by my apparatus, exercises
on the different parts of our body which the current attacks and passes
through; an action which is not instantaneous, but which lasts, and is maintained during the whole time that this current can follow the chain not interrupted in its communications; in a word, an action the effects of which vary
according to the different degrees of excitability in the parts, as has been
seen; all these facts, sufficiently numerous, and others which may still be
discovered by multiplying and varying the experiments of this kind, will open
a very wide field for reflection, and of views, not only curious, but particularly
interesting to Medicine. There will be a great deal to occupy the anatomist,
the physiologist, and the practitioner.

Volta, the physicist, believed that the electricity in his pile, or artificial electric organ, arose from the contact of metals. Sir Humphry
Davy, the chemist who experimented with the pile and observed that
the zinc became more and more corroded, believed that it came from
a chemical change. This controversy lasted for many decades and need
not be reviewed here. Both views were, of course, partly right since
the location of an electromotive force at any particular site in a circuit is not operational. It arises from the summation of all the metal-
metal, metal-liquid, and liquid-liquid junctions.

Perhaps Davy's greatest contribution to electrochemistry was his
assistant at the Royal Institution, Michael Faraday, who was born in
the year Galvani published his work and a year after Franklin's death.
Faraday's contributions, which established the modern science of electrochemistry, are so well known as to require no discussion beyond

stating his law: The magnitude of the chemical effect, in chemical equivalents, is the same at each of the metallic-electrolytic boundaries in an electric circuit and is determined solely by the amount of electricity passed.[3]

In the chapters that follow the authors discuss a wide variety of topics that fall under one or the other of the two categories that have been indicated at the beginning of this introduction relating electrochemistry to biology and medicine. These papers are individual contributions to a symposium which indicate the trend of present work and thinking in a very wide field, some of it highly controversial. They can make no pretense of a glib, exhaustive treatise on the subject but, rather, serve the purpose of highlighting certain spots in the fascinating dark area between physical science and life.

Living matter or a living cell is not a mere assembly of chemical compounds. It is an oriented, dynamic system of complex materials in constant interaction with its environment, a complex chemical laboratory manufacturing many compounds no chemist has yet been able to synthesize, and electrochemical in many if not perhaps all of its functions. Between the inside and the outside of a living cell there exists normally an electrical potential usually of about a tenth of a volt. It is true of plant cells as well as cells of mammals, birds, or fishes. This is the so-called "resting" potential. In certain cells like nerve cells, this potential may be quickly altered and restored again, giving rise to electric "action potentials" in response to various stimuli. In nerve, this happens within a few milliseconds and is in the nature of electric transients. The theory of the fundamental electrochemical mechanism underlying these bio-electric phenomena is now an active and controversial subject of research.

A symposium has the character of a forum, and, of course, no author of the following chapters assumes any responsibility for any others. If the book stimulates thought, discussion, and research, it should also stimulate constructive controversy in a field that was, perhaps, too dormant until relatively recently.

In conclusion I should like to quote a passage that shows remarkable speculative foresight from Felice Fontana's "Treatise on the Venom of the Viper."[4,5]   He was a Florentine who published this work a decade before Galvani's papers.

The considerable size of the nervous cylinders and blood vessels, when compared with the primitive fleshy threads, leads me to suspect that these threads are not put in motion, in any immediate way however, either by the blood or by the nerves. In a word, we are not only ignorant of muscular motion, but we cannot even imagine any way to explain it, and we shall apparently be driven to have recourse to some other principle; that principle, if it be not common electricity, may be something, however, very analogous to it. The electrical gymnotus and torpedo, if they do not render the thing very probable, made it at least possible, and this principle may be believed to follow the most common laws of electricity. It may likewise be more modified in the nerves than in the torpedo or gymnotus. The nerves should be the organs destined to conduct the fluid, and perhaps also to excite it. But here everything yet remains to be done. We must first assure ourselves by certain experiments whether there is really an electrical principle in the contracting muscles; we must determine the laws that this fluid observes in the human body; and after all it will yet remain to be known what it is that excites this principle, and how it is excited. How many things are left in an uncertain state to posterity!

REFERENCES

1. Bern Dibner, *Galvani-Volta*, Burndy Library, Norwalk, Conn., 1952.
2. From Volta's letter (Como in the Milanese, March 20, 1800), to Sir Joseph Banks, "On the Electricity Excited by the Mere Contact of Conducting Substances of Different Kinds" (published in French in *Phil. Trans.*, Part 2, 1800) ; translation in: E. C. Watson, *Am. J. Phys.*, *13*, 397 (1945).
3. D. A. MacInnes, *The Principles of Electrochemistry*, Reinhold Publishing Corp., New York, 1939.
4. Felice Fontana, *Traité sur le Venin de la Vipère*, Florence, 1781.
5. H. E. Hoff, *Ann. Sci.*, *1*, 157 (1936).

2·

Membrane Potentials in
the Donnan Equilibrium

DAVID I. HITCHCOCK [*,1]

HISTORICAL INTRODUCTION

The thermodynamic relations that form the basis of the theory of membrane equilibria were stated by Gibbs [2] in 1875. Since Arrhenius had not yet formulated the theory of electrolytic dissociation, this part of Gibbs's paper contains no mention of ions or of an electric potential difference. Indeed, as Guggenheim [3] has inferred from a later remark of Gibbs, he would have recognized that the difference of electric potential between two phases of different composition "involves the consideration of quantities of which we have no apparent means of physical measurement." Any discussion of membrane potentials must therefore include the admission that it is not possible to measure such a single potential difference, or to calculate its value exactly, without relying on some arbitrary, non-thermodynamic assumption.

The theory of ionic membrane equilibrium was developed by Donnan [4] in 1911. He considered a system in which two solutions containing electrolytes are separated by a membrane freely permeable to most of the ionic species but impermeable to at least one of them. A system in which the non-permeating ion is a protein cation, while the diffusible ions are those of hydrochloric acid, may be represented by the following diagram:

$$z \quad R^{n+}$$
$$y \quad H^{+} \quad \bigg| \quad H^{+} \quad x$$
$$y + z \quad Cl^{-} \quad \bigg| \quad Cl^{-} \quad x$$

The vertical line represents a membrane impermeable to the cation R^{n+}, and the lower-case letters x, y, and z denote the normalities or equivalent concentrations of the ions at equilibrium. This notation is

* From the Department of Physiology, Yale University School of Medicine, New Haven, Conn.

6

consistent with the rule of electroneutrality for each solution. By the application of thermodynamics and the laws of dilute solutions, Donnan obtained a simple equation showing an unequal distribution of the diffusible ions at equilibrium. This may be written in the form

$$x^2 = y(y + z)$$

from which it may be seen that x is greater than y and that $y + z$ is greater than x. The presence of the non-diffusible ion on one side causes the diffusible electrolyte (in this case, hydrochloric acid) to become more concentrated on the other side. Donnan's equation may also be written as an equality of the ionic ratios,

$$r = \frac{x}{y} = \frac{y + z}{x} \qquad (1)$$

and here the ratio r is greater than unity. Donnan also obtained an expression for the electric potential difference commonly known as the membrane potential between the two phases. This expression may be written in the form

$$E_M = \frac{2.303 RT}{F} \log r \qquad (2)$$

for univalent diffusible ions. The value of $2.303\ RT/F$ is 59.15 mv. for 25° C. A positive value of E_M means that the solution containing the non-permeating cation is at the higher (i.e., more positive) electric potential.

Both Donnan [4] and Gibbs [2] pointed out that in such equilibria the two parts of the system will, in general, be at unequal pressures. Osmotic or membrane equilibria have been called by Guggenheim [3,5] partial equilibria, to emphasize the fact that the two phases are not in equilibrium with respect to the non-permeating substance.

The membrane potential is commonly taken to be the electromotive force measured between identical reference electrodes (e.g., calomel half-cells), connected by salt bridges with the two solutions on opposite sides of the membrane. This would be a measurement of the true membrane potential only if the liquid junction potentials at the ends of the salt bridges were equal and opposite. It is assumed that this is true when the salt bridge is a saturated potassium chloride solution, although no way to prove this assumption is known. The same assumption is made in estimating the activities of single ionic species (cf. Scatchard [6]). The results reported by Loeb [7] for membrane potentials in the equilibrium of proteins with electrolytes are all based on this assumption.

If a Donnan system at equilibrium is converted into a galvanic cell by inserting into the two solutions identical electrodes, reversible to one of the diffusible ion species, the resulting electromotive force must be zero. This conclusion, based on thermodynamic reasoning, was stated by Donnan and Allmand,[8] Michaelis,[9] and Hill.[10] As a result of this property of the system, it is possible to obtain a rough estimate of the membrane potential by making a measurement in the absence of the membrane, provided the solutions have first come to equilibrium across the membrane. The electromotive force between such reversible electrodes, in direct contact with the two solutions, is measured after the solutions have been connected by a salt bridge. This is essentially what Loeb[7] did in obtaining the figures reported as "calculated P.D." or "hydrogen electrode potentials." The solutions were placed in turn in a vessel provided with a hydrogen electrode and a salt bridge leading to a calomel half-cell; the difference between the e.m.f. readings obtained with the two equilibrated solutions was numerically equal to the e.m.f. between two calomel half-cells, each containing saturated potassium chloride, which made contact with the experimental solutions on opposite sides of the membrane. Similar results may be obtained with a glass electrode in place of the hydrogen electrode. Scatchard, Batchelder, and Brown[11] used two silver-silver chloride electrodes dipping directly into the two solutions, which were connected by a salt bridge. The rational basis for this procedure may be understood by considering the following galvanic cells:

$$\underset{e_1}{\text{Ag, AgCl;}} \quad \text{HCl,} \underset{E_M}{\text{membrane:}} \quad \text{HCl + protein;} \underset{e_2}{\text{AgCl, Ag}} \quad \text{(I)}$$

$$E_I = e_1 + E_M + e_2 = 0$$

$$\underset{e_3}{\text{Hg, HgCl;}} \quad \underset{e_4}{\text{KCl(sat.):}} \quad \text{HCl,} \underset{E_M}{\text{membrane:}}$$

$$\text{HCl + protein:} \underset{e_5}{\text{KCl(sat.);}} \quad \underset{-e_3}{\text{HgCl, Hg}} \quad \text{(II)}$$

$$E_{II} = e_3 + e_4 + E_M + e_5 - e_3 = E_M + E_J$$

Here E_J is written for the net liquid junction potential, the algebraic sum of e_4 and e_5.

$$\underset{e_1}{\text{Ag, AgCl;}} \quad \underset{-e_4}{\text{HCl:}} \quad \underset{-e_5}{\text{KCl(sat.):}} \quad \text{HCl + protein;} \underset{e_2}{\text{AgCl, Ag}} \quad \text{(III)}$$

$$E_{III} = e_1 - e_4 - e_5 + e_2 = E_I - E_{II}$$

$$-E_{III} = E_{II} = E_M + E_J$$

The last equation shows that cells II and III have equal and opposite electromotive forces if that of cell I is zero. Neither cell, however, gives a measure of the true membrane potential E_M unless it can be shown that E_J is zero.

EXPERIMENTS

Some years ago Nims [12] expressed the opinion that the e.m.f. of cell II would not be changed appreciably by removal of the membrane. This prediction was approximately verified by experiments in which the membrane was pierced by a thick needle, and the result was mentioned in textbooks.[13] In order to avoid flow through the hole, diffusion of potassium chloride, and the possible effect of large areas of intact membrane, further experiments were carried out by starting with cell I instead of cell II and by placing the electrodes and solutions, after equilibration across the membrane, in separate glass vessels with side arms dipping into a beaker of the outer solution. This constituted cell IV:

$$\text{Ag, AgCl; \quad HCl: \quad HCl + protein; \quad AgCl, Ag} \qquad \text{(IV)}$$

Readings for cell III were obtained with the side arms of the same vessels dipping into a beaker of saturated potassium chloride. The e.m.f. of cell V,

Glass electrode;   HCl: KCl(sat.):

$$\text{HCl + protein; \quad glass electrode} \qquad \text{(V)}$$

was the difference between e.m.f. readings used for the determination of pH. The actual cell included only one glass electrode of the bulb type, supported in a water-jacketed vessel at $25° \pm 0.05°$ C. The solution was connected by a salt bridge of saturated potassium chloride with a reference half-cell, also at $25°$ C. Reproducible liquid junctions were made by means of a three-way, $120°$ stopcock of 2-mm. bore.

Protein solutions were prepared from granular gelatin (Cooper's), purified according to Northrop and Kunitz,[14] or edestin, extracted from hemp seed, crystallized according to Osborne,[15] and washed free from salt. One gram of air-dried protein was treated with 100 ml. of dilute hydrochloric acid. The gelatin was dissolved by warming to $50°$ C., and the edestin by rubbing with a glass rod. In each case, a small residue was removed by filtration. The protein concentrations, as determined by drying at $110°$ C. for a day or two, were 8.7 grams of gelatin per liter of initial solution and 8.1 grams of edestin per liter.

Membranes were prepared from USP collodion in test tubes about 25 by 100 mm. The inside of the tube was twice coated, each application being followed by drying until the odor of ether was no longer perceptible. After the membranes had been washed in distilled water and the hard rim had been cut off, each was fitted with a rubber stopper, held tightly in place by a stretched rubber band, and tested for leaks by gentle squeezing. Membranes prepared in this simple way proved to be remarkably strong and free from leaks if they were made in dry weather. Before use, each membrane was soaked in dilute acid of the same concentration as that to be used for the external solution.

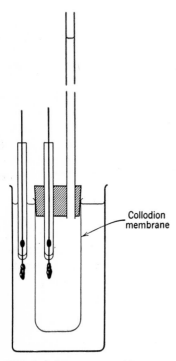

Silver-silver chloride electrodes were prepared either by the thermal-electrolytic method of Harned,[16] the electrolytic method of Brown,[17] or by fusing a silver wire to a platinum wire and then forming silver chloride by electrolysis. In each case, it was necessary to have a good seal of the supporting platinum wire through the end of a soft glass tube. Electrodes differing by more than 0.2 mv. in the same solution were not used.

The electromotive force across the membrane (cell I) was measured to 0.1 mv. by means of a reliable potentiometer and galvanometer. For the other cells it was necessary to add to the measuring circuit a thermionic ampli-

Fig. 1. Osmometer with silver chloride electrodes, used to study the Donnan equilibrium in systems containing protein and acid.

fier (Leeds and Northrup Co.) or electronic bridge (Hitchcock and Mauro [18]).

Figure 1 is a diagram of the system used for equilibration, with silver chloride electrodes to form cell I. The initial volume of the inner solution was 25 ± 2 ml., whereas that of the outer solution was 250 ml. The temperature remained constant within 1° during each period of equilibration and was always within 2° or 25° C.

Figure 2 shows the time course of the equilibration in terms of the electromotive force between the silver chloride electrodes on opposite sides of the membrane (cell I). The initial values could be varied at

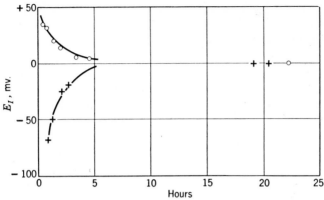

Fig. 2. Time course of approach to the Donnan equilibrium in systems containing gelatin and hydrochloric acid.

will by starting with different concentrations of acid in the two compartments, but in each case E_I was practically zero within 8 hours and
remained constant thereafter. The osmotic pressure difference between
the two solutions reached a maximum value in about 8 hours and did
not change more than a few millimeters of water in 24 or 48 hours.

In the experiment represented by the lower curve of Fig. 2, the initial concentrations of total acid were 0.01 N in the gelatin solution and
0.001 N in the outer solution. The temporary negative potential of
the inner electrode may be explained by unequal electrode potentials,
added to a diffusion potential during the outward diffusion of the acid.
The data plotted in the upper curve of Fig. 2 were obtained by starting with 0.001 N acid in both compartments. The initial positive potential of the inner electrode may be explained as a diffusion potential
caused by unequal ionic mobilities as acid moved in to establish the
equilibrium state, in which Cl^- was more concentrated in the inner
solution. Most of the experiments were begun with equal initial concentrations of acid throughout.

In order to determine the influence on electromotive force of the
excess pressure on the protein solution, two experiments were set up
with a T-tube inserted near the lower end of the straight osmometer
tube. After equilibrium had been reached and E_I measured, the pressure was decreased from about 23 cm. to only 2 cm. of water by allowing the liquid in the osmometer tube to run out through the T-tube.
This caused a decrease in e.m.f. of 0.1 mv. in one case and zero in the
other. Although the excess pressure is necessary for equilibrium, it is
without appreciable effect on electromotive force.

After E_I had been measured, equilibrated solutions were removed from contact with the membrane by the following procedure. A short rubber tube was put on the upper end of the osmometer tube and closed with a screw clamp, in order to keep unequilibrated solution in the tube. The membrane with its tube was lifted out of the external solution, wiped on the outside, and held over a dry beaker. The membrane was then pierced several times with a needle, so that the equilibrated protein solution flowed into the beaker. The electrodes were supported

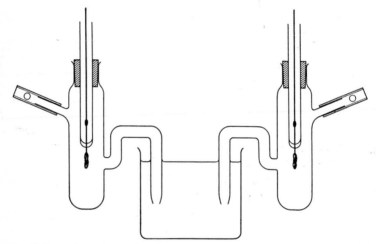

Fig. 3.   Cells used to determine the effect of removal of the membrane and to estimate membrane potentials in the absence of the membrane.

by small rubber stoppers in two Ostwald electrode vessels, which were then filled by suction with the two solutions. Cell IV was constructed by dipping the side arms of the Ostwald vessels into a beaker containing some of the inner or outer solution, as shown in Fig. 3. The effect of time for diffusion at the junction in cell IV was investigated in three cases by leaving the cell with a free junction for 17 or 18 hours; the changes in E_{IV} were -0.1, $+0.1$, and $+0.5$ mv.

In most of the experiments cell III was constructed by flushing out the side arms of the Ostwald vessels with a few drops of solution and dipping them into a beaker of saturated potassium chloride (Fig. 3).

The electromotive force of cell V was obtained as the difference between the e.m.f. values obtained with the two solutions in the glass electrode pH cell at 25° C. (Hitchcock and Mauro [18]).

In about half of the experiments, the total chloride concentrations of the inner and outer solutions were determined by the modified

Volhard method of Wilson and Ball.[19] Samples were digested on a
steam bath with 10 ml. of 0.01 N silver nitrate and 2 ml. of concentrated nitric acid until the silver chloride had coagulated and the
supernatant liquid was no longer cloudy. After the solutions had been
cooled with ice water, the back titration with 0.02 N potassium thiocyanate was carried out rapidly. The method was standardized by
analyzing samples of 2 and 7 ml. of 0.01 N hydrochloric acid. Recovery of known amounts of chloride in gelatin solutions was complete
within 1%.

RESULTS

Tables 1 and 2 give the electromotive force data obtained with
gelatin and edestin solutions. The values of E_I differ from zero by
only a few tenths of a millivolt, indicating that each system was practically in equilibrium. The values of E_{IV}, obtained with a direct liquid
junction, tend to be somewhat less than E_I, but the differences are not
more than 2 or 3 mv. for gelatin and 3 or 4 mv. for edestin. If the
only effect of the removal of the membrane had been to abolish the
membrane potential E_M, it might have been expected that E_{IV} would
have been equal to the difference between the electrode potentials,

TABLE 1. ELECTROMOTIVE FORCE IN MEMBRANE EQUILIBRIUM OF 0.87%
GELATIN WITH HYDROCHLORIC ACID

Date, 1953	Initial Acid N	ΔP mm. H$_2$O	E_I mv.	E_{IV} mv.	$-E_{III}$ mv.	$-E_V$ mv.	pH_i
3/27	0.001	310	0.2	−0.5	28.0	30.5	3.759
3/27	0.001	332	0.3	−2.5	31.0	31.3	3.740
9/22	0.001	320	−0.1	−2.0	29.6	33.9	3.846
9/22	0.001	330	0.0	−2.0	29.9	32.2	3.751
10/30	0.002	372	±0.1	....	24.7	24.6	3.269
10/30	0.002	373	±0.2	....	24.6	24.8	3.286
9/30	0.005	261	0.4	0.0	12.5	13.5	2.637
9/30	0.005	251	0.0	0.0	12.9	13.2	2.607
10/12	0.005	231	0.4	0.0	12.3	12.0	2.661
10/12	0.005	234	0.5	−0.7	12.9	12.3	2.637
10/17	0.005	248	....	....	13.6	....	....
10/17	0.005	242	....	....	13.5	....	....

ΔP = Osmotic pressure difference.
E_I: AgCl electrodes, measured through membrane.
E_{IV}: AgCl electrodes, direct liquid junction.
E_{III}: AgCl electrodes with KCl bridge.
E_V: Glass electrodes with KCl bridge.
pH_i: Refers to the inner solution; pH_o may be obtained by subtracting
$-E_V/59.15$.

TABLE 2. ELECTROMOTIVE FORCE IN MEMBRANE EQUILIBRIUM OF 0.81%
EDESTIN WITH ACID

Date, 1953	Initial Acid N	ΔP mm. H_2O	E_I mv.	E_{IV} mv.	$-E_{III}$ mv.	$-E_V$ mv.	pH_i
5/25	0.001 *	350	−0.5	−4.5	32.0	31.2	3.876
5/25	0.001 *	364	0.0	−2.5	30.0	32.8	3.797
11/23	0.002 *	417	±0.9	−3.0	26.9	27.8	3.288
11/23	0.002 *	414	±1.1	....	26.2	25.1	3.271
6/3	0.02 †	277	−0.6	−3.5	22.0	20.8	3.752
6/3	0.02 †	286	−0.3	−1.9	21.6	22.6	3.733

* Hydrochloric acid.
† Acetic acid, with 0.001 N sodium chloride.

which is usually assumed to be E_{III}, the e.m.f. obtained with the salt bridge. Since this was not the case, it must be inferred that cell IV contained a liquid junction potential E_L which was only a few millivolts less than the membrane potential E_M.

The agreement between the values of E_{III} and E_V, which should theoretically be perfect, is best in the experiments dated 10/30 in Table 1. On this occasion a single silver chloride electrode was placed in the water-jacketed vessel beside the glass electrode. After equilibration across the membrane, the solutions were placed successively in this vessel, and the electromotive force of the cell without liquid junction

Glass electrode; inner or outer solution; AgCl, Ag

was measured. Since the e.m.f. of this cell depends on the product of the activities of the hydrogen and chloride ions, its value should have been the same for the two solutions if the Donnan equilibrium had really been attained. The actual values were 189.4 and 189.5 mv. in one experiment, 190.5 and 190.7 mv. in the other. The value of E_{III} was obtained by difference, from the e.m.f. of cells containing the silver chloride electrode and the reference electrode with the salt bridge. E_V was obtained in the same way with the glass electrode instead of the silver chloride electrode. The failure of other values of E_{III} and E_V to agree well may have been due to the sensitivity of silver chloride electrodes to mechanical shock; in most of the experiments the glass tube of a silver chloride electrode was withdrawn from the stopper on the membrane and inserted into the stopper used on the Ostwald vessel.

Table 3 provides a comparison of ion ratios calculated in three ways: from total chloride concentrations, as given by analysis; from chloride

TABLE 3. ION RATIOS IN MEMBRANE EQUILIBRIA OF GELATIN AND
HYDROCHLORIC ACID

Date, 1953	$[Cl]_i$ mEq./ liter	$[Cl]_o$ mEq./ liter	$\dfrac{[Cl]_i}{[Cl]_o}$	$\dfrac{(Cl^-)_i}{(Cl^-)_o}$	$\dfrac{(H^+)_o}{(H^+)_i}$
9/22	3.07	0.78	3.93	3.17	3.74
9/22	3.11	0.77	4.04	3.20	3.50
10/30	5.21	1.65	3.16	2.62	2.61
10/30	5.16	1.63	3.16	2.61	2.62
9/30	8.98	4.70	1.91	1.63	1.69
9/30	9.12	4.68	1.95	1.66	1.67
10/12	8.68	4.72	1.84	1.61	1.60
10/12	8.77	4.68	1.87	1.65	1.61
10/17	9.12	4.77	1.91	1.70	....
10/17	8.94	4.70	1.90	1.69	....

$[Cl]$ = total chloride, by analysis.
(Cl^-) = chloride ion activity, from E_{III}.
(H^+) = hydrogen ion activity, from E_V.

ion activities, as given by E_{III}; and from hydrogen ion activities, as given by E_V. The figures in the two last columns would have agreed perfectly if E_{III} and E_V had been identical, and the agreement was quite good in six cases. The concentration ratios, however, were all considerably greater than either of the activity ratios. This may have been due to combination of chloride ion with protein, so that the concentration of free chloride ions was less than the total chloride concentration in the protein solution.

DISCUSSION

The principal result of the present work is the finding that the electromotive force, in these equilibrium systems, is not greatly affected by the absence of the membrane. Because of this fact, it is necessary to modify an earlier assertion [20] that "the difference of potential must depend on the fact that the protein cannot get through the membrane." It would be better to say that even though a membrane may provide the constraint necessary for the establishment of the Donnan equilibrium in systems containing protein and acid, the removal of the membrane, after the difference in pressure has been abolished, does not necessarily produce any great or rapid change at the boundary. This may be a result of the very low mobility of the protein. The comparison of E_I and E_{IV} indicates that cell IV must have included a diffusion potential E_L not much less than the membrane potential E_M of cell I.

The liquid junction potential E_L might be estimated by the formulas of Planck and Henderson, which are admittedly inexact (cf. Mac-Innes [21]). It can be shown that the Planck equation becomes identical with equation 2, the Donnan equation, if it is assumed that the protein ions have a negligibly low mobility. With this assumption, the Henderson equation yields a somewhat lower value for E_L. The value calculated by either equation would be less if a mobility greater than zero were assigned to the protein cation.

The results obtained in this work on the Donnan equilibrium differ sharply from those obtained with the dried collodion membranes of Michaelis.[22] When such a membrane separates 0.1 N and 0.01 N potassium chloride solutions, provided with silver chloride electrodes, an electromotive force of 90 to 100 mv. may be measured. On piercing the membrane, this falls to 54 mv., the e.m.f. of the ordinary concentration cell with transference. The difference may be taken as the membrane potential, since in this case E_L is probably close to zero.

The results of this work may have a bearing on the validity of a theory of bioelectric potentials in excitable tissues. Hodgkin [23] considers that the resting potential in muscle or nerve arises from a condition resembling the Donnan equilibrium, with K^+ and Cl^- playing the part of diffusible ions, unequally distributed according to the Donnan ratio. Activity of the tissue is supposed to be accompanied by a sudden increase in permeability to Na^+, which has hitherto been a non-permeating ion outside of the cell. Entrance of Na^+ into the cell is believed to account for a reversal in sign of the potential difference at the peak of activity. The present experiments are by no means a fair model for testing this theory, because of the very low mobility of the protein cation. They do suggest, however, that in ionic membrane equilibria the removal of the membrane, corresponding to an increase in permeability, may not have a very significant effect. There is need for further model experiments with a membrane impermeable to some ion of high mobility.

SUMMARY

Measurements were made of e.m.f. in the Donnan equilibrium of systems containing dilute solutions of protein and acid. Removal of the membrane produced a decrease of no more than 2 to 4 mv. in electromotive force, whereas the membrane potentials, as estimated by the usual arbitrary assumption, were of the order of 12 to 34 mv. Ion ratios, as calculated from analyses for total chloride, were definitely greater than those calculated from the e.m.f. of cells with salt bridges, indicating a probable combination of some of the chloride ion with protein.

Acknowledgment. The writer is indebted to Dr. Alexander Mauro for many helpful discussions during the progress of this work.

REFERENCES

1. Aided by a grant from the Medical Fluid Research Fund of the Yale University School of Medicine.
2. J. W. Gibbs, *Collected Works, 1,* 83, Longmans, Green and Co., New York, 1928.
3. E. A. Guggenheim, in: F. G. Donnan and A. Haas, eds., *A Commentary on the Scientific Writings of J. Willard Gibbs, 1,* 198–200, Yale University Press, New Haven, 1936.
4. F. G. Donnan, *Z. Elektrochem., 17,* 572 (1911); *Chem. Revs., 1,* 73 (1924).
5. E. A. Guggenheim, *Modern Thermodynamics by the Methods of Willard Gibbs,* pp. 24, 82, 140, Methuen & Co., London, 1933.
6. G. Scatchard, in: E. J. Cohn and J. T. Edsall, *Proteins, Amino Acids, and Peptides as Ions and Dipolar Ions,* pp. 44–48, Reinhold Publishing Corp., New York, 1943.
7. J. Loeb, *Proteins and the Theory of Colloidal Behavior,* 2nd ed., p. 177, McGraw-Hill Book Co., New York, 1924.
8. F. G. Donnan and A. J. Allmand, *J. Chem. Soc., 105,* 1941 (1914).
9. L. Michaelis, *Die Wasserstoffionenkonzentration,* 2nd ed., p. 190, J. Springer, Berlin, 1922.
10. A. V. Hill, *Proc. Roy. Soc. (London), A 102,* 705 (1923).
11. G. Scatchard, A. C. Batchelder, and A. Brown, *J. Am. Chem. Soc., 68,* 2320 (1946).
12. L. F. Nims, personal conversation, ca. 1941.
13. D. I. Hitchcock, *Physical Chemistry for Students of Biology and Medicine,* 4th ed., p. 176, Little, Brown & Co., Boston, 1953; also in: R. Höber, *Physical Chemistry of Cells and Tissues,* p. 68, Blakiston Co., Philadelphia, 1945.
14. J. H. Northrop and M. Kunitz, *J. Gen. Physiol., 11,* 477 (1928).
15. T. B. Osborne, *J. Am. Chem. Soc., 24,* 28 (1902).
16. H. S. Harned, *J. Am. Chem. Soc., 51,* 417 (1929).
17. A. S. Brown, *J. Am. Chem. Soc., 56,* 646 (1934).
18. D. I. Hitchcock and A. Mauro, *Yale J. Biol. Med., 22,* 309 (1950).
19. D. W. Wilson and E. G. Ball, *J. Biol. Chem., 79,* 221 (1928).
20. D. I. Hitchcock, *J. Gen. Physiol., 5,* 661 (1923).
21. D. A. MacInnes, *The Principles of Electrochemistry,* pp. 231–236, Reinhold Publishing Corp., New York, 1939.
22. L. Michaelis, *J. Gen. Physiol., 8,* 33 (1925).
23. A. L. Hodgkin, *Biol. Revs., Cambridge Phil. Soc., 26,* 339 (1951).

3.

Transport of Ions
Across Charged Membranes

GEORGE SCATCHARD *

My own interest in charged membranes has been the search for some that are impermeable to proteins and as highly selective as possible to small cations or anions. An ion exchanger membrane that meets these requirements well can be made sufficiently thick to be treated as a bulk phase. Many properties may be measured. It may make a satisfactory model for protein containing membranes, which also have ionic charges fixed in a rigid lattice.

MEMBRANES

These membranes should not be pictured as diaphragms; that is, as very thin plates with holes that are small but not nearly so small as the thickness of the plates, for the holes are very small relative to the thickness of the membrane. They should not be pictured with right-cylindrical circular pores, like a honeycomb with rounded cells. They are much more like a sand pile, a brush pile, a sponge, or a dish of spaghetti. The membrane consists of a continuous resin network and a continuous aqueous network, which are interpenetrating. In ion exchangers the volumes of the two are about equal. The interstices in the lattice are continuously branching and coming together. One common type of ion exchanger is based on polystyrene (polyvinylbenzene)

cross-linked with divinylbenzene. The unit is $(RC_6H_4)-(HC)-(CH_2)$,

and the cross link is $(CH_2)-(CH)-(RC_6H_3)-(CH)-(CH_2)$. An-

* From the Department of Chemistry, Massachusetts Institute of Technology, Cambridge, Mass.

other common lattice is based on phenol-formaldehyde. The unit is —(RC₆H₂OH)—(CH₂)—, and the cross link is $\rangle$(C₆H₂OH)—. The most useful exchangers for most purposes are the strong electrolytes, in which R is SO_3^- for the cation exchanger and a quaternary ammonium ion for the anion exchanger. The corresponding weak acid or base, in which R is COO^- or a tertiary ammonium ion, might serve as an even better model of a protein membrane.

Juda et al. have published a rather complete description of one membrane,[1] Neptonic CR-51, of the phenol-formaldehyde sulfonate type. It contains 1.26 milliequivalents of sulfonate per cubic centimeter of resin, or 1.72 milliequivalents per gram of water. The distribution of sodium chloride between membrane and water indicates that the activity coefficient of sodium chloride in the membrane changes rapidly with its concentration. The conductance of the sodium resin is 0.0080 ohm^{-1} cm.$^{-1}$, which is about a fifth of the conductance of sodium ion in 1.26 aqueous solution. The increased conductance due to 0.35 milliequivalents of sodium chloride per cubic centimeter is 0.010, which is about a third of its conductance in water. They have also measured the quantities that can be measured for thinner films, the transfer of water, and of salt and the electromotive force. Through the sodium form of the resin without sodium chloride, 300 cc. of water are transferred per equivalent of electricity.

ELECTRICAL TRANSFERENCE

A cell for the measurement of either transference or electromotive force consists of a pair of reversible electrodes and one or more solutions between. If two solutions meet at a liquid junction we will indicate the junction by |; if they are separated by an uncharged membrane we will use |O|; if the membrane has a fixed negative charge, and is therefore a cation exchanger, we will use |C|; and we will designate an anion exchanger membrane by |A|.

For the measurement of a transference number in solution, there is but a single solution, and we represent the cell as

Electrode α, solution, electrode ω

or, for a specific case,

Ag-AgCl, NaCl(0.1 *M*), AgCl-Ag

We will consider that there are three components in the system: sodium ion, chloride ion, and water; and one restriction: the solution must be everywhere neutral. If positive current goes through the cell from left to right, for each equivalent of electricity one chloride ion is used up at α by the reaction $Ag + Cl^- = AgCl + \epsilon^-$, and one is formed at ω by the reverse reaction. About 0.4 Na^+ goes to the right and about 0.6 Cl^- to the left. There is also a transference of a certain amount of water. We are interested only in the motion of the components relative to each other, therefore we may consider any one of them as standing still. Since the days of Hittorff, it has been customary to consider motion relative to the water. Therefore, the net effect of the current is to transfer 0.4 equivalent of sodium chloride from α to ω. The transference number of water is zero, that of sodium ion is 0.4, and that of chloride ion is -0.6.†

As soon as this transfer starts there is a deficiency of sodium chloride at electrode α, and an excess at electrode ω; sodium chloride begins to diffuse from right to left near the electrodes. In a successful transference experiment, the portions for analysis are taken large enough to include all parts that have changed in concentration due to diffusion.

It is considerably more difficult to measure transference in a cell containing a membrane in which the transference numbers are not the same as in the solution. Consider the cell

$$Ag\text{-}AgCl, \ NaCl(0.1 \ M) \,|\, C \,|\, NaCl(0.1 \ M), \ AgCl\text{-}Ag$$

If we consider the water to be fixed, the membrane must be considered to move. It is more convenient to consider that the membrane is stationary. If the membrane is Neptonic CR-51, the transference number of the sodium ion is more than 0.9 and that of chloride ion less than -0.1. As a result, sodium chloride will accumulate at the right of the membrane as well as at electrode ω, and there will be a deficiency at the left of the membrane as well as at electrode α. As soon as the transference begins, sodium chloride will diffuse away from the right-hand side of the membrane and toward the left-hand side, both through the solutions and through the membrane. If the transference numbers in the membrane vary with the concentration, the transference will

† There is a great advantage in defining the transference number of component i, t_i, as the number of moles of i carried in the direction of the positive current per equivalent of electricity so that the transference number of an anion, t_i, like its valence, z_i, is negative, for it is much more important to know which way a component travels than how fast it goes. This is particularly true of a neutral component, which may have either a positive or negative transference number. The transport number or fraction of the current carried, T_i, is then equal to $t_i z_i$, which is positive for any ion and zero for any neutral component.[2] It is also convenient to consider the mobility, u_i, as having the same sign as the transference number.

correspond to a higher concentration than 0.1 M because of the easier availability of chloride ion on the right-hand side. The experimental difficulties are also greater because now the portion for analysis must contain everything to the very edge of the membrane.

The concentration changes at the edges of the membrane are compensated to a small extent by the transfer of water, which has a transference number of 300/18 in this membrane. The transference number of water is

$$t_w = \frac{u_w m_w}{\Sigma_j z_j u_j m_j}$$

in which m is the number of moles per kilogram of water. The mobility of the water when the membrane is stationary is minus one times the mobility of the membrane when the water is stationary. The mobility of the membrane so calculated is almost the same as that of sodium ion relative to the water. I would expect it to be of the same order of magnitude but not so large.

ELECTRICAL POTENTIALS

The simplest cell for the measurement of electrical potential differences consists of two different electrodes and a single solution. It is not interesting for our present discussion. The next simplest cell is two identical electrodes with two solutions of different concentrations but the same electrolyte and with no membrane. An example would be

$$\text{Ag-AgCl, NaCl(0.1 } M)\,|\,\text{NaCl(0.01 } M), \text{ AgCl-Ag}$$

The electrical potential difference for the general case with any number of liquid junctions or membranes is given by

$$E\mathfrak{F}/RT = -\Delta G/RT = E_{0\alpha}\mathfrak{F}/RT$$

$$- \Sigma_i \nu_{i\alpha} \ln a_{i\alpha} - \int_\alpha^\omega \Sigma_i t_1 \, d\ln a_i - \Sigma_i \nu_{i\omega d} \ln a_{i\omega} - E_{0\omega}\mathfrak{F}/RT$$

in which, $-\Delta G$ is the decrease in Gibbs free energy per equivalent of electricity passed through the cell; $E_{0\alpha}$ and $E_{0\omega}$ are the standard electrode potentials, written as anode potentials; $\nu_{i\alpha}$ and $\nu_{i\omega}$ are the number of moles of component i formed at electrodes α and ω per equivalent of electricity, and the sums include all components, charged or uncharged.

In this special case, the electrode potentials cancel, the water may be considered stationary, and the equation reduces to

$$E\mathfrak{F}/RT = -\int_\alpha^\omega t_{\mathrm{Na}}\, d \ln a_{\mathrm{Na}}a_{\mathrm{Cl}}$$

Relating the electrical potential difference to the change in free energy, or even stating that there is a change in free energy, requires more than classical thermodynamics, for the system is not in equilibrium. As soon as the two solutions are placed in contact, sodium chloride will diffuse from left to right. A successful measurement requires that the concentrations at the electrodes be not changed measurably either by diffusion or by the electrical current. In the usual potentiometric method a very small current flow is imposed on the diffusion, first in one direction and then in the other, and the electrical potential difference is taken as the electromotive force when no current flows.

To justify our expression, we use the most fundamental principle of non-equilibrium thermodynamics, which is so basic that it is often not stated, that in a system not too far from equilibrium the potentials such as temperature, pressure, and chemical potentials exist at each point, and that the chemical potential of any component is a function only of the temperature, pressure, and composition at that point and does not depend upon their rates of change with distance or with time. Professor Debye has offered the criterion that the change in composition must be small over distances comparable to the thickness of the ionic atmosphere, which is about three over the square root of the ionic strength angstroms in aqueous solutions. There is a second criterion that depends somewhat upon the geometry of the apparatus. The equations in general assume constant temperature, but the diffusion across a boundary may absorb or evolve heat, and thus tend to change the temperature. Unless the conduction of heat away from the junction is sufficiently rapid to make the temperature difference very small, there may be an effect on the electrical potential.[3]

Provided that these two criteria are satisfied, it is not necessary to know the details of the boundary between two solutions of different concentrations of the same salt, for the transference numbers are single-valued functions of the mean activity since all are single-valued functions of the concentration. If the solute composition is different on the two sides, however, we do need to know the details of the composition of the boundary layer. We need to consider only the integral $\int_\alpha^\omega \Sigma_i t_i\, d \ln a_i$, and in many cases the integrand will be sufficient. In the ideal case with $a_i = m_i$ the integrand becomes $(\Sigma_i u_i\, dm_i)/(\Sigma_j z_j u_j m_j)$. Obviously the integral depends upon the relation of each m_j to m_i.

The simplest boundary is the Henderson,[4] or mixture, boundary in which each $m_j = (1 - x)m_{j\alpha} + xm_{j\omega}$, and x varies from zero to unity across the boundary, so that each portion is equivalent to $(1 - x)$ parts of solution α and x parts of solution ω.

The initial boundary in the Clark cell for pH measurement [5] is a mixture boundary about 1 cm. thick. Diffusion is so slow that the change from the initial state is usually unimportant during a measurement. A flowing junction [6-8] is an extremely thin mixture boundary that is maintained in a quasi-stationary state by continued renewal. Any boundary formed by shearing, such as the boundary at the stopcock in the MacInnes glass electrode,[9] is initially a mixture boundary, usually quite thin.

The change with time of a boundary at which two solutions meet initially in a plane is closely reproduced when the flow of a flowing junction is stopped.[8] The theory has been studied by Taylor [10] and by Guggenheim.[11]

The first theoretical study of a liquid junction was that of Max Planck,[12] who treated the case of an ideal mixture of any number of ions, each with valence $+z$ or $-z$, in a region between two boundaries; each concentration is kept constant at $m_{j\alpha}$ or $m_{j\omega}$ outside the respective boundary, and between the boundaries a stationary state is maintained by diffusion without current flow. This type of junction requires a diaphragm or membrane, at the opposite sides of which are the solutions α and ω. Their compositions may be kept constant by continuous flow. This is the simplest model of a membrane and should be the (idealized) limit which a charged membrane approaches as the fixed charge on the lattice approaches zero. Although Planck makes very clever use of the fact that the sum of the molal concentrations of cations is the same as that of the anions, his answer is an implicit exponential equation in

$$\int_\alpha^\omega \Sigma_i t_i\, d \ln a_i.$$

Cumming and Gilchrist [13] have compared the values calculated by the Henderson and Planck equations for boundaries between hydrochloric acid and the alkali chlorides. Their discussion of the thickness of the junction is irrelevant, for both expressions are independent of the thickness. For a single salt they both reduce to the classical Nernst expression. For equal total concentrations they also agree. If the concentration ratio is greater than ten, they differ by 10–20%. This difference depends entirely on the different assumptions as to the structure of the boundary layer.

In a cell such as

$$\text{Ag-AgCl, NaCl}(\alpha)\,|\,\text{C}\,|\,\text{NaCl}(\omega),\ \text{AgCl-Ag}$$

the membrane should be regarded as stationary, therefore,

$$\Sigma_i t_i\, d\ln a_i = t_{\text{Na}}\, d\ln a_{\text{Na}} + t_{\text{Cl}}\, d\ln a_{\text{Cl}} + t_w\, d\ln a_w$$

$$= d\ln a_{\text{Na}} + t_{\text{Cl}}\, d\ln a_{\text{Na}}a_{\text{Cl}} + t_w\, d\ln a_w$$

The first term may be integrated directly to give $\ln a_{\text{Na}\omega}/a_{\text{Na}\alpha}$, which is the same as would result from a pair of sodium electrodes, one in each solution. The other terms, which measure the inefficiency of the membrane electrode, are expressed in terms of activities of neutral components. Since t_{Cl} is negative and $d\ln a_w$ has the opposite sign to $d\ln a_{\text{Na}}a_{\text{Cl}}$, both diminish the measured electrical potential difference.

The sodium chloride will diffuse through the membrane from the more concentrated solution to the more dilute. The desired potential is for the steady state with uniform composition outside the two limits, just as in a Planck boundary. Although the thickness of the membrane makes no difference, it is important that these limits should come just at the surface of the membrane, for t_{Cl} varies from almost zero within the membrane to about 0.6 outside. Presumably the change does not come at a mathematical surface but in a transition layer in which there is enough structure to prevent efficient stirring. If so, the measured transference number of chloride ion will be larger than that within the membrane. Once more the effect of water transfer is compensatory, for the water transfer will be reduced in the transition layers.

MEMBRANE POTENTIALS

Our measurements have been made on cells of the type

$$\text{Hg-Hg}_2\text{Cl}_2,\ \text{KCl(sat.), NaCl}(\alpha)\,|\,\text{C}\,|\,\text{NaCl}(\beta)\,|\,\text{A}\,|\,\text{NaCl}(\alpha),$$

$$\text{KCl(sat.), Hg}_2\text{Cl}_2\text{-Hg}$$

The cell is symmetrical except for the section

$$\text{NaCl}(\alpha)\,|\,\text{C}\,|\,\text{NaCl}(\beta)\,|\,\text{A}\,|\,\text{NaCl}(\alpha)$$

The electrical potential difference is given by

$$E\mathfrak{F}/RT = \ln\frac{(a_{\text{Na}}a_{\text{Cl}})_\beta}{(a_{\text{Na}}a_{\text{Cl}})_\alpha} + \int_\alpha^\beta (t_{\text{Cl}\,\text{C}} - t_{\text{Na}\,\text{A}})\, d\ln a_{\text{Na}}a_{\text{Cl}}$$

$$+ \int_\alpha^\beta (t_{w\,\text{C}} - t_{w\,\text{A}})\, d\ln a_w$$

The solution α was always 0.01 M, and the solution β was varied over a wide range. The figures show the measured electrical potential dif-

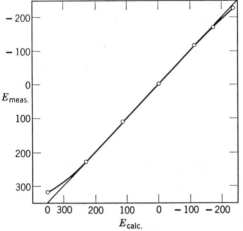

Fig. 1. Potential of ion exchanger electrodes HCl ($m_0 = 0.01$ M) with Amberple X A-1 and C-1.

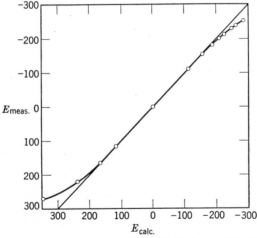

Fig. 2. Potential of ion exchanger electrodes NaCl ($m_0 = 0.01$ M) with Nepton CR-51 and ARX-102.

ference plotted against the value calculated from the first term alone.[14] Figure 1 shows hydrochloric acid, from 10^{-5} M to 1 M; Fig. 2 shows sodium chloride, from 10^{-5} M to 3 M. In the middle of the range both show excellent agreement. Both begin to deviate at about 0.1 M. The curves in concentrated solutions are almost superposable. This must be a coincidence, for membranes and solutes are both very different. In dilute solutions the deviations of the hydrochloric acid solutions begin only at one-tenth the concentration at which deviations for sodium chloride appear.

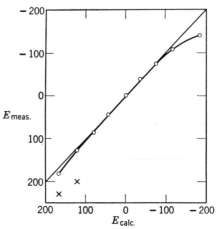

Fig. 3. Potential of ion exchanger electrodes $CaCl_2$ ($m_0 = 0.01$ M) with Nepton CR-51 and ARX-102.

Figure 3 shows the measurements for $CaCl_2$ from 10^{-4} M to 1 M. For this cell,

$$\frac{E\mathfrak{F}}{RT} = \ln \frac{(a_{Ca}^{\frac{1}{2}} a_{Cl})_\beta}{(a_{Ca}^{\frac{1}{2}} a_{Cl})_\alpha} + \int_\alpha^\beta (t_{ClC} - 2t_{CaA}) \, d \ln a_{Ca}^{\frac{1}{2}} a_{Cl}$$

$$+ \int_\alpha^\beta (t_{wC} - t_{wA}) \, d \ln a_w$$

The deviations at high concentrations are about the same as those for sodium chloride or hydrochloric acid at twice the chloride ion concentration, or four times the salt concentration. In dilute solutions the deviations give too large a slope.

Figure 4 shows the effect of stopping the flow along one side of the membrane. For both curves solution α was 0.01 M sodium chloride continuously flowing. The upper curve shows the small effect of stopping flow in a solution β twentyfold more concentrated than α. The lower shows the effect with a solution β one-twentieth as concentrated as α. There is a very rapid drop immediately and a rapid drop at least for half an hour.

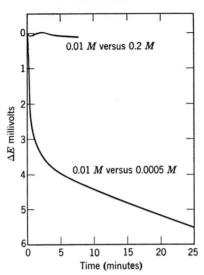

Fig. 4. Change of potential on stopping flow NaCl with Nepton CR-51 and ARX-102.

BI-IONIC POTENTIALS

The solutions in the cells we use, as in many other arrangements, may contain any number of ion components. The separation of $d \ln a_S$ is still convenient if all the cations at a cation exchanger have the same valence. The correcting terms become more complicated, and a new one is added depending upon the variation of $u_i \gamma_S / u_S \gamma_i$ across the membrane; the main term integrates to

$$\ln \Sigma_i{}^+ (a_i u_i \gamma_S / u_S \gamma_i)_\beta / \Sigma_i{}^+ (a_i u_i \gamma_S / u_S \gamma_i)_\alpha$$

in which $\Sigma_i{}^+$ indicates summation over the cations, and S is a standard component. If S is Na^+ and the only other cation is H^+ this becomes

$$\ln [a_{Na} + (u_H \gamma_{Na} / u_{Na} \gamma_H) a_H]_\beta / [a_{Na} + (u_H \gamma_{Na} / u_{Na} \gamma_H) a_H]_\alpha$$

$(RT/\mathfrak{F}) \ln (u_H \gamma_{Na} / u_{Na} \gamma_H)$ is called the bi-ionic potential. It is the potential corresponding to hydrogen ion in β and sodium ion at the same activity in α. Figure 5 shows the potential difference when α is 0.01 M NaCl and β is a 0.01 M mixture of sodium chloride and hydrochloric acid. The curve corresponds to $u_H \gamma_{Na} / u_{Na} \gamma_H = 4$. We have also found that $u_{OH} \gamma_{Cl} / u_{Cl} \gamma_{OH} = \frac{1}{4}$.

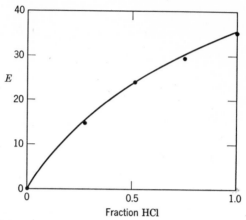

Fig. 5. Potential of ion exchanger electrodes NaCl + HCl (total $m = 0.01$ M) with Nepton CR-51 and ARX-102.

INTERPRETATION

A pioneer theoretical study of membranes was made by Michaelis,[15] who considered that the charge on the membrane was due to the adsorption of one kind of ions. Then, almost simultaneously, Teorell[16] and Meyer and Sievers[17] developed the theory of membranes with charges fixed in the lattice. Later workers have attempted to remove the restrictions of ideal solutions from this theory. Goldman[18] and Teorell[19] have replaced the Henderson equation by the generally more appropriate Planck equation within the membrane.

There are two problems. The first is to determine the transference numbers of the various species as functions of the salt concentration, and the second is to learn about the membranes themselves from these relations.

To determine transference numbers from electrical potential measurements, it is convenient to consider the deviations from efficiency separately. We may use the Gibbs-Duhem relation in the aqueous solution of concentration m', in equilibrium with the membrane to give

$$d \ln a_w = -0.018 m' \, d \ln a_{Na} a_{Cl}$$

For generality we will now include the transference of the ions of water. Then with an aqueous solution of sodium chloride and a cation exchanger we have

$\Sigma_i t_i \, d \ln a_i = d \ln a_{\mathrm{Na}}$

$$+ \; (t_{\mathrm{Cl}} - 0.018 m' t_w) \, d \ln a_{\mathrm{Na}} a_{\mathrm{Cl}} + (t_{\mathrm{H}} - t_{\mathrm{OH}}) \, d \ln a_{\mathrm{H}}$$

and with an anion exchanger

$\Sigma_i t_i \, d \ln a_i = -d \ln a_{\mathrm{Cl}}$

$$+ \; (t_{\mathrm{Na}} - 0.018 m' t_w) \, d \ln a_{\mathrm{Na}} a_{\mathrm{Cl}} + (t_{\mathrm{H}} - t_{\mathrm{OH}}) \, d \ln a_{\mathrm{H}}$$

It is obvious that in the range in which the efficiency is nearly unity we will find out nothing further about the membrane for we measure only the first term. The deviations in concentrated solutions arise from the second terms. Those in solutions so dilute that the concentration of the ions of water is only one order of magnitude smaller than the concentration of salt may come from the last term. Then only hydrogen ion in the cation exchanger and hydroxyl ion in the anion exchanger need to be considered.

In the cation exchanger, in solutions so dilute that m_{Cl} may be neglected,

$$t_{\mathrm{H}} = \frac{u_{\mathrm{H}} m_{\mathrm{H}}}{u_{\mathrm{Na}} m_{\mathrm{Na}} + u_{\mathrm{H}} m_{\mathrm{H}}} = \frac{u_{\mathrm{H}} \gamma_{\mathrm{Na}}}{u_{\mathrm{Na}} \gamma_{\mathrm{H}}} \frac{a_{\mathrm{H}}}{a_{\mathrm{Na}}} \bigg/ \left(1 + \frac{u_{\mathrm{H}} \gamma_{\mathrm{Na}}}{u_{\mathrm{Na}} \gamma_{\mathrm{H}}} \frac{a_{\mathrm{H}}}{a_{\mathrm{Na}}} \right) \cong \frac{u_{\mathrm{H}} \gamma_{\mathrm{Na}}}{u_{\mathrm{Na}} \gamma_{\mathrm{H}}} \frac{m_{\mathrm{H}}'}{m_{\mathrm{Na}}'}$$

The coefficient is the 4 which we determined from the bi-ionic potential. Since the low concentration deviations are much larger for sodium chloride than for hydrochloric acid, which cannot hydrolyze, it is tempting to attribute this effect to hydrolysis. However, quantitative calculations show that hydrolysis accounts for less than a tenth of the measured effect. We are, in fact, unable to explain the deviations in dilute solutions.

In concentrated solutions the deviations are the sums of two effects; transfer of chloride ion and of water. The water transfer is the more important in the first deviations. In our membranes it is the more important even to high concentrations. Let us suppose however that the two transference numbers can be separately determined. Then

$$t_w = \frac{u_w m_w}{u_{\mathrm{Na}} m_{\mathrm{Na}} - u_{\mathrm{Cl}} m_{\mathrm{Cl}}} = \frac{u_w / 0.018}{u_{\mathrm{Na}} m_{\mathrm{Na}} - u_{\mathrm{Cl}} m_{\mathrm{Cl}}}$$

The denominator is proportional to the electrical conductance of the membrane. If u_w is a constant, the electrical conductance is inversely proportional to the transference number of water. The proportional factor is undetermined. This relation has been verified for Neptonic CR-51 for various concentrations of sodium chloride and for the replacement of sodium by other ions.

For the chloride ion

$$t_{Cl} = \frac{u_{Cl} m_{Cl}}{u_{Na} m_{Na} - u_{Cl} m_{Cl}}$$

For Michaelis' assumptions $m_{Cl} = m_{Na}$, therefore, $t_{Cl} = u_{Cl}/(u_{Na} - u_{Cl})$, and any variation in the transference number must arise from variation in the relative mobilities. With a fixed charge of concentration m_R, $m_{Na} = m_R + m_{Cl}$, and

$$t_{Cl} = \frac{(u_{Cl}/u_{Na}) m_{Cl}/m_R}{1 + (1 - u_{Cl}/u_{Na}) m_{Cl}/m_R}$$

moreover

$$m_{Cl}(m_R + m_{Cl}) = a_{Na} a_{Cl}/\gamma_{Na}\gamma_{Cl} = a_{\pm}^2/\gamma_{\pm}^2$$

$$\frac{m_{Cl}}{m_R}\left(1 + \frac{m_{Cl}}{m_R}\right) = a_{\pm}^2/\gamma_{\pm}^2 m_R^2$$

The ratio m_{Cl}/m_R may be eliminated, and the relation between t_{Cl} and $a_{\pm}$ depends upon the two parameters (u_{Cl}/u_{Na}) and $\gamma_{\pm}/m_R$. If each of the quantities is constant, the two may be determined from the relation of t_{Cl} to $a_{\pm}$. Then m_{Cl}/m_R may be determined from either equation. This is essentially the method of Teorell and of Meyer and Sievers. They assumed that $\gamma_{\pm}$ is unity and that all the deviations in the electrical potential arise from t_{Cl}, none from t_w. Measurements of the distribution of sodium chloride between CR-51 and water indicate a large variation in $\gamma_{\pm} m_R$, and the conductance measurements indicate a large variation in u_{Cl}/u_{Na} in this membrane.

Let us return to a consideration of the dilute solutions of calcium chloride shown in Fig. 3. In these experiments the first measurements after conversion of the membranes from sodium form were with 0.01 M solution throughout and then by progressive dilution to 10^{-4} M in β giving the crosses in the two most dilute solutions. Then the concentration was progressively increased from 0.03 M to 1 M. Since the crosses did not fall on a smooth curve, the measurements at these concentrations were repeated giving the circles.[20] The first measurements seem to have been made with some sodium ion remaining in the exchanger. It was found that very irregular behavior resulted from using cation exchanger membranes containing much sodium ion with calcium chloride solutions. An asymmetry potential of 0.1 volts resulted in one case. We are not sure that we did not cause considerable chemical changes in the membranes in converting from one form to the other, and this effect needs further investigation. It is possible, however, that this phenomenon, which we cannot now explain, may be more important in physiological systems than those others which we understand at least partially.

CONCLUSION

Our results indicate that the ion exchanger membranes may be very useful as electrodes at which there is no oxidation or reduction and no restriction to special classes of ions except as to size. They show almost no specificity. Our results also indicate that these membranes may serve as useful models for physiological membranes, since they can be studied in more detail because the measurements of electromotive force and transference may be supplemented by measurements of electrical conductance, Donnan distributions, and so on. At present, the knowledge of ion exchanger membranes is very limited, and the variety of membranes available is not very great. They can be made in much greater variety, however, and the study of their properties is not very difficult.

REFERENCES

1. W. Juda, J. A. Marinsky, and N. W. Rosenberg, *Ann. Rev. Phys. Chem., 4,* 373 (1953).
2. G. Scatchard, *J. Am. Chem. Soc., 75,* 2883 (1953). This paper contains the mathematical treatment of transport through charged membranes.
3. G. Scatchard and T. F. Buehrer, *J. Am. Chem. Soc., 53,* 574 (1931).
4. P. Henderson, *Z. physik. Chem., 59,* 118 (1907); *63,* 325 (1908) gives equations for the ideal case.
5. W. M. Clark, *The Determination of Hydrogen Ions,* 3rd ed., William & Wilkins Co., Baltimore, 1928.
6. A. B. Lamb and A. T. Larson, *J. Am. Chem. Soc., 42,* 229 (1920).
7. D. A. MacInnes and Y. L. Yeh, *J. Am. Chem. Soc., 43,* 2563 (1921).
8. G. Scatchard, *J. Am. Chem. Soc., 47,* 696 (1925).
9. D. A. MacInnes, *The Principles of Electrochemistry,* Reinhold Publishing Co., New York, 1939.
10. P. B. Taylor, *J. Phys. Chem., 31,* 1478 (1927).
11. E. A. Guggenheim, *J. Am. Chem. Soc., 52,* 1315 (1930).
12. M. Planck, *Ann. der Physik und Chemie, 40,* 561 (1890). See also reference 9.
13. A. C. Cumming and E. Gilchrist, *Trans. Faraday Soc., 9,* 174 (1913).
14. J. S. Coleman, Ph.D. Thesis, Department of Chemistry, Massachusetts Institute of Technology, 1953. Some of the measurements were made by Amy L. Shen.

The Neptonic membranes were prepared by Ionics, Inc., and the Amberplex membranes by Rohm and Haas. We are indebted to both of these companies for supplying us with membranes before they were commercially available. In both cases the membranes had sufficient conductivity and diffusion so that they were used as ribbons (edgewise) rather than as membranes.

15. L. Michaelis and A. Fujita, *Biochem. Z.*, *158*, 28 (1925) (first paper); L. Michaelis, *Kolloid Z.*, *10*, 575 (1933) (review); *J. Gen. Physiol.*, *10* (1927).

16. T. Teorell, *Proc. Soc., Exp. Biol. Med.*, *33*, 282 (1935).

17. K. H. Meyer and J. F. Sievers, *Helv. Chim. Acta, 19,* 649 (1936).

18. D. E. Goldman, *J. Gen. Physiol., 27,* 37 (1943).

19. T. Teorell, *Z. Elektrochem., 55,* 460 (1951).

20. Similar results with calcium chloride have been noted earlier by M. R. J. Wyllie, private communication.

4.

The Electrochemistry
of Porous Membranes

Karl Sollner *

I. PHYSICOCHEMICAL MEMBRANES—MEMBRANES
AS MACHINES

This chapter does not attempt to review the vast literature on the electrochemistry of membranes. Its purpose is to present briefly certain phases of work on the basic electrochemistry of non-living, artificial membranes that was carried out in the author's laboratory.

The most characteristic feature of membranes is their selective permeability, in other words, their function as barriers. Thus, membranes considered from the physicochemical point of view—*"physicochemical membranes"*—can be defined properly only in relation to their surroundings.[1] For example, a sheet of platinum separating oxygen and nitrogen does not show any characteristic membrane features; it is merely an inert separating wall. However, if the same sheet of platinum separates hydrogen from nitrogen, it assumes a typical membrane function. Although it completely prevents diffusion of nitrogen across its thickness, it is freely permeable to hydrogen (particularly if heated).[2]

Membranes, while regulating the movement of particles and the flow of energy across their thickness, cause a great variety of effects such as movement of solute, the closely related development of (not necessarily static) hydrostatic pressures, and the partial or complete separation of solutes from the solvent. With electrolytes numerous additional effects may be observed, such as static or dynamic membrane potentials, anomalous osmosis, movement of third ions against concentration gradients, electroösmosis, etc. In all these cases the membranes act as physicochemical machines, transforming by various

* From the Laboratory of Physical Biology, National Institute of Arthritis and Metabolic Diseases, National Institutes of Health, Public Health Service, Department of Health, Education, and Welfare, Bethesda, Maryland.

33

mechanisms the free energy of the adjacent phases (or energy applied through them) into other forms of energy (mechanical, concentration, electrical, etc.), sometimes in a reversible but ordinarily in an irreversible manner. Physicochemical membranes are in this respect strictly analogous to mechanical machines—they regulate energetic processes, essentially without thereby being changed, exhausted, or consumed. They cannot by expenditure of energy of their own bring about any transport phenomena.[3]

One may define a physicochemical membrane as follows:

A membrane is a phase or structure interposed between two phases or compartments which obstructs or completely prevents gross mass movement between the latter, but permits passage, with various degrees of restriction, of one or several species of particles from the one to the other or between the two adjacent phases or compartments, and which thereby acting as a physicochemical machine transforms with various degrees of efficiency according to its nature and the nature and composition of the two adjacent phases or compartments the free energy of the adjacent phases or compartments, or energy applied from the outside to the latter, into other forms of energy.[1]

As long as only ideal "semipermeable" membranes and reversible equilibria across them are considered (as was done by the classical physicochemists), the special mechanisms by which the membranes act are of no importance whatsoever from the point of view of thermodynamic theory.[1,4] However, as soon as we consider the *dynamics of membrane processes* either across ideal semipermeable or across nonideal membranes of various degrees of selective permeability, the questions of mechanisms and of membrane structure become of paramount importance. The correlation between the restrictive barrier functions of membranes and their machine actions is thus a central topic of the physical chemistry of the dynamics of membrane systems.

Accordingly, the electrochemistry of membranes is concerned with the barrier action that is exerted by membranes on electrolytes or, more precisely, on ions and with the resulting electrical machine actions of the membranes, that is, with the electrical effects that arise under various conditions from the interplay of membranes and solutions of electrolytes.

II. THE FUNDAMENTAL ELECTROCHEMISTRY OF MEMBRANES OF POROUS CHARACTER

In a discussion of the physical and electrochemistry of membranes, it is necessary to distinguish two basic classes of membranes, "homogeneous phase membranes" (oil membranes) and "membranes of porous

character." Homogeneous phase membranes exert their typical membrane functions by means of selective, differential solubility.[5] Membranes of porous character act as sieves that screen out the various
species of solute particles according to their different sizes and to some
extent according to their different adsorbabilities and, in the case of
ions, also according to the sign and magnitude of their charge. The
membranes to be discussed here are *membranes of porous character.*[1, 6, 7]

Membranes of this type can be prepared at will with a great variety
of characteristics. In addition, they show some effects of great interest to the biologist, such as ultrafiltration, electroösmosis, and (electrical) anomalous osmosis, which cannot be obtained with membranes
of the homogeneous phase type.

Membranes of porous character can arbitrarily be classified into two
groups: *membranes of high porosity,* as exemplified by ordinary dialyzing membranes; and "molecular sieve" or *"ion sieve" membranes* with
pores so narrow that different low-molecular-weight species of molecules and ions are retarded to a differential degree or are prevented
altogether from passing across them.

The basic observations in the electrochemistry of membranes refer
to their electromotive action, which becomes conspicuous when a membrane separates two solutions that are not identical in electrolyte content, the simplest case of this nature being the membrane concentration chain or cell.

If a membrane prepared from collodion, silicates, proteins, or almost
any other material is interposed between two solutions, e.g., of different
concentration of the same electrolyte, an electromotive force arises that
is different in most instances from the liquid junction potential that
would arise between the same two solutions on free diffusion, that is,
in the absence of a membrane. The electromotive forces arising in such
membrane concentration cells customarily are referred to as *"concentration potentials."*

The sign and the magnitude of the concentration potential depend on
the absolute concentrations and the concentration ratio of the electrolyte in the two adjacent solutions, also on its nature, and last but not
least on the nature of the membrane.

With membranes of highest porosity (porous diaphragms) the concentration potentials are in sign and magnitude identical with or not
much different from the corresponding liquid junction potentials. The
concentration potentials deviate more and more from the liquid junction potential if stepwise denser membranes are used.

The direction of the deviation of the concentration potential from
the liquid junction potential is functionally correlated with the elec-

trokinetic charge of the membrane. With electropositive membranes the dilute solution is more negative and with electronegative membranes it is more positive than on free diffusion. From this it may be concluded that electronegative membranes are preferentially cation permeable and electropositive membranes preferentially anion permeable, as is readily confirmed by direct observation. This is the most fundamental fact in the whole electrochemistry of membranes of porous character.

With certain membranes of very low porosity the concentration potential may reach the magnitude of the potential difference that would arise between the two solutions if they were connected to each other through a pair of reversible electrodes, specific either for the cations or the anions in solution, as the case may be. This "thermodynamically possible maximum value" of the concentration potential represents the upper limit of the possible dynamic membrane potentials in concentration cells, the liquid junction potential being the other limit.

Concomitant with the just-described electrical effects that are observed in membrane concentration cells there arises also an "osmotic" effect, the translocation of liquid across the membrane. With membranes of the highly porous, dialyzing type these effects can be very pronounced, being in many instances much larger than those arising with non-electrolyte solutions of equal concentration; sometimes they are even in the opposite direction. This "anomalous osmosis" will be treated below.

The correlation of ionic membrane selectivity and concentration potential in formal electrochemical terms is the basic concept in the electrochemistry of these membranes.[8, 9] This correlation can readily be visualized along the following lines of thought. The virtual transportation of electricity across the membranes is divided between anions and cations in a proportion that is different from the ratio of the *transference numbers* of these ions in free solution. In electronegative membranes a greater fraction of the current is transported by cations across the membrane than in free solution; the transference number of the cations in the pores of the membrane (τ_+) is larger than the transference numbers of the cations in free solution t_+ ($\tau_+ > t_+$; and $\tau_- < t_-$). With positive membranes the inverse holds true.[8, 9]

The correlation of membrane concentration potential ϵ and the transference numbers τ_+ and τ_- may be expressed quantitatively by the use of a modified Nernst equation. For the case of a uni-univalent electrolyte, it reads:

$$\epsilon = \frac{\tau_+ - \tau_-}{\tau_+ + \tau_-} \frac{RT}{F} \ln \frac{a_\pm^{(1)}}{a_\pm^{(2)}}$$ (1)

where $a_\pm^{(1)}$ and $a_\pm^{(2)}$ are the activities of the electrolyte in the two solutions, the sum τ_+ plus τ_- by definition being unity. If a membrane is exclusively permeable to cations, the transference number of the cation in the membrane, τ_+, is unity; it is an electronegative *"membrane of ideal ionic selectivity."* Correspondingly, an electropositive membrane of ideal ionic selectivity is permeable exclusively to anions, τ_- being unity.

The charges (ions) that form the immovable part of the electric double layer at the pore wall-solution interface are attached firmly to the pore walls; they are unable to move and thus do not participate in ionic processes across the membrane, such as diffusion or the transportation of electricity. The counter ions of the fixed wall charges are dissociated off into the liquid in the pores; they are freely movable and therefore able to participate in ionic processes across the membrane, for instance, in the transportation of electricity, the current being transported by the counter ions of the fixed wall charges and whatever other electrolytes, both anions and cations, may be present in the pores. Thus, the movable counter ions of the fixed wall charges are the vehicle for a larger and larger fraction of all ionic processes across the membranes as membranes of decreasing porosity are considered.

Ions of the same sign of charge as the membrane are prevented by electric repulsion from approaching the spots at the pore walls where the fixed charges of the same sign are located. From sufficiently narrow pores such ions (and therefore their electrically compensating counter ions, too) are virtually excluded. In this case the membrane will act as a membrane of ideal ionic selectivity; all the possible pathways across it are blocked completely for the ions in solution that carry the same charge as the membrane itself.

The correlation of pore diameter and membrane selectivity is shown in a highly schematized manner in Figs. 1a to 1c for electronegative pores. In these figures the cross-hatched parts indicate the solid wall material; the protuberances on the solid wall material denote the charges (ions or ionized groups) that are fixed to the pore walls (and form the immovable part of an electrical double layer). The plus and minus signs represent the movable (univalent) cations and anions in the pore water. In the widest pore (Fig. 1a) there are eleven movable cations and four movable anions; in the next narrower pore (Fig. 1b) these numbers are eight and one, respectively. Figure 1c shows a pore

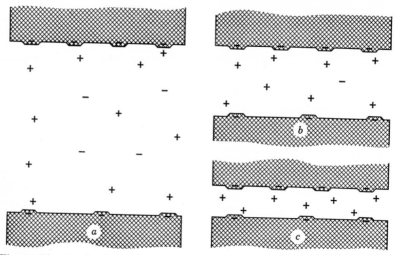

Fig. 1. The distribution of ions in three pores of different diameter at the same concentration of the outside electrolyte solution.

of ideal ionic selectivity; it contains only seven movable cations but no movable anions.

With increasing concentration of the outside electrolyte solutions, an increasing quantity of electrolyte, having equivalent quantities of anions and cations, enters the pores. The specific influence of the membrane is thereby decreased. This explains why the ionic selectivity of a given membrane decreases if the concentration of the adjacent electrolyte solutions is increased.

It is easy to see how under suitable conditions a single charge in a given pore may block it completely for the passage of ions of the same sign. This occurrence is indicated in Fig. 2a. The continuous circles

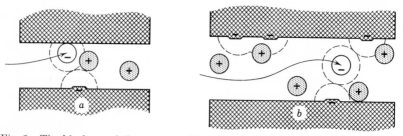

Fig. 2. The blockage of the passage of ions by charges of the same sign that are fixed at the walls of a pore. (a) Blockage by one fixed charge in a narrow pore. (b) The influence of the relative location of several fixed charges at the walls of a wider pore.

around the plus or minus signs represent here the size of the ions including their effective shell of hydration; the dashed circles indicate the
effective range of the electrical force of repulsion acting at the given
ionic strength between the fixed charges situated on the pore walls and
ions of identical signs in the solution. The tip of the arrow indicates
how far the ions identical in sign with the charged wall groups may
move from the left side.[10]

In somewhat wider pores, the situation may easily arise in which a
single charge at the pore walls would not effect complete blockage to
the passage of ions of the same sign. Even with several charges on
the walls of the pore the same situation may prevail, unless the
charged groups are properly located as is indicated in the right half of
the pore of Fig. 2b.

Polyvalent ions with a charge of the same sign as the membrane are
much more restricted in their permeation across the membrane than
univalent ions because polyvalent ions are large and have a high
charge that prevents them by electric repulsion from entering narrow
pores which are accessible to univalent ions of the same sign.

At this point it is necessary to introduce the often neglected but
highly important concept of *membrane heteroporosity*.[8-12] Any membrane that is available at present for experimental investigation must
be assumed to be heteroporous, a mosaic of wider and narrower channels. The pores are the interstices between micelles, which in many
instances must be assumed to be arranged in a more or less random
manner.[6, 10]

The availability of any particular pathway across a membrane for
non-electrolytes of a given molecular size is obviously determined by
its narrowest spot; with electrolytes or, more correctly, with ions the
availability of a pathway depends upon a combination of this geometrical factor and the electrical factor, the repelling action being
exerted by the fixed charges on the pore walls on ions of the same sign.

With artificial membranes, except perhaps in the rarest instances,
branching of pores as well as dead-end cavities must occur.[10]

Figures 3a and 3b indicate how in geometrically identical pores the
location of fixed charges may determine the electric characteristics of
the pore. In Fig. 3a a single fixed wall charge is located at a fairly
narrow part of the pore with no alternate pathway around it; the pore,
therefore, is blocked for ions of the same sign of charge as the membrane. In Fig. 3b, five less strategically located wall charges leave the
pore permeable to ions of the same sign of charge as the membrane.[10]

The concept of membrane heteroporosity leads to the following important considerations. If a heteroporous membrane that is not strictly

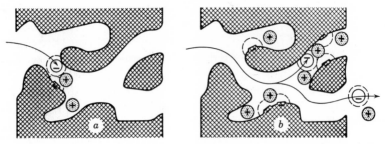

Fig. 3. The influence of the location of fixed charges at the pore walls of a hetero-
geneous pore upon the blockage of ions of the same sign.

impermeable to ions of the same charge separates two solutions with
differing concentrations of the same electrolyte, the various pores of the
membrane yield different potentials. The different pores act upon one
another and thereby set up local electrical circuits. The measurable
membrane potential is the over-all *resultant of the interaction of the
different* individual *pore potentials.* The electrical heterogeneity of
pores may be due to differences in effective width or to differences in
the number and distribution of the dissociable groups in geometrically
similar pores.[10, 12]

One specific instance in which the concept of membrane heteroporosity has played an important role is the elucidation of the mechanism of the phenomenon of *"anomalous osmosis."* [12]

It has been known since the days of Dutrochet [13] that, in many instances, seemingly rather erratic osmotic phenomena arise when membranes of the dialyzing type separate electrolyte solutions of different
concentration, or one such solution and pure water. The rate of "osmotic" movement of liquid across membranes, particularly at low electrolyte concentration, may be far greater than that caused by non-
electrolytes of equal concentration or, in some instances, the "osmotic"
flow is in the direction opposite from that expected on the basis of the
concentration difference.

These effects are designated "anomalous osmosis." If the anomalous
movement of liquid is from the dilute to the concentrated side of the
system, it is called anomalous positive osmosis; if it is in the opposite
direction, it is called anomalous negative osmosis or negative osmosis.

Anomalous osmotic effects are never observed with strictly semipermeable membranes, impervious to the solute under consideration.
Anomalous osmosis is a dynamic, transient phenomenon. After a sufficiently long time the electrolyte concentration on both sides of the

membrane is the same and hydrostatic heads that have developed intermediately disappear.

Anomalous osmosis is of interest not only from the point of view of the fundamental electrochemistry of membranes, but it also has attracted considerable attention on the part of investigators in the biological sciences as a conceivable mechanism of the translocation of liquid in cells and tissues, a problem that will be taken up in the next chapter. Moreover, anomalous osmosis furnishes a convenient method of characterizing, from the electrochemical point of view, membranes of high porosity.

The technique of studying anomalous osmosis as used, for instance, by Loeb is essentially as follows.[14-18] A collodion bag is tied to a glass ring that is fitted to a rubber stopper carrying a capillary manometer tube. The membrane is filled in succession with solutions of graded concentrations of different electrolytes, and of sucrose, and suspended in a large beaker filled with water. After a stated time (20 min. in Loeb's experiments) the rise of the meniscus in the manometer is read.

If the manometer readings are plotted in a pressure/concentration diagram, non-electrolytes give curves that are strictly proportionate to the concentration of the solute; with electrolytes the curves have a characteristic N shape. A pressure rise that deviates significantly from that obtained with non-electrolytic reference substances of the same concentration is commonly considered to be due to anomalous osmosis.

Some typical results of studies on anomalous positive osmosis with membranes of about equal porosity are summarized in Fig. 4. The differences in the magnitude of the effects with different membranes are of subordinate interest here; they are due to electrochemical differences between the membranes, which will be discussed later. Of interest here is the typical N shape of the curves in electrolytes that have a maximum, in many instances a maximum of considerable height, at fairly low concentrations, and the contrasting curves obtained with the non-electrolyte sucrose which at the same low concentrations gives only minimal, barely detectable osmotic effects.

As suggested already by Graham,[19] anomalous osmosis according to the work of Girard,[20] Bartell,[21] Loeb,[14-16] and others[22, 23] is essentially a spontaneous electroösmosis that occurs when an electrolyte diffuses across a charged membrane.

According to Loeb's observations, the extent of anomalous osmosis is approximately proportional to the electrokinetic potential ζ of the membrane times the concentration potential ϵ measured across the

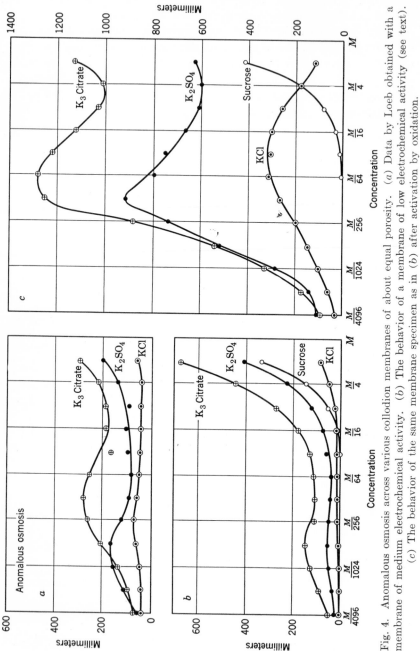

Fig. 4. Anomalous osmosis across various collodion membranes of about equal porosity. (*a*) Data by Loeb obtained with a membrane of medium electrochemical activity. (*b*) The behavior of a membrane of low electrochemical activity (see text). (*c*) The behavior of the same membrane specimen as in (*b*) after activation by oxidation.

membrane. The driving energy of the process is obviously derived
from the diffusion of the electrolyte across the membrane.

The remaining question was to find a specific mechanism that would
explain the existence of a continuous flow of electric current, which is
necessary to bring about electroösmosis.[12]

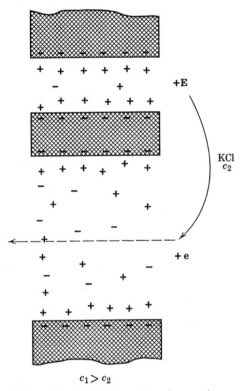

$c_1 > c_2$

Fig. 5. The mechanism of the origin of anomalous osmosis.

Suppose an electrolyte with ions having the same diffusion velocity,
say potassium chloride, diffuses across a heteroporous electronegative
membrane as shown schematically in Fig. 5. The two pores in this
figure are similar to the pores (a) and (b) in Fig. 1, the concentration
difference across the membrane being indicated in Fig. 5 by the uneven
distribution of movable electrolyte, both anions and cations, along the
axis of the pores. According to our premises, the electromotive forces
that arise across the two pores differ, the **E** and the **e** at the right side
of the picture indicating the larger and smaller pore potential. The
two pores are connected electrically to each other by the two solutions

at the left and the right sides of the membrane. Thus, an all-electrolytic electrical circuit in the sense of Dolezalek and Krüger [24] with two electromotive forces, E and e in series is established. An electric current flows through the system that consists of the two pores and the adjacent parts of the two solutions. The positive current, indicated in the figure by a solid arrow, is driven passively through the wider pore. Since the membrane is charged negatively, the movable part of the Helmholtz electric double layer in the pores is positive, and an electroosmotic flow of liquid occurs from the right side of the system to the left, from the dilute to the side of the more concentrated solution, as is indicated by a dotted arrow. In other words, the circuit flowing in our two-pore system brings about anomalous positive osmosis.[12, 25, 26]

With electrolytes whose ions have different diffusion velocities the situation can be more involved, depending on whether the ion that in free solution diffuses more rapidly has the same charge as the membrane itself.

If the faster-diffusing ion carries a charge opposite to that of the membrane, in other words, when the ions that form the movable part of the double layer are those with the higher diffusion velocity in free solution, the situation is analogous to that shown in Fig. 5. The two pore potentials are of the same sign as the ions of the movable part of the electrical double layer with the result that anomalous positive osmosis occurs.

If, however, the more rapidly diffusing ion is of the same sign as the electrokinetic charge of the membrane, the situation is more complicated. According to the widths of the different pores, the sign of the potentials across them can either be determined by the more rapidly diffusing ions—this is true of wide pores (where the situation in free solution is approached)—or a pore may be so narrow that the influence of those ions that form the movable part of the double layer is preponderant. The sign of the pore potential in such narrow pores is therefore identical with that of the more slowly diffusing species of ions. The different possible cases arising from this situation have been worked out in detail.[12] Briefly, it may be stated that wide pores and high concentrations will favor the occurrence of anomalous negative osmosis; also, the same membrane can be expected to give at low concentrations anomalous positive osmosis, at higher concentrations, anomalous negative osmosis.

Bivalent and multivalent ions, because of their smaller diffusion velocity and the greater steric hindrance exerted on them by the membrane, give particularly strong effects (Fig. 4).

The outlined theory of the interaction of two membranes of different porosity has been tested successfully in a macroscopic model system with two membranes of different porosity.[27, 28]

For all the foregoing considerations concerning the electrochemical behavior of membranes it has not been necessary to make any special assumptions as to the specific *mechanism by which the charge of the membrane arises*. This mechanism can be considered to be immaterial up to a point, though it is of primary importance for the further conceptual development of the theory and any attempt at a quantitative theoretical treatment.

Contrary to former, widely held views,[29, 30] the basic electrochemical behavior in the presence of strong, poorly adsorbable, inorganic electrolytes, even of the presumably inert materials such as, for example, collodion, is due to dissociable groups such as carboxyl groups (probably stray and end groups), which form an integral part of the molecules, or at least a fraction of the molecules, of these substances. Thus, the supposedly inert materials are, strictly speaking, ionizable substances and, therefore, in their electrochemically important properties qualitatively identical with materials like clays, zeolites, or protein gels that are customarily classified as ion exchangers. If acidic in character, they are cation exchangers; if basic, anion exchangers. The difference between the substances that are conventionally classed as ion exchangers and the more inert materials is only quantitative.[1, 7, 18, 31–33]

Inert membranes have been "activated" by the adsorption of dissociable substances of high molecular weight, such as proteins.[14–16] Proteins, like other polyelectrolytes, when adsorbed on an inert membrane skeleton, impress on its microstructure the essential property of ion exchangers, namely, a definite, and usually fairly high charge density or number of fixed, dissociable groups per unit area.

The concept of membranes as ion exchange bodies leads to the fixed-charge theory of electrical membrane behavior. This theory, on the basis of a clear physical picture, namely, the ion exchange character of the membranes, correlates in a quantitative manner the previously outlined facts and ideas concerning membrane selectivity and the concomitant electrical effects.

The physical essence of the fixed-charge theory can be stated qualitatively in a simple manner. The terms in which this theory was originally presented by Teorell[34] and later in greater detail by Meyer and Sievers[35] are rather complex and do not need to be outlined here, particularly since Teorell has recently published two detailed expositions of his current views on this matter.[36]

According to the fixed-charge theory, the walls of the pores of the membranes carry inherently a definite number of potentially dissociable groups, anionic (acidic) groups, such as carboxyl groups in electronegative membranes, and cationic (basic) groups, such as amino groups in electropositive membranes. These dissociable groups are an integral, invariable part of the membrane structure; their number is independent of the nature or concentration of the adjacent electrolyte solutions. Any current that flows across the membrane is transported by the counter ions of the fixed charged wall groups and whatever other "non-exchange" electrolyte may be present in the pores. The concentration of other non-exchange electrolytes is determined by a distribution equilibrium existing between the electrolytic pore structure of the membrane and the adjacent outside electrolyte solution, the fixed wall groups being a "non-diffusible" species of ions which is restricted to the membrane phase. In a concentration cell, two such distribution equilibria are set up between the two solutions and the two adjacent surface layers of the membrane, with a corresponding concentration drop across the membrane. The concentration potential is considered the algebraic sum of the two phase boundary potentials (which are treated by some authors as Donnan potentials) plus the liquid junction potential within the pores.

Although based on assumptions that are oversimplified as far as membranes of porous character are concerned, the core of the fixed-charge theory is destined to play a dominant role in the further development of the theory. Whether it will ultimately be advisable to split up the observed membrane potential into three parts, two non-operational distribution potentials (of doubtful meaning) and one diffusion potential, or whether it may not be preferable to consider statistically the probability that individual ions will pass critical spots in a heteroporous structure, cannot yet be decided. The first method of approach has the advantage of being based on rather fully developed concepts; but it will be applicable only after considerable modification of the actual physical situation, which involves microheterogeneous interphases, where the conventional electrochemical concepts, of phase boundary potentials for instance, become blurred.[37, 38] The second method of approach, namely, a consideration of molecular processes occurring at individual spots, might be much closer to the physical facts and, conceptually, less involved. However, it could not be connected quite as conveniently to earlier work in theoretical electrochemistry.[10]

PREPARATION AND PROPERTIES OF MEMBRANES OF HIGH POROSITY AND HIGH ELECTROCHEMICAL ACTIVITY

The fixed-charge theory implicitly gives directions towards the *preparation of membranes of highest electrochemical activity.* It postulates that, *ceteris paribus,* the electrochemical properties of membranes of porous character will be the more pronounced, the greater the number of potentially dissociable groups per unit area on the walls of the pores. The obvious objective is to prepare membranes that would yield to a very pronounced degree the electrical and permeability phenomena under investigation.

The technical details of the methods of preparation of membranes of highest electrochemical activity are without specific interest in the present connection; they have been discussed repeatedly.[39-42] One may use a membrane-forming material that carries inherently an adequate number of dissociable groups; or an activating material of polyelectrolyte nature may be dissolved in the solution of an electrochemically fairly inert material, such as collodion, from which membranes are prepared; electrochemically active polyelectrolyte molecules are thus embedded in the inert matrix when the membrane is formed;[42,43] or an inherently inert membrane can be activated by the adsorption of some polyelectrolyte, which attaches itself in a virtually irreversible manner to the preformed membrane structure.[42-45] Finally, membranes may be activated by a chemical reaction, for instance, oxidation, which results in the formation of dissociable groups (carboxyl groups) on the accessible pore walls of the membrane structure.[17,18,31,39]

Electronegative membranes of high porosity and a very high degree of electrochemical activity have been prepared by all these methods. Membranes with carboxyl groups as functional groups (which have the acid strength of benzoic or salicylic acid)[32] lose in acid solutions a good part of their characteristic electrochemical properties. Membranes prepared by the use of strong-acid-type polyelectrolytes, for instance, polystyrene monosulfonic acid $(-CH_2-CH-C_6H_4-SO_3H)x$,

are free of this shortcoming.[42-44]

Electropositive membranes of high porosity and high electrochemical activity have been obtained by the adsorption on collodion membranes of protamines, basic proteins with an isoelectric point of about pH 12 and a molecular weight of around 3000.[45]

Two basic parameters for the *electrochemical characterization of membranes of high porosity* are the membrane concentration potential and the rate of electroösmosis across them, the rate of electroösmosis being determined by the electrokinetic potential of the membranes. The higher the concentration potential and the higher the rate of electroösmosis, the greater the "electrochemical activity" of a membrane (of given porosity).

The influence of activation by oxidation on the *concentration potential* across a formed collodion membrane is seen from these data. A membrane of the dialyzing type before oxidation gave, in the concentration cell KCl 0.1 N membrane KCl 0.01 N, a concentration potential of 1.6 mv., after oxidation of 25.0 mv. The behavior of the membrane towards non-electrolytes, it must be stressed, was not significantly changed by the oxidation.

With protamine collodion membranes the result of activation is analogous, the activated membranes being electropositive, the concentration potentials being of opposite sign.

The influence of activation by oxidation on *electroösmosis* across a membrane of high porosity can be seen in columns 1 to 3 of the self-explanatory Table 1. Activation by sulfonated polystyrene has virtually the same effect. Column 4 of Table 1 shows the analogous effect of activation by the adsorption of protamine.[45]

TABLE 1. ELECTROÖSMOSIS THROUGH A TYPICAL UNOXIDIZED COLLODION MEMBRANE OF HIGH POROSITY, THE SAME MEMBRANE AFTER OXIDATION, AND A PROTAMINE COLLODION MEMBRANE OF ABOUT EQUAL POROSITY

1	2	3	4
	Electroösmotic Flow in mm.^{3} per 100 cm.^{2} per hour with a Current Intensity of 0.1 milliamp. per cm.^{2} *		
Concentration of KCl Solution equiv./liter	Unoxidized Collodion Membrane mm.^{3}	Oxidized Collodion Membrane mm.^{3}	Protamine Collodion Membrane mm.^{3}
0.00100	+2840	+4640	−4380
0.0100	+360	+1800	−1680
0.100	±0	+210	−80

* A plus sign indicates transport towards the cathode, a minus sign transport towards the anode.

The rate of *anomalous osmosis,* because it is a function both of the magnitude of the electrokinetic potential of the membrane and of the dynamic membrane potential, is another and particularly sensitive indicator of the electrochemical activity of membranes of high porosity, especially if membranes of similar water permeability are compared. In our work, this method has been used routinely, in most instances with membranes that, when filled with 0.25 M sucrose solution and placed in a large beaker of water for 20 min., yielded, without artificial stirring, an osmotic rise of about 120–140 mm. of liquid in a capillary manometer of about 1.5 mm. inside diameter.[1, 7, 17, 18, 31–33]

Figures 4b and 4c allow the comparison of the activity of a membrane that was prepared from pure commercial collodion, which is nearly devoid of dissociable groups, and of the activity of the same membrane after oxidative production of a considerable number of dissociable groups at the walls of its pores.[17] The abscissas give the concentration of the solution inside the test-tube-shaped membrane, which is immersed in distilled water; the ordinates represent the pressure rise observed after 20 min. The influence of increasing the charge density at the pore walls of the membrane is clearly evident from these figures. The behavior of the membranes towards solutions of sucrose, a typical non-electrolyte, is hardly changed by the oxidation. Loeb's membrane, referred to before (see Fig. 4a), which was prepared from a fairly impure, distinctly acidic collodion, shows a medium degree of activity.

The extent of anomalous osmosis with neutral electrolytes across strong-acid-type membranes is closely similar to that across the weak-acid-type oxidized collodion membranes.[42] With solutions of strong acids the anomalous osmotic effects with weak-acid-type oxidized collodion membranes are much smaller than with the neutral electrolytes because of the nature of their functional groups. This difference in behavior with neutral electrolytes and with acids is, of course, not found with strong-acid-type membranes.[42]

Anomalous osmosis across a typical electropositive protamine collodion membrane is shown in Fig. 6. The similarity of the curves in the upper half of this figure and the analogous curves in Fig. 4 hardly needs to be pointed out. As predicted by the theory, the anomalous osmotic effects in positive membranes become greater when electrolytes with two- and three-valent cations are used, the inverse holding true with the electronegative membranes.

The lower half of Fig. 6 shows also some of the most pronounced cases of *negative* osmosis, which were obtained with acids at relatively high concentrations, as predicted by the theory.

The pH range over which the behavior of protamine collodion membranes is strongly electropositive is about pH 2.8–8.5, which compares with the range of pH 2.6–3.8 of the oxyhemoglobin membranes of Loeb.

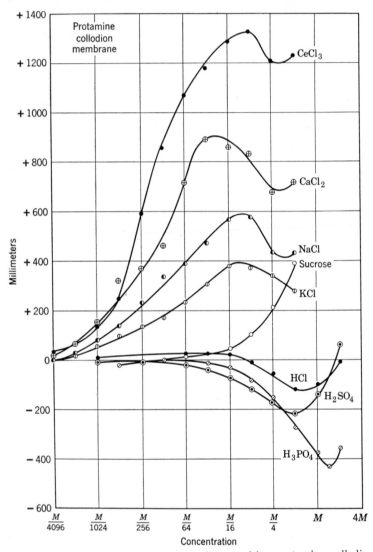

Fig. 6. Anomalous osmosis across an electropositive protamine collodion membrane.

PREPARATION AND PROPERTIES OF MEMBRANES OF HIGHEST IONIC SELECTIVITY—PERMSELECTIVE MEMBRANES

The first thoroughly investigated *electronegative membranes,* of a relatively *high degree of ionic selectivity,* are the "dried" collodion membranes used by Michaelis and collaborators in their classical studies on ion sieve membranes.[8, 9, 46] They were characterized by the measurement of the "characteristic concentration potential," the electromotive force which arises when 0.1 N and 0.01 N potassium chloride solutions are separated by a membrane. The values of the characteristic concentration potential, corrected for the asymmetry of the liquid junctions at the salt bridges used in the measurements, varied between $+47$ and $+52$ mv. with occasional values slightly higher, the maximum thermodynamically possible value being $+55.1$ mv. The resistance of these membranes was high, even for fairly thin membranes of the order of 10^5 ohms for 1 cm.² in 0.1 N potassium chloride solutions.

Electropositive membranes of low porosity and *high ionic selectivity* which are analogous to the dried collodion membranes have been described repeatedly. They are dried collodion membranes impregnated with basic dyestuffs and alkaloids. Their ionic selectivity in most cases is not satisfactory, their stability is rather limited, and their absolute permeability is extremely low.

With *membranes of ion sieve character,* it was obvious to strive for membranes that would be of virtually ideal ionic selectivity. At the same time, these membranes should allow a fast rate of diffusion of the critical ions across their thickness. In other words, they should be membranes of low resistance. Such membranes would be much more useful for physicochemical experimentation and also for model studies of biological interest. For this type of ion sieve membrane of highest ionic selectivity and high permeability, the designation "megapermselective" or *"permselective"* membranes was suggested, permselective being now commonly used.[47]

The same *general methods* that are useful in the preparation of membranes of high porosity can also be employed with success *for the preparation of* the ion sieve type, *permselective membranes.*

"Permselective" electronegative membranes of very high ionic selectivity and low resistance have been prepared by a variety of methods. Collodion membranes of high porosity are oxidized and dried over glass mandrels under carefully controlled conditions.[39, 47] For easy

handling, the glass-clear, test-tube-shaped, perfectly smooth membranes are tied with linen thread to glass rings that fit inside their open end.

The thickness of these membranes is 30–40 microns; their water content by weight is 14–23 per cent. Their resistance can be adjusted over a wide range; membranes of lower resistance have at higher concentrations a somewhat smaller ionic selectivity.

Analogous, strong-acid-type membranes of excellent mechanical strength and improved ionic selectivity have been prepared by using as activating agents strong-acid-type polyelectrolytes, such as sulfonated polystyrene. Sulfonated polystyrene may either be adsorbed from aqueous solutions on collodion membranes of high porosity that are dried later on their casting tubes, or it may be incorporated in the collodion solutions from which the membranes are cast.[42, 43, 44]

The first *"permselective" electropositive membranes* were prepared by the adsorption of protamine on one-, two-, or three-layer collodion membranes of high porosity, which were later dried under carefully controlled conditions.[40, 48]

Ion exchangers of the commercial type, because of their high charge density per unit area and their low inherent porosity, are obviously suitable materials for the preparation of permselective membranes. Having an exchange capacity of several equivalents per liter, membranes prepared from such material can be expected to have a very low resistance, that is, a very high permeability for the critical ions.[41] The first successful work in this direction was carried out by Wyllie and Patnode.[49]

Later, several groups of investigators took up this general line of work.[50] However, none of the membranes prepared seems to offer as yet any advantages for physicochemical investigations over the here-described permselective collodion-base membranes, nor do they seem desirable as yet for model studies of biological interest.

The subsequent paragraphs review some of the systematic investigations on *the electrochemistry of permselective collodion-base membranes.* Other types of permselective membranes seem to follow the same general pattern.

The measurement of the *membrane concentration potentials* consisted of the determination of the electromotive force that arises in the cell electrolyte c_1 | membrane | electrolyte c_2, the sign referring to the solution with the concentration c_2, the more dilute solution.

It is immaterial whether specific reversible electrodes are used (if they exist) or calomel electrodes with KCl-agar bridges. The results are the same within the limits of the experimental error, provided the appropriate corrections for the asymmetry of the two liquid junction potentials arising at the potassium chloride bridges are introduced.

Membranes of ion exchange character in such concentration cells can respond electromotively in a correct manner only if their movable, "critical" ions are the same as those contained in the outside solution; in other words, the membranes, or at least their electromotively functional pores, must be saturated by ion exchange with the critical species of ions under consideration. The periods required for this depend upon the thickness and density of the membrane as well as the nature of the critical ion, lasting from half an hour to several hours with the permselective collodion and collodion-base membranes.[51] If a membrane that is already saturated with a particular species of critical ions is transferred to solutions of different concentration containing the same species of critical ion, its electromotive response in most instances is immediately correct and reproducible; adaptation periods of more than 2 min. are rare.[51] This is important in the use of these membranes as practical physicochemical tools, for instance, as membrane electrodes.

The final, stable concentration potential across a given membrane is a function of the nature, the concentration ratio, and the absolute concentrations of the electrolyte in solution. Following an established procedure, we use the concentration ratio 1:2 in our experimental work.

The significance and the physical meaning of membrane concentration potential ϵ can be visualized by reference to its theoretical upper limit, the calculated potential ϵ_{max}, which would arise if the membrane behaved under a given set of conditions as an ideal machine for the reversible transfer of the critical ion.

The calculations of the theoretically possible maximum values of the concentration potential ϵ_{max} are based on well-known conventional assumptions concerning the meaning of single-ion activities, a topic that cannot be discussed here.[52] The computation of ϵ_{max} is based on the general equation

$$\epsilon_{max} = \frac{RT}{nF} \ln \frac{a_+^{(1)}}{a_+^{(2)}} \tag{2a}$$

and

$$\epsilon_{max} = \frac{-RT}{nF} \ln \frac{a_-^{(1)}}{a_-^{(2)}} \tag{2b}$$

for negative and positive membranes respectively. $a_+^{(1)}$ and $a_+^{(2)}$ are the activities $c_+^{(1)}\gamma_+^{(1)}$ and $c_+^{(2)}\gamma_+^{(2)}$ of the cations in solutions 1 and 2; $a_-^{(1)}$ and $a_-^{(2)}$ correspondingly are $c_-^{(1)}\gamma_-^{(1)}$ and $c_-^{(2)}\gamma_-^{(2)}$. In the case of uni-univalent electrolytes, the mean activity coefficients were used ($\gamma_+ = \gamma_\pm$; $\gamma_- = \gamma_\pm$). With the uni-bivalent and bi-univalent electrolytes, potassium sulfate and magnesium chloride, the activity coefficient for the univalent critical ions is calculated with the assumption that their activities are the same as those of the potassium and chloride ions, respectively, in potassium chloride solution of the same ionic strength.

The accuracy of the calculated ϵ_{max} values in the more dilute solutions, depending on the electrolyte used, might be estimated to be of the order of about 0.05 to ±0.10 mv.; with the highest concentrations, the error might be appreciably greater.

Table 2 presents the data for potassium chloride and hydrochloric acid cells obtained with an oxidized collodion membrane and a sul-

TABLE 2. CONCENTRATION POTENTIALS (c_1:c_2 = 2:1) OF TWO ELECTROLYTES ACROSS A TYPICAL PERMSELECTIVE OXIDIZED COLLODION MEMBRANE AND A REPRESENTATIVE PERMSELECTIVE SULFONATED POLYSTYRENE COLLODION-BASE MEMBRANE (T = 25.00 ± 0.05° C.)

1	2	3	4	5	6	7
		Potassium Chloride			Hydrochloric Acid	
		Concentration Potential ϵ			Concentration Potential ϵ	
Concentration of Electrolyte Solutions c_1:c_2	Theoretical Maximum, ϵ_{max}	Oxidized Collodion Membrane	Sulfonated Polystyrene Collodion Membrane	Theoretical Maximum, ϵ_{max}	Oxidized Collodion Membrane	Sulfonated Polystyrene Collodion Membrane
equiv./liter	mv.	mv.	mv.	mv.	mv.	mv.
0.002/0.001	17.45	17.20	17.25	17.45	17.45	17.45
0.004/0.002	17.31	17.04	17.19	17.34	17.26	17.26
0.01/0.005	17.10	16.95	16.97	17.15	17.02	17.08
0.02/0.01	16.86	16.74	16.74	16.97	16.66	16.88
0.04/0.02	16.63	16.47	16.52	16.84	16.04	....
0.1/0.05	16.30	15.80	16.10	16.76	15.31	16.59
0.2/0.1	16.11	15.09	15.74	16.87	15.33	....
0.4/0.2	15.95	13.90	15.40	17.49	15.66	17.37
1.0/0.5	16.32	10.93	14.58	19.89	17.7	19.1
2.0/1.0	17.34	8.01	13.86	24.39	22.0	23.2

fonated polystyrene collodion-base membrane.[42, 43] The reproducibility of the individual measurements is here better than ±0.05 mv., except at the highest concentrations of hydrochloric acid. Analogous data for lithium chloride and potassium sulfate measured (±0.1 mv.) across a typical oxidized permselective collodion membrane are presented for easier visualization in Fig. 7.[52] The broken line represents

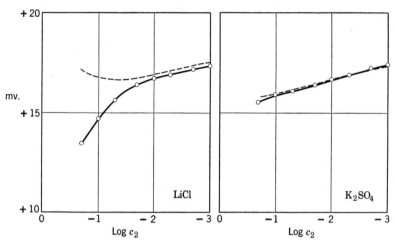

Fig. 7. Concentration potentials $c_1{:}c_2 = 2{:}1$ across a typical permselective oxidized collodion membrane.

calculated ϵ_{max} values, the circles are experimental points, the concentrations noted in the figure being the lower concentration in each cell. The deviation of the experimentally determined concentration potential ϵ from ϵ_{max} at any given concentration level, with the below-stated restrictions, can be considered a direct measure of the deviation of the membrane from ideality.

Table 3 and Fig. 8 bring corresponding data for four electrolytes and a typical permselective protamine collodion membrane.[53]

TABLE 3. CONCENTRATION POTENTIALS $(c_1{:}c_2 = 2{:}1)$ OF TWO ELECTROLYTES ACROSS A TYPICAL PERMSELECTIVE PROTAMINE COLLODION MEMBRANE $(T = 25.00 \pm 0.05°C.)$

Concentration of Electrolyte Solutions, $c_1{:}c_2$	Potassium Chloride		Potassium Iodate	
	Theoretical Maximum, ϵ_{max}	Concentration Potential ϵ	Theoretical Maximum, ϵ_{max}	Concentration Potential ϵ
equiv./liter	mv.	mv.	mv.	mv.
0.002/0.001	−17.5	−16.7	−17.5	−16.2
0.004/0.002	−17.3	−16.8	−17.3	−16.2
0.01/0.005	−17.1	−16.5	−16.9	−16.1
0.02/0.01	−16.9	−16.5	−16.7	−16.0
0.04/0.02	−16.6	−16.2	−16.1	−14.9
0.1/0.05	−16.3	−15.5	−15.1	−12.4
0.2/0.1	−16.1	−14.8	−14.1	−10.2
0.4/0.2	−16.0	−13.5	....	....

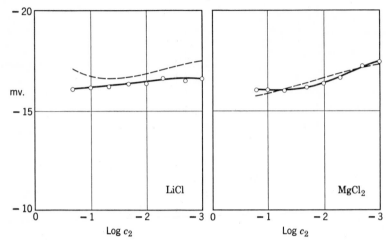

Fig. 8.   Concentration potentials $c_1 : c_2 = 2:1$ across a typical permselective protamine collodion membrane.

The results presented in Tables 2 and 3 and Figs. 7 and 8 are in
best agreement with the theoretical expectation.   Most conspicuous is
the close agreement over wide concentration ranges of the experimental
and the calculated ϵ values, with the electrolytes having bivalent non-
critical ions, K_2SO_4 and $MgCl_2$, respectively.

With the acidic membranes (Table 2 and Fig. 7) the experimental
ϵ values in chains with uni-univalent electrolytes at low concentrations
very closely approach the calculated ones.   As the concentration increases the deviations become larger: the membranes lose a significant
part of their ionic selectivity due to the mechanism which was mentioned in discussing Fig. 1.

A loss of ionic selectivity is most pronounced and occurs at the lowest concentration with the oxidized collodion membrane in the cells
with hydrochloric acid.   The sulfonated polystyrene collodion membrane, because of its strong acid character, maintains its high ionic
selectivity even in fairly highly concentrated solutions of acid.

The higher selectivity at higher concentrations of neutral electrolytes of the sulfonated polystyrene collodion membrane as compared
to the oxidized collodion membrane is due to the higher charge density
in the pores of the sulfonated polystyrene collodion membrane.

It might be added that the sulfonated polystyrene collodion-base
membranes show a close agreement, at least at low concentrations, between experimental and calculated ϵ values in concentration cells involving the alkaline earth-metal ions as critical ions.[54]

The data obtained with permselective protamine collodion membranes and uni-univalent electrolytes (Table 3 and Fig. 8) show that an ideal degree of ionic selectivity is not reached in a single instance. Even at the lowest concentrations a highly significant difference exists between the measured and the theoretically possible maximum concentration potentials.

The minor differences between the various uni-univalent electrolytes can readily be understood on the basis of steric hindrance; some pores that are accessible on a purely steric basis to one species of ions may be inaccessible to ions that (in the hydrated state) are of a larger size.

The permselective protamine membranes, with which the data of Table 3 and Fig. 8 were obtained, have not the same degree of perfection as that of the electronegative permselective membranes. More highly selective protamine membranes have been obtained more recently [44] but have not yet been studied in detail.

We are refraining from an evaluation of the data on concentration potentials in terms of transference numbers according to equation 1, mainly for the following reasons.

The calculated maximum potential values are based on somewhat arbitrary non-thermodynamic assumptions and may, therefore, involve a significant systematic error, also the accuracy of the experimental data is limited, 0.05 to 0.1 mv. in most instances. Thus, in the region of highest membrane selectivity, which is of primary interest in the present context, transference numbers calculated from such data are all so close to unity that the existing minor variations become uncertain and thus lose most of their significance. Moreover, in evaluating transference numbers and thus also ionic selectivities of membranes from concentration potential data according to equation 1 it is assumed that a leak of non-critical ions across the membranes is the only factor that causes the measured potential to be less than the calculated theoretical maximum. However, several complicating factors may conceivably arise, which would become particularly significant with membranes of high selectivity; they are poorly understood as yet and await further experimental exploration. Water transport, for instance, across the membrane must be expected to lower the potentials significantly whenever the transfer of ions is unavoidably coupled with the transport of water against its activity gradient. This effect could be due to the hydration of ions or to electrophoretic effects.[41, 55] Membrane hydrolysis, too, may conceivably lower the measured potential in dilute solutions of neutral electrolytes (but not in solutions of acids). It therefore becomes inadvisable to equate a putative deficit in membrane concentration potential with a lack of ionic selectivity. Small deviations of membranes from ideal ionic selectivity are better studied by more direct methods, particularly by the determination of the (relative) rates of exchange of both critical and non-critical ions across a membrane (see below); such studies should be carried out preferentially with radioactive tracers.[52, 56]

The *resistance* data available on permselective membranes are still quite inadequate in scope. Moreover, in the most extensive measurements presented thus far,[57, 58] alternating current of a single frequency only was used, but truly reliable and meaningful data can generally result only from carefully designed impedance studies at a great variety of frequencies.[57]

Representative resistance data obtained with a permselective collodion and a permselective protamine collodion membrane of medium resistance between test-tube-shaped platinized platinum electrodes at $25.00 \pm 0.05°$ C. are listed in Table 4.[57] Collodion-base permselective membranes of considerably lower resistance than those shown in Table 4 have been prepared, as can be seen below in column 1 of Table 5.[42]

A thorough study of the resistance of different types of permselective membranes is urgently needed, particularly in the concentration range of highest ionic selectivity. Such data are bound to throw much light

TABLE 4. THE ELECTRICAL RESISTANCES OF TWO TYPICAL PERMSELECTIVE COLLODION-BASE MEMBRANES OF MODERATELY HIGH RESISTANCE IN CONTACT WITH SOLUTIONS OF SEVERAL ELECTROLYTES AT THREE CONCENTRATION LEVELS

Electrolyte Solution	Oxidized Collodion Membrane	Protamine Collodion Membrane	Electrolyte Solution	Oxidized Collodion Membrane	Protamine Collodion Membrane
equiv./liter	Ω cm.^{2}	Ω cm.^{2}	equiv./liter	Ω cm.^{2}	Ω cm.^{2}
KCl			MgCl$_2$		
0.1	230	1,180	0.1	9,610	2,110
0.01	480	3,930	0.01	14,800	8,330
0.001	1,760	7,830	0.001	21,600	35,300
K$_2$SO$_4$			HCl		
0.1	240	36,300	0.1	250	....
0.01	610	39,500	0.01	510	....
0.001	3,260	45,700	0.001	2,120	....
K$_3$-Citrate			K-Acetate		
0.1	200	....	0.1	....	6,320
0.01	490	....	0.01	....	11,000
0.001	3,980	....	0.001	....	22,300
LiCl			KF		
0.1	630	1,660	0.1	....	2,250
0.01	1,100	4,980	0.01	....	6,740
0.001	5,130	9,080	0.001	....	13,600

on the geometrical and electrical structure of membranes and, more important, on the details of the ionic transport mechanisms in membranes in general. Of considerable interest here, particularly from the theoretical point of view, is a series of papers, three by G. Schmidt and two by G. Schmidt and H. Schwarz.[59]

The conductance of commercial-type ion exchangers was studied in a pioneering paper by Heymann and O'Donnell;[60] their work is of fundamental interest in the membrane field. Some more data on the resistance of ion exchange resin membranes of considerable ionic selectivity[50] were subsequently presented by several investigators.

The *water permeability* of the permselective collodion base membranes is low, being practically negligible in many instances.[42,47] For example, a solution of 0.2 M sucrose was placed inside a membrane which had a resistance of about 2.4 ohms per 100 cm.^{2} in 0.1 N potassium chloride solution. The rate of water movement under these conditions (corresponding to a hydrostatic pressure of 50 meters of water pressure) amounted to only 0.02 ml. per 100 cm.^{2} of membrane surface per hour.[42] In this respect the collodion-base permselective membranes offer a great advantage in many physicochemical experiments over the commercial-type resin membranes.

Closely related to the resistance of the membranes is the *rate of exchange* of ions across them. This rate, under standard conditions, is a convenient measure of ionic membrane permeability. It is of great practical importance in the use of the membranes in various physicochemical studies.

If an ideally ion-selective membrane separates two solutions of strong electrolytes, only the critical ions exchange across the membrane; if a membrane is not ideally ion-selective, a "leak" of non-critical ions also occurs.

For the determination of the rates of ion exchange and the leak of non-critical ions, test-tube-shaped permselective membranes (active area about 50 cm.^{2}) were filled with 25 ml. solution of one electrolyte, e.g., KNO$_3$, and immersed in a test tube containing a 25-ml. solution of the same concentration of some other electrolyte, e.g., NH$_4$Cl. Both solutions were stirred. After measured time intervals portions of the solution initially containing the potassium nitrate were analyzed for ammonia and for chloride. The initial rates obtained in such experiments with 0.1 N solutions of the mentioned pair of uni-univalent electrolytes and several sulfonated polystyrene collodion-base membranes of different standard resistance in 0.1 N potassium chloride solution, ρ^*, are summarized in Table 5; some analogous experiments[42] were carried out also with solutions of a pair of electrolytes with bivalent

TABLE 5. THE RATES OF MOVEMENT OF CRITICAL AND NON-CRITICAL IONS ACROSS VARIOUS PERMSELECTIVE SULFONATED POLYSTYRENE COLLODION-BASE MEMBRANES IN THE SYSTEM, 0.1 N KNO$_3$ || 0.1 N NH$_4$Cl ($T = 22° \pm 2°$ C.)

1	2	3	4
Resistance of Membrane in 0.1 N KCl, ρ^* Ω cm.^{2}	Initial Rate of Movement of NH$_4^+$ μequiv./hr.-cm.^{2}	Initial Rate of Movement of Cl$^-$ μequiv./hr.-cm.^{2}	Ratio of Initial Rates of Movement of NH$_4^+$ to Cl$^-$
22	93	0.167	560
27	156	0.28	560
38	37	0.050	740
75	12.0	0.0076	1580
195	4.9	0.00234	2100
420	1.63	0.00098	1660

non-critical ions (NH$_4$)$_2$C$_2$O$_4$ || K$_2$SO$_4$. Data obtained at various concentrations with a pair of uni-univalent electrolytes and a membrane of medium resistance ($\rho^* = 80\Omega$ cm.^{2}) are given in Table 6.[42]

TABLE 6. THE RATES OF EXCHANGE OF CRITICAL AND NON-CRITICAL IONS ACROSS A TYPICAL PERMSELECTIVE SULFONATED POLYSTYRENE COLLODION-BASE MEMBRANE AT VARIOUS CONCENTRATION LEVELS IN THE SYSTEM, NH$_4$Cl(c_1) || KNO$_3$(c_1) ($T = 25.0°$ C.)

1	2	3	4
Concentration (c_1) equiv./liter	Initial Rate of Movement of NH$_4^+$ μequiv./hr.-cm.^{2}	Initial Rate of Movement of Cl$^-$ μequiv./hr.-cm.^{2}	Ratio of Initial Rates of Movement of NH$_4^+$ to Cl$^-$
0.01	9.8	0.000147	67,000
0.02	9.8	0.00054	18,100
0.05	10.2	0.00223	4,600
0.10	11.5	0.0090	1,280
0.20	12.3	0.0277	440
0.50	14.5	0.143	101
1.00	17.0	0.44	39
2.00	19.0	1.34	14.2

Comparing first the *initial rate of movement of the critical ions*, the cations (column 2 of Table 5), across various membranes with their standard membrane resistance (column 1), it can be seen that there is a rough inverse proportionality except for the second membrane listed, which falls out of line for some unknown reason. The *initial rate of movement of the* (univalent) *non-critical ions*, the anions (column 3), shows a similar but considerably steeper inverse relationship with the membrane resistance.

The *ratio of the initial rates* of movement of the cations to that of the anions (column 4 of Table 5) can be taken as a direct *measure of the ionic selectivity* of the membranes under the conditions of the experiment; its reciprocal may be defined as the *relative "leak"* of non-critical ions.

In the experiments with 0.1 N $(NH_4)_2C_2O_4$ || 0.1 N K_2SO_4 the leak of anions was so small that after a month it could be detected only in the case of the first two membranes in Table 5, which are of rather low resistance. The rate of leak of oxalate ions with these relatively leaky membranes was approximately 1000 times less than the rates of leak of chloride ions; the selectivities of even these membranes in the uni-bivalent 0.1 N electrolyte system are, therefore, of the order of 500,000 to 1. The selectivities with the uni-bivalent electrolyte system of the more highly selective membranes of Table 5 would be expected to be considerably higher.[42]

The data on the *concentration dependence of the rates of exchange of critical ions*, the cations (column 2, Table 6), show that for a 200-fold concentration change there is only a 2-fold change in the rate of exchange of cations across the membrane. The *rate of leak of non-critical ions*, the anions (column 3), however, changes by a factor of more than 9000 over this concentration range.[42] The data on the ratio of the rates of movement of the critical and non-critical ions (column 4) demonstrate in a striking manner how the selectivity changes with concentration. The considerable change in selectivity with concentration which is observed in the range of the more dilute solutions could not have been predicted from concentration potential data, as was explained before.

The data of Tables 5 and 6 help to define the conditions under which the sulfonated polystyrene collodion-base membranes can be used without significant disturbances due to leak. In fairly dilute solutions of uni-univalent electrolytes and in dilute and in rather concentrated solutions of uni-bivalent electrolytes, the better membranes are nearly perfect tools for exacting membrane studies, e.g., studies on membrane equilibria.

Similar less detailed studies of the rate of exchange of critical ions (anions in this case) across permselective protamine membranes of the older, significantly leaky type yielded results analogous to those obtained with the acidic membranes. The leak of non-critical ions (cations), however, is known to be considerably larger.

It might be added that the *exchange capacity* of even the most highly active collodion-base membranes is only several tenths of a micro-equivalent per square centimeter. This might be of considerable advantage for certain physicochemical studies involving limited quantities of solutions.

The importance of the permselective membranes from a wider point of view lies in the fact that membranes are available which have a degree of ionic selectivity which is higher by several orders of magnitude than any previously available membranes of high ionic selectivity; equally important, their resistance per unit area is several orders of magnitude lower.[1, 41, 47] Ionic processes across permselective membranes occur therefore at rates that are several orders of magnitude greater than those obtainable with the older types of membranes. The permselective membranes provide thus a new and unique tool for a great variety of studies that formerly were not in the realm of experimental possibility.

Acknowledgments. The author wishes to thank the editors of the *Journal of General Physiology* and of the *Journal of Physical (and Colloid) Chemistry* for permission to quote freely from earlier papers and to reproduce a number of graphs. He is particularly indebted to the Electrochemical Society, to the editors of the *Journal of the Electrochemical Society,* and to the editors of the *Annals of the New York Academy of Sciences* for kind permission to utilize verbatim lengthy sections of some of his earlier reviews.

REFERENCES

1. K. Sollner, *J. Phys. Chem., 49,* 47 (1945).
2. M. Planck, *Vorlesungen über Thermodynamik,* 5th Ed., pp. 218 ff., Veit & Co., Leipzig, 1917.
3. A. Krogh, *Trans. Faraday Soc., 33,* 912 (1937).
4. J. H. van't Hoff, *Z. physik. Chem., 9,* 485 (1892).
5. R. Beutner, *Die Entstehung elektrischer Ströme in lebenden Geweben,* Ferdinand Enke, Stuttgart, 1920; *Physical Chemistry of Living Tissues and Life Processes,* Williams & Wilkins Co., Baltimore, 1933; "Bioelectricity," in O. Glasser, *Medical Physics,* Year Book Publishers, Chicago, 1944 (also re-edited separately with an explanatory introduction, Hahnemann Medical College and Hospital, Philadelphia, 1944).
6. K. Sollner and C. W. Carr, *J. Gen. Physiol., 26,* 17 (1942); *26,* 309 (1943).
7. K. Sollner, *J. Phys. Chem., 49,* 171 (1945).
8. L. Michaelis, *Bull. Natl. Research Council* (U. S.), *69,* 119 (1929); *Kolloid-Z., 62,* 2 (1933).
9. L. Michaelis and A. Fujita, *Biochem. Z., 158,* 28 (1925); *164,* 23 (1925); L. Michaelis and S. Dokan, *Biochem. Z., 162,* 258 (1925); L. Michaelis and K. Hayashi, *Biochem. Z., 173,* 411 (1926); L. Michaelis and W. A. Perlzweig, *J. Gen. Physiol., 10,* 575 (1927); L. Michaelis, R. McL. McEllsworth, and A. A. Weech, *J. Gen. Physiol., 10,* 671 (1927); L. Michaelis, A. A. Weech, and

A. Yamatori, *J. Gen. Physiol.*, *10*, 685 (1927); L. Michaelis and A. A. Weech, *J. Gen. Physiol.*, *11*, 147 (1927).

10. K. Sollner, *J. Phys. Chem.*, *49*, 265 (1945).
11. R. Collander, *Kolloidchem. Beih.*, *19*, 72 (1924); *20*, 273 (1925); *Soc. Sci. Fennica, Commentationes Biol.*, *2*, No. 6 (1926).
12. K. Sollner, *Z. Elektrochem.*, *36*, 36, 234 (1930).
13. M. Dutrochet, *Ann. chim. et phys.*, *60*, 337 (1835).
14. J. Loeb, *J. Gen. Physiol.*, *1*, 717 (1919); *2*, 87, 173, 225, 387, 563, 659, 673 (1920); *4*, 213, 463 (1922); *5*, 89 (1923).
15. J. Loeb, *J. Gen. Physiol.*, *2*, 173 (1920).
16. J. Loeb, *J. Gen. Physiol.*, *2*, 577 (1920).
17. K. Sollner and I. Abrams, *J. Gen. Physiol.*, *24*, 1 (1940).
18. K. Sollner, I. Abrams, and C. W. Carr, *J. Gen. Physiol.*, *24*, 467 (1941).
19. T. Graham, *Trans. Roy. Soc. (London)*, *144*, 177 (1854).
20. P. Girard, *Compt. rend.*, *146*, 927 (1908).
21. F. E. Bartell, "Membrane Potentials and Their Relation to Anomalous Osmosis," in J. H. Mathews, *Colloid Symposium Monograph*, *1*, Department of Chemistry, University of Wisconsin, Madison, 1923; F. E. Bartell and O. E. Madison, *J. Phys. Chem.*, *24*, 444, 593 (1920); F. E. Bartell and D. C. Carpenter, *J. Phys. Chem.*, *27*, 101, 252, 346 (1923).
22. H. Freundlich, *Kolloid-Z.*, *18*, 11 (1916).
23. G. Preuner and O. Roder, *Z. Elektrochem.*, *29*, 54 (1923).
24. F. Dolezalek and F. Krüger, *Z. Elektrochem.*, *12*, 669 (1906).
25. R. Höber, *Physiol. Revs.*, *16*, 52 (1936).
26. R. Höber, *Physical Chemistry of Cells and Tissues*, Blakiston Company, Philadelphia, 1945.
27. K. Sollner and A. Grollman, *Z. Elektrochem.*, *38*, 274 (1932).
28. A. Grollman and K. Sollner, *Trans. Elektrochem. Soc.*, *61*, 487 (1932).
29. L. Michaelis, *The Effects of Ions in Colloidal Systems*, Williams & Wilkins Co., Baltimore, 1925.
30. R. A. Gortner, *Outlines of Biochemistry*, 2nd Ed., John Wiley & Sons, Inc., New York, 1938.
31. K. Sollner, I. Abrams, and C. W. Carr, *J. Gen. Physiol.*, *25*, 7 (1941).
32. K. Sollner and J. Anderman, *J. Gen. Physiol.*, *27*, 433 (1944).
33. K. Sollner, C. W. Carr, and I. Abrams, *J. Gen. Physiol.*, *25*, 411 (1942).
34. T. Teorell, *Proc. Soc. Exptl. Biol. Med.*, *33*, 282 (1935); *Proc. Natl. Acad. Sci. U. S.*, *21*, 152 (1935).
35. K. H. Meyer and J.-F. Sievers, *Helv. Chim. Acta*, *19*, 649, 665, 987 (1936); K. H. Meyer, *Trans. Faraday Soc.*, *33*, 1073 (1937).
36. T. Teorell, *Z. Elektrochem.*, *55*, 460 (1951); *Progr. Biophys. and Biophys. Chem.*, *3*, 305 (1953).
37. R. Loosjes, *pH-Meting in Suspensies*, Scheltema en Holkema's Boekhandel en Uitgeversmaatschappij, N. V. Amsterdam, 1942; *Chem. Weekblad*, *46*, 902 (1950).
38. K. Sollner, *J. Colloid Sci.*, *8*, 179 (1953).
39. H. P. Gregor and K. Sollner, *J. Phys. Chem.*, *50*, 53 (1946).
40. H. P. Gregor and K. Sollner, *J. Phys. Chem.*, *50*, 88 (1946).
41. K. Sollner, *J. Electrochem. Soc.*, *97*, 139C (1950).
42. R. Neihof, *J. Phys. Chem.*, *58*, 916 (1954).
43. K. Sollner and R. Neihof, *Arch. Biochem. and Biophys.*, *33*, 166 (1951).

44. R. Neihof, Ph.D. Thesis, University of Minnesota, Minneapolis, 1950.
45. I. Abrams and K. Sollner, *J. Gen. Physiol., 26,* 369 (1943).
46. L. Michaelis and A. Fujita, *Biochem. Z., 161,* 47 (1925).
47. C. W. Carr and K. Sollner, *J. Gen. Physiol., 28,* 119 (1944).
48. C. W. Carr, H. P. Gregor, and K. Sollner, *J. Gen. Physiol., 28,* 179 (1945).
49. M. R. J. Wyllie and H. W. Patnode, *J. Phys. & Colloid Chem., 54,* 204 (1950).
50. K. F. Bonhoeffer, L. Miller, and U. Schindewolf, *Z. physik. Chem., 198,* 270 (1951); K. F. Bonhoeffer and U. Schindewolf, *Z. physik. Chem., 198,* 281 (1951); J. T. Clark, J. A. Marinsky, W. Juda, N. W. Rosenberg, and S. Alexander, *J. Phys. Chem., 56,* 100 (1952); W. Juda and W. A. McRae, *J. Am. Chem. Soc., 72,* 1044 (1950); W. Juda, N. W. Rosenberg, J. A. Marinsky, and A. A. Kasper, *J. Am. Chem. Soc., 74,* 3736 (1952); T. R. E. Kressman, *Nature, 165,* 568 (1950); G. Manecke, *Z. Elektrochem., 55,* 672 (1951); G. Manecke, *Z. physik. Chem., 201,* 193 (1952); A. G. Winger, G. W. Bodamer, and R. Kunin, *J. Electrochem. Soc., 100,* 178 (1953).
51. K. Sollner and H. P. Gregor, *J. Phys. Chem., 50,* 470 (1946); *54,* 325 (1950).
52. K. Sollner and H. P. Gregor, *J. Phys. Chem., 51,* 299 (1947).
53. K. Sollner and H. P. Gregor, *J. Phys. & Colloid Chem., 54,* 330 (1950).
54. C. W. Carr, *Arch. Biochem. and Biophys., 43,* 147 (1953); *46,* 424 (1953).
55. G. Scatchard, *J. Am. Chem. Soc., 75,* 2883 (1953).
56. R. Schlögl and F. Helfferich, *Z. Elektrochem., 56,* 644 (1952); R. Schlögl, *Z. Elektrochem., 57,* 195 (1953).
57. K. Sollner and H. P. Gregor, *J. Colloid Sci., 6,* 557 (1951); *7,* 37 (1952).
58. G. Manecke, *Z. physik. Chem., 201,* 193 (1952).
59. G. Schmidt, *Z. Elektrochem., 54,* 424 (1950); *55,* 229 (1951); *56,* 181 (1952); G. Schmidt and H. Schwarz, *Z. Elektrochem., 55,* 295, 684 (1951); *56,* 35 (1952).
60. E. Heymann and I. J. O'Donnell, *J. Colloid Sci., 4,* 405 (1949).

5·

Membranes of High Electrochemical Activity in Studies of Biological Interest

Karl Sollner, Sheldon Dray,
Eugene Grim, and Rex Neihof *

The membranes described in the preceding chapter lend themselves readily to a great variety of studies of biological interest. Some of our investigations in this direction, in part unpublished, are reviewed in the following pages.

ANOMALOUS OSMOSIS

Anomalous osmosis across membranes of significant electrolyte permeability—of the dialyzing type—has been of interest to physiologists for over a hundred years because this phenomenon seems to offer some basis for an explanation of the translocation of liquids across living membranes, which seems to defy any explanation based on the concept of the normal Pfeffer-van't Hoff osmosis.

Although the basic physicochemical mechanism of anomalous osmosis, as outlined in the preceding chapter, is now reasonably well understood, it has not been demonstrated clearly that anomalous osmosis can occur to a significant extent under conditions that are at least superficially similar to those existing *in vivo*, the published data referring almost exclusively to the rates of pressure rise in systems in which a membrane separates the solution of an electrolyte from distilled water.

Grim and Sollner [1,2] have studied certain aspects of this question in some detail. The first problem was to find a method that permits a

* From the Laboratory of Physical Biology, National Institute of Arthritis and Metabolic Diseases, National Institutes of Health, Public Health Service, Department of Health, Education, and Welfare, Bethesda, Maryland.

clear distinction between the contribution of normal osmosis and the contribution of anomalous osmosis towards the over-all, observed effect. Although the available data indicate that the contribution of normal osmosis is relatively small in the region of low concentrations in which these investigators were primarily interested, this is not true at the higher concentrations which are of physiological significance. Customarily, it is assumed that the extent of normal osmosis across a given membrane at a given concentration can be determined with solutions of the same concentration of some arbitrarily chosen non-electrolyte. This, however, is not true. Non-electrolytes of different molecular weight differ greatly in their osmotic efficacy because of the difference in permeability of a membrane for various solutes. Thus, it is inadvisable to estimate the magnitude of normal osmotic effects by the use of an arbitrarily chosen non-electrolytic reference solute.[1]

The solution of this problem lies in the use of membranes that can be brought in a reversible manner and without changes in geometrical structure into a charged state, positive or negative, and into the uncharged, isoelectric state.[1] With the membranes in the charged state anomalous osmosis can occur; the observed, gross osmotic effect is composed of a normal and an abnormal component. With the membrane in the isoelectric state anomalous osmosis does not occur; here the total observed osmotic effect is due to normal osmosis. Thus, the difference Δ between the effects with the membrane in the charged state and the effects with the membrane in the isoelectric state is a measure of the true anomalous osmosis. Amphoteric, essentially non-swelling membranes are the tool of choice for an investigation along these lines.

We have used preferentially oxyhemoglobin collodion membranes that are prepared, according to the method of Loeb, by the adsorption of hemoglobin on collodion membranes of suitably high porosity. These membranes have an isoelectric point near pH 6.75 at which they do not show any net charge; they can be readily charged positively or negatively by adjusting the pH of the solutions with which they are in contact. pH 4 and pH 10 were chosen in our work.

The experiments on osmotic transport rates were carried out with bag-shaped membranes tied to glass rings that were fitted with a rubber stopper carrying a cut-off part of a burette. The membrane was filled with one solution and immersed in a beaker containing the other solution. The liquid level of the inside solution was a few centimeters higher than the outside solution, back-filtration at this pressure being negligible. Both solutions were stirred. After the membrane had reached a satisfactory quasi-stationary state in preliminary runs, the initial rates of liquid movement were determined in experiments of 5-min. duration with fresh portions of the two solutions. These initial transport rates are expressed as milliliters per 100 cm.² of membrane area per hour.

Figure 1 demonstrates how the outlined method permits the separation of the anomalous osmotic effect from the over-all observed liquid movement, both in anomalous positive and anomalous negative osmosis, a minus sign indicating a movement of liquid into the more dilute solution. The osmolar concentration given in the graph refers

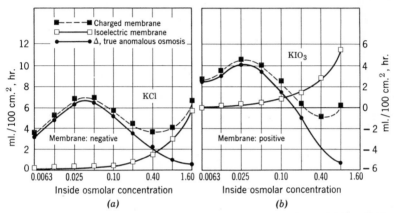

Fig. 1. The rates of transportation of liquid through an oxyhemoglobin collodion membrane in the charged state and in the isoelectric state, and the rates of true anomalous osmosis. $c_{in}:c_{out} = 2:1$.

to the inside solution that has twice the concentration of the outside solution. The heavy solid-line curves give the difference Δ between the effects observed in the charged state and those observed in the isoelectric state and thus represent the true anomalous osmotic component of the observed effect.

Figure 2 presents the rates of liquid transport by true anomalous osmosis through an oxyhemoglobin collodion membrane arrived at in this manner for several systems giving anomalous positive as well as anomalous negative osmosis. The data in this figure are also plotted on an osmolar, not on a molar basis, the concentration range of particular interest in mammalian physiology being indicated by crosshatching.

Figures 1 and 2 prove that, for single-solute, low-concentration-ratio systems, anomalous osmosis can occur at a rather conspicuous rate at physiological concentration levels. Thus, the main question

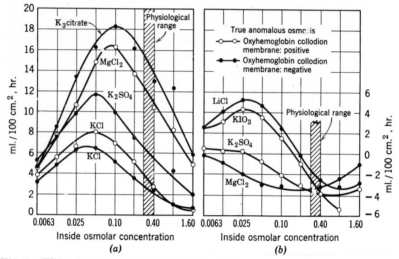

Fig. 2. The rates of transportation of liquid by true anomalous osmosis across an oxyhemoglobin collodion membrane in the charged state. $c_{in}:c_{out} = 2:1$. (a) Systems in which the theory predicts anomalous positive osmosis only. (b) Systems in which the theory predicts anomalous positive osmosis for low concentrations and anomalous negative osmosis for higher concentrations.

concerning the possibility that this phenomenon can occur in mammalian organisms is answered in the affirmative.

Of greater specific interest for mammalian physiology, however, than the just-discussed single-solute systems with 2:1 concentration ratios are systems containing more than one solute, particularly systems of this nature in which two solutions of identical over-all concentration (in the physiological range) are separated by the membrane.

Anomalous osmosis in systems with more than one solute has not been considered in the literature from a theoretical viewpoint. Space does not permit a discussion of this rather involved matter in any detail. Suffice it to say that such systems can be considered theoretically on the same basis as single-solute systems according to the general treatment of Sollner.[3]

Data of the type presented in Figs. 1 and 2 make it possible to predict semiquantitatively the extent of anomalous osmosis that can be expected in a particular system with two or more solutes, the situation being relatively simple in systems in which single-solute solutions are used.

The rates of true anomalous osmosis in two-or-more-solute systems can be determined by measuring the liquid transport rates with the membrane in the charged and in the isoelectric state, in the same manner as was done in the single-solute systems of Figs. 1 and 2.

Several experiments of this general nature with positive membranes and solutions of equal osmolar concentration are summarized in Table 1. The results with negative membranes, omitted here, are

TABLE 1. REPRESENTATIVE RATES OF TRANSPORTATION OF LIQUID AND OF TRUE ANOMALOUS OSMOSIS ACROSS AN OXYHEMOGLOBIN COLLODION MEMBRANE IN THE ELECTROPOSITIVE AND IN THE ISOELECTRIC STATE

Inside Solution		Outside Solution		Rates of Transport of Liquid		
				Membrane		True Anomalous Osmosis, Δ
Solute	Concentration Osmolarity	Solute	Concentration Osmolarity	Charged ml./100 cm.^{2} hr.	Isoelectric ml./100 cm.^{2} hr.	ml./100 cm.^{2} hr.
KCl	0.40	Glucose	0.40	+13.2	−7.0	+20.2
MgCl$_2$	0.20	Glucose	0.20	+70.0	+2.2	+67.8
MgCl$_2$	0.40	Glucose	0.40	+53.1	+1.7	+51.4
K$_2$SO$_4$	0.40	Glucose	0.40	−16.2	+0.8	−17.0
MgCl$_2$	0.40	KCl	0.40	+17.3	+3.4	+13.9
MgCl$_2$	0.40	KIO$_3$	0.40	+31.2	+1.4	+29.8
MgCl$_2$	0.40	K$_2$SO$_4$	0.40	+15.4	−1.8	+17.2
MgCl$_2$+ Glucose	0.20 0.20	Glucose	0.40	+58.5	+0.2	+58.3
MgCl$_2$+ KCl	0.20 0.20	KCl	0.40	+8.7	0.0	+8.7
MgCl$_2$+ KCl	0.20 0.20	K$_2$SO$_4$+ KIO$_3$	0.20 0.20	+12.1	−3.7	+15.8

analogous. In Table 1 a movement of liquid from the outside to the inside solution is indicated by a plus sign; a movement in the opposite direction by a minus sign.

Table 1 shows that true anomalous osmosis occurs at a very considerable rate in systems with more than one solute. With isoösmotic, 0.40 osmolar solutions of electrolytes the true anomalous osmotic liquid transport rates found are in the range of 8 to 30 ml./100 cm.^{2} hr. If one of the solutes is a non-electrolyte, these rates are about twice as high.

The potential physiological significance of the data on transport rates in Table 1 can be seen from the fact that they are, for instance, several times as high as the highest reported rates of intestinal absorption. They are of the same order of magnitude and in some cases considerably higher than the unidirectional rates of fluid movement which have been postulated as the physical basis of intestinal absorption.[4]   However, it must be emphasized that the foregoing data do not prove in any way that anomalous osmosis actually is an important mechanism in the translocation of liquid in the mammalian organism; it only furnishes evidence that such a process from the strictly physico-chemical point of view is a possibility.

PERMSELECTIVE MEMBRANES IN PREPARATIVE CHEMISTRY

The use of permselective membranes in preparative chemistry (and in industrial operations) for the purpose of the exchange, between solutions, of ions (including the exchange of the ions of water) is beginning to be explored.[5]   For example: The salts of pH-sensitive organic acids may be converted into the free acid either by membrane hydrolysis or by dialytic ion exchange against an acid without ever coming into contact with the latter as occurs in precipitation reactions. Non-electrolytes of medium and even of low molecular weight might be separated from electrolytes by the simultaneous use of both electropositive and electronegative membranes in diffusion dialysis; or ion exchange dialysis against outside solutions of an acid and a base, respectively, might be employed for the same purpose in a three-cell outfit; or, most promising, electrodialysis might be used to accelerate the speed of electrolyte removal from the middle cell.[5]   This latter possibility has recently attracted considerable industrial and popular interest.   The movement to the middle cell of anions from the cathode compartment and of cations from the anode compartment can be eliminated by the use of permselective membranes; outside solutions of considerable conductance become thus feasible.   Their use would greatly increase the efficiency of the process.

PERMSELECTIVE MEMBRANES AS MEMBRANE ELECTRODES

Of considerable scientific and practical interest is the use of permselective membranes as "membrane electrodes," which was demonstrated ten years ago.[6, 7]

The potential usefulness of membrane electrodes was first recognized by Haber,[8] after Nernst and Riesenfeld [9] had shown that any interphase (membrane) which in a concentration cell selectively allows the reversible transfer of only a single ion species from the one solution to the other gives rise to a potential and acts electromotively in a manner strictly analogous to a conventional reversible electrode for this ion.

The general theory of membrane electrodes has been discussed in some detail by Haber and collaborators,[8] Horowitz,[10] Marshall,[11] and most recently by Scatchard,[12] and therefore need not be reiterated here.

For many years the only membrane electrode of practical usefulness was the glass electrode until Marshall and collaborators succeeded in the preparation of clay membranes which, though sluggish in their electromotive response, are useful in the determination of the activities of univalent and in some instances also of bivalent cations.[11]

A detailed discussion of Marshall's pioneering work in this field is outside the scope of this review, since he now seems to consider his membranes rather as solid electrolyte phases than as porous membranes as the term is used here.

Permselective membranes, by virtue of their ability to act electromotively in the presence of a single species of critical ions like specific reversible electrodes, may be used for the electrometric determination of ion activities in such solutions. By their use it becomes possible to determine (with the restriction indicated) the activities of many ions for which specific reversible electrodes do not exist,[6,7] as with many anions, F^-, NO_3^-, acetate, ClO_3^-, ClO_4^-, IO_3^-, etc., or where specific reversible electrodes of the conventional type involve considerable experimental difficulties, as with the alkali and alkaline earth cations, Li^+, Na^+, K^+, Rb^+, Cs^+, Mg^{++}, Ca^{++}, etc., and with NH_4^+. For cation determinations the strong-acid-type sulfonated polystyrene collodion membranes [13,14] will be preferable in the future to the oxidized collodion membranes originally used.

The determination of ion activities by means of the permselective "membrane electrodes" may be made in various ways. The potential difference that arises between a known solution on the one side of the membrane and the solution of unknown concentration on the other side of the membrane may be evaluated on the basis of some calculated standard curve. Or better, it may be compared to an empirical curve determined for a specific membrane in advance. A third method consists of an electrometric titration: the membrane separates the solution of unknown concentration from water, to which electrolyte solution of known higher concentration is added stepwise; thereby the potential difference is diminished stepwise, and finally it is reversed. Zero potential difference indicates that the activity of the critical ion is the same on both sides of the membrane. The zero point is obtained conveniently and with considerable accuracy by plotting potential versus concentration data. The titration method makes it possible to minimize the uncertainties of the asymmetry of the liquid junction potentials arising from the use of nonspecific (e.g., calomel) electrodes. It also is less sensitive towards slight "leaks" in the membrane than the two other methods. With membranes that are already saturated with the critical ions under investigation, activity determinations can be made within a few minutes. Results with an error of less than ± 1 per cent may now routinely be obtained in wide concentration ranges. This method is readily applicable on the semimicrochemical and microchemical levels.[6, 7]

The variety of ions, the activity of which can be determined by means of the permselective collodion-base and similar membranes, has not been explored; the examples mentioned before by no means circumscribe the range of their usefulness. Generally speaking, the determination of the activities of all critical ions that form highly dissociated surface compounds with the fixed wall groups can be expected to fall within the range of the method.

The concentration range within which the membranes described in this paper can be used as membrane electrodes has likewise not been explored fully; it depends considerably upon the accuracy which is desired. At higher concentrations in which the membranes are significantly leaky, the nature of the non-critical ion in the two solutions becomes gradually more significant. However, it can be stated that the methods of empirical calibration curves and titration through zero, judiciously applied, permit the performance of fairly accurate determinations at least up to concentrations of several tenths normal, in which other factors such as the asymmetry of the liquid junction potentials begin to play a significant role.

It is obvious that any exchange resin type of membranes with adequate electromotive response may in principle be used as membrane electrodes. Their relative merits have to be decided on the basis of practical experimental considerations.

The obvious usefulness of membrane electrodes in protein chemistry, for instance, in connection with the problems of ion binding, is borne out by the pioneering work of Carr in this direction.[15]

GIBBS-DONNAN MEMBRANE EQUILIBRIA

The theoretical investigation of the Gibbs-Donnan membrane equilibrium has in the past outrun its experimental study. Extensive theoretical discussions of Gibbs-Donnan membrane equilibria can be found in the literature; their experimental study, however, was long confined to systems containing colloidal or semicolloidal ions as non-diffusible ions and to a few systems in which the ferrocyanide ion acted as the non-diffusible ion in conjunction with a copper-ferrocyanide membrane.[16, 17] Except for this last case, Donnan equilibria involving only strong inorganic electrolytes in which relatively small ions act as "non-diffusible" ions could not be studied; suitable membranes for such investigations were non-existent. Now, however, the permselective membranes lend themselves admirably to this purpose as is shown in a preliminary series of experiments.[18, 19]

In order to demonstrate the existence of a membrane equilibrium across a certain membrane it is only necessary to test experimentally the classical Donnan equations. For two uni-univalent electrolytes A^+X^- and B^+X^- and a membrane permeable for the cations A^+ and B^+, and impermeable for the anion X^- (such as the permselective collodion membranes), the Donnan equation, written in a convenient manner, reads:

$$\frac{a_{A^+}{}^{(1)}}{a_{B^+}{}^{(1)}} = \frac{a_{A^+}{}^{(2)}}{a_{B^+}{}^{(2)}} \tag{1}$$

where a is the activity of the respective ions in solutions 1 and 2. If the experimental system is selected so that the ions A^+ and B^+ have the same activities in solutions of the same ionic strength, then the ratios of the activity coefficients will be unity and one may use concentration c instead of activity; equation 1 becomes the expression

$$\frac{c_{A^+}{}^{(1)}}{c_{B^+}{}^{(1)}} = \frac{c_{A^+}{}^{(2)}}{c_{B^+}{}^{(2)}} \tag{2}$$

The theoretically predicted equilibrium conditions hold true if the ratio of the analytical concentrations of the two ions on both sides of the membrane, as determined by analytical procedures, is identical (and if the same final condition is reached independent of the original distribution of the diffusible ions between the two solutions).

Equation 2 was tested with the same experimental arrangement as described in the preceding chapter for the studies on the rate of exchange of ions across membranes. Osmotic equilibration can be established by the addition of the proper amount of a non-diffusible non-electrolyte (sucrose) to the more dilute solution, though this is not always necessary from the experimental point of view on account of the low water permeability of the permselective membranes.

The Donnan membrane equilibrium was established in the various systems in 3 to 24 hours according to the nature (resistance) of the membrane used. The systems did not change further significantly for periods of several days; thereafter a slight "leak" of non-critical ions became noticeable in many instances.

The results of three typical experiments on membrane equilibria across permselective collodion membranes are given in the self-explanatory Table 2. The ratio of the activity coefficients of the K^+ and NH_4^+ salts used in the pairs of solutions given in this table are nearly identical.

TABLE 2. GIBBS-DONNAN EQUILIBRIA ACROSS PERMSELECTIVE COLLODION MEMBRANES THAT INVOLVE ONLY STRONG INORGANIC ELECTROLYTES
(The anions are the non-diffusible ions.)

Ratio of Volumes of Solution in / Solution out	Solute	Original State millimoles/liter		Equilibrium State				Concentration Ratio $\frac{In}{Out}$	
				Experimental millimoles/liter		Calculated millimoles/liter			
		In	Out	In	Out	In	Out	Experimental	Calculated
1:1	NH_4^+	20.0	10.0	22.4	7.5	22.5	7.5	2.99 ± 0.05	3.00
	K^+	10.0	....	7.4	2.4	7.5	2.5	3.08 ± 0.10	3.00
	Cl^-	30.0	10.0	30.0	10.2	30.0	10.0	2.94 ± 0.05	3.00
	Sucrose	....	33	....	(33)	....	(33)	....	....
1:1	NH_4^+	30.0	....	22.4	7.5	22.5	7.5	2.99 ± 0.05	3.00
	K^+	....	10.0	7.5	2.5	7.5	2.5	3.00 ± 0.10	3.00
	Cl^-	30.0	10.0	29.8	10.1	30.0	10.0	2.95 ± 0.05	3.00
	Sucrose	....	33	....	(33)	....	(33)	....	....
1:10	NH_4^+	50.2	2.51	37.4	3.79	37.5	3.78	9.9 ± 0.3	9.9
	K^+	....	2.56	12.0	1.27	12.7	1.29	9.4 ± 0.4	9.9
	$C_2O_4^-$	25.1	2.54	24.7	2.53	25.1	2.54	9.8 ± 0.2	9.9
	Sucrose	....	39	....	(39)	....	(39)	....	....

Preliminary tests have shown that protamine collodion membranes are also usable for Donnan experiments.

The *determination of the activities of several coexisting species of ions of the same sign* for which specific electrodes are lacking can be based on the membrane equilibrium, namely, the consideration of the ion distribution under equilibrium condition *and* of the concomitant membrane potential.[20]

MOSAIC MEMBRANES

The heterogeneities that can be found in real membranes are by no means confined to differences in pore size, charge density and distribution, or a combination of these factors. Layered membranes and "mosaic" membranes composed of parts varying in other respects must likewise be considered. A convenient starting point in this field is the study of the simplest possible mosaic membranes, namely, membranes composed of parts that are strictly anion selective and other parts that are strictly cation selective. A quantitative theory of the electrolyte permeability of cation-selective membranes outlined more than 20

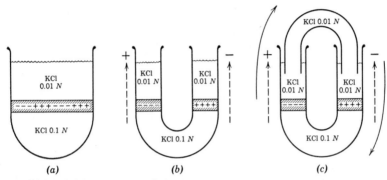

Fig. 3. Pictorial development of the theory of electrolyte permeability of mosaic membranes that are composed of ideally anion-selective and ideally cation-selective parts. (a) Mosaic membrane with adjacent cation-selective and anion-selective parts. (b) Spatial and electrical separation of the cation-selective and anion-selective parts of the membranes. (c) The spatially separated cation-selective and anion-selective parts joined electrically by a bridge of solution in an all-electrolytic circuit.

years ago by one of us [21] could more recently be tested, owing to the availability of the permselective collodion and protamine collodion membranes.

The theory of the electrolyte permeability of mosaic membranes that are composed of ideally anion-permeable and cation-permeable parts is most easily developed by reference to a sequence of line drawings.[21]

Figure 3a illustrates schematically a system in which a mosaic membrane of this type separates a lower compartment (of invariable volume) from an upper compartment, the striated structure in the figure indicating the membrane. The electronegative, cation-permeable (anion-impermeable) parts of the membrane are indicated by minus signs, and the electropositive, anion-permeable (cation-impermeable) parts by plus signs. The lower compartment is assumed to be filled with 0.1 N potassium chloride solution; and the upper compartment, with 0.01 N solution of the same electrolyte.

Contrary to certain ideas that are reviewed in Höber's book,[22] it was postulated that such membranes must permit the penetration of electrolytes from the lower compartment to the upper one. Cations move through the electronegative parts of the membrane and anions through the electropositive parts, neutralizing each other electrically. Thus a continuous movement of the electrolyte occurs across the membrane, which does not cease until equilibrium between the two compartments is established.

In formulating this qualitative concept in a manner that is susceptible to a quantitative test it is necessary to consider a system in which the cation-permeable and anion-permeable parts are separated from each other. Figure 3b shows a U-tube containing in its left arm an electronegative (cation-permeable) and in its right arm an electropositive (anion-permeable) membrane, both membranes being assumed to be of an ideal degree of ionic selectivity. The lower part of the system (having an invariable volume) is filled with 0.1 N potassium chloride solution, whereas the two separate compartments above the membranes contain 0.01 N solution of the same electrolyte. The only processes, according to the premises, that can occur in this system consist of the establishment of static membrane potentials (concentration potentials) across the two membranes and the establishment of a hydrostatic pressure in the lower compartment, because of the difference in water activity between the concentrated and the dilute solution.

The magnitude of each of the two membrane potentials in the system of Fig. 3b is numerically defined by the Nernst equation, as applicable to membranes of ideal ionic selectivity,

$$\epsilon = RT \ln \frac{a_1}{a_2} \tag{3}$$

where ϵ is the electromotive force and a_1 and a_2 are the molar activities of the electromotively active ion. The direction of the two electromotive forces is shown in Fig. 3b by broken-line arrows pointing at a plus and a minus sign, respectively, their numerical values being +55.1 mv. and −55.1 mv. for the pair of solutions indicated.

In order to reestablish in Fig. 3b the essential features of the situation represented in Fig. 3a, it would be necessary to connect the two compartments containing dilute solution by a liquid conduit filled with 0.01 N potassium chloride solution, as shown in Fig. 3c.

The system of Fig. 3c may be considered as a "Flüssigkeitsring," an "all-electrolytic electrical circuit," a (positive) electric current flowing in a clockwise direction through the system, as is indicated by the solid arrows in Fig. 3c. The total e.m.f. in the system, **E**, is $2 \times 55.1 = 110.2$ mv. The strength of the current, I, is defined by Ohm's law,

$$I = \frac{\mathbf{E}}{R} \tag{4}$$

where R is the total resistance of the system.

The current that flows in a clockwise direction in the system of Fig. 3c is transported through the negative membrane in the left arm of the system exclusively by cations that move clockwise, in the direction of the broken-line arrow; through the positive membrane in the right arm the electricity is transported exclusively by an equivalent quantity of anions that move in a counterclockwise direction, as indicated by a broken-line arrow.

Accordingly, the quantity of electrolyte (in equivalents) that moves in a given time in the mosaic system of Fig. 3c from the concentrated to the dilute solution must be numerically identical with the number of electrochemical equivalents of current (faradays) that flow in the system during the same period. The experimental proof of the theory of the electrolyte permeability of mosaic membranes thus consists in testing this prediction in model systems identical in all essential features with the all-electrolytic ring system of Fig. 3c.

The obvious approach to this problem lies in some alteration in the simple theoretical model of Fig. 3c that will permit the accurate determination of the current that flows in the system. One practical way of doing this is to cut the system at some suitable point and attach to the two open ends of the interrupted circuit two symmetrical electrodes that can reversibly take the current from and return it to the system. The two electrodes in turn are connected to each other by some conventional current-measuring instrument, a coulometer or a microammeter, and a closed circuit is thus reestablished. The electrodes must be chosen so that they do not bring about any significant change in the original system that would not occur on closed circuit in their absence. They may be either specific electrodes for one of the ions in the solutions or non-specific electrodes of the $Cu \mid CuSO_4 \mid$ agar bridge type.[23, 24]

The system shown in Fig. 4a illustrates schematically one possible arrangement, which makes use of silver-silver chloride electrodes in chloride solutions. It may be represented as a galvanic cell in the

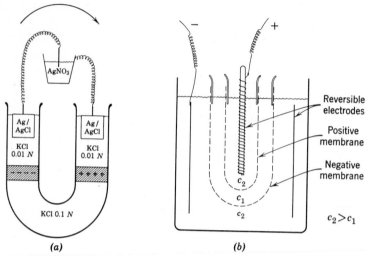

Fig. 4.   Mosaic membrane models with auxiliary electrodes through which the current flows. (a) A schematic model. (b) The experimental model.

conventional way, double vertical lines representing the negative and the positive membranes:

$$\text{Ag} \mid \text{AgCl} \mid \text{KCl } c_1 \overset{-}{\parallel} \text{KCl } c_2 \overset{+}{\parallel} \text{KCl } c_1 \mid \text{AgCl} \mid \text{Ag}$$
$$\quad\;\, \epsilon_1 \qquad\;\; \epsilon_2 \qquad\;\; \epsilon_3 \qquad\;\; \epsilon_4 \qquad\;\; \epsilon_2' \qquad\; \epsilon_1'$$

In this chain, the electromotive forces ϵ_1 and ϵ_1', and ϵ_2 and ϵ_2' are equal but opposite in direction; they cancel out and do not contribute to the total, effective e.m.f. of the cell.   The introduction of reversible and symmetrical electrodes in a mosaic model system makes it, therefore, possible to determine directly and accurately the number of faradays that flow in it during the period for which the circuit is closed.

Another possible approach, which avoids the use of auxiliary electrodes through which the current flows, consists in determining the current by measuring the potential difference by means of feeler electrodes across an element of the circuit whose resistance is known and does not change during the course of the experiment.[23]   Figure 5a sketches such an arrangement in a highly schematic manner; the planes of the direction of the probe electrodes are indicated by Y and Y'.

Space does not permit a discussion of the difficulties in building systems that are suitable from the experimental point of view.   The essentials of the geometry of the working models are shown in the schematic Figs. 4b and 5b.   The fundamental electrical identity of the systems in Figs. 4a and 4b and of Figs. 5a and 5b is evident.

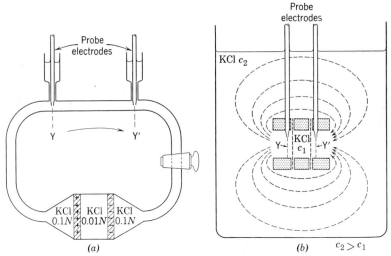

Fig. 5. All-electrolytic mosaic membrane models. (a) A schematic model. (b)
The experimental model.

The self-explanatory Table 3 summarizes some of the results obtained with model systems both with and without auxiliary electrodes
through which the current flows.[23, 24] The necessary correction for
"leak" of electrolyte across the membranes, due to their imperfection,
is noted in the sixth column of this table. The theory postulates numerical agreement of the data in the last two columns of this table.

TABLE 3. A COMPARISON OF THE QUANTITIES OF ELECTROLYTE AND OF ELEC-
TRICITY MOVED IN MODEL SYSTEMS OF MOSAIC MEMBRANES THAT ARE COM-
POSED OF NEARLY IDEALLY ANION- AND CATION-SELECTIVE PARTS

Electrolyte Solutions			Volume of Dilute Solution	Increase in Concentration of Dilute Solution	Correction for Leak	Equivalents of Electrolyte Moved	Electricity Moved
Electrolyte Used	Concentration on Closing of Circuit	Electrodes					
	equiv./liter		ml.	equiv./liter	equiv./liter	equiv. $\times$ 10^{-6}	$F \times$ 10^{-6}
KCl	0.050/0.00521	Ag | AgCl	70.0	0.00116	None	81.2	82.2
KCl	0.100/0.01050	Ag | AgCl	65.0	0.00105	0.00008	63.1	61.8
KCl	0.050/0.001500	Cu | CuSO$_4$ | agar	80.0	0.000420	None	33.6	33.5
K$_2$SO$_4$	0.050/0.001681	Cu | CuSO$_4$ | agar	74.0	0.000417	0.000064	26.1	25.7
KCl	0.050/0.001554	None	19.00	0.001308	0.000046	24.0	24.6
LiCl	0.050/0.004898	None	19.00	0.000657	0.000009	12.3	12.2
KIO$_3$	0.050/0.004938	None	19.00	0.000435	0.000019	7.90	8.08

The agreement between the data of the last two columns of Table 3
seems fully satisfactory in view of the experimental difficulties involved
in these experiments.

The more general importance of this study lies in the fact that it demonstrates that fairly complex membrane systems can be considered from a theoretical viewpoint and that quantitative predictions based on these considerations can be verified experimentally. This indicates that the time is ripe for a similar attack on more complex membrane problems that may be of much more immediate and wider biological interest, such as the problem of specific uptake of ions by living cells and the question of accumulation by living matter of electrolytes, both anions and cations, against concentration gradients.

DYNAMIC MEMBRANE POTENTIALS

Whereas the membrane potentials that arise in equilibrium systems and quasi-equilibrium systems are clearly and quantitatively understood on the basis of the theory of the Donnan membrane potential, no general statement can be made concerning the dynamic membrane potentials that arise in systems that drift toward equilibrium.

Relatively simple cases of dynamic membrane systems with more than one species of potential determining ions are the cells with membranes of ideal or nearly ideal ionic selectivity, the simplest possible systems of this type being those in which the so-called *bi-ionic potentials* arise.

The bi-ionic potential (b.i.p.) was defined as the dynamic membrane potential that arises across a membrane separating the solutions of two electrolytes at the same concentration having different "critical" ions, which are able to exchange across the membrane, and the same "non-critical" ion species for which the membrane is (ideally) impermeable.[25, 26]

The general scheme of a cell in which a b.i.p. arises across an electronegative membrane can be represented in the following manner:

Solution 1 Electrolyte A^+X^- c_1	Electronegative membrane	Solution 2 Electrolyte B^+X^- c_1

Here A^+ and B^+ represent univalent cations that are able to exchange freely across the membrane, and X^- an anion that is unable to penetrate through it.

Systems of this type have been investigated experimentally only in a limited number of instances.[19, 25–29] Bi-ionic potentials, according to the nature of the membrane and the combination of critical ions, may be up to 150 mv. or more. This magnitude is nearly independent of the nature and valency of the non-critical ions, provided complete dissociation prevails. In a medium concentration range the b.i.p. is likewise fairly independent of the absolute concentration; at high concentrations it is slightly lower in most instances;[19,30] at very low concentrations the drop may become quite considerable, particularly with membranes of low resistance. This drop in potential can be assumed to be due primarily to the influence of the unstirred diffusion layers at the membrane solution interfaces. For this reason, the use of membranes of relatively high resistance is often indicated in the study of the b.i.p. and related phenomena.

The chemical nature of the membrane, its charge density, and its porosity have a rather involved, at present in part unpredictable influence on the absolute magnitude of the bi-ionic potentials. Table 4

TABLE 4. SEVERAL REPRESENTATIVE BI-IONIC POTENTIALS ACROSS A TYPICAL PERMSELECTIVE OXIDIZED COLLODION AND A TYPICAL PERMSELECTIVE PROTAMINE COLLODION MEMBRANE ($T = 25.0 \pm 0.1°$ C.)

1	2	3	4	5	6	7	8
Oxidized Collodion Membrane ($\rho^* = 1550\ \Omega$ cm.^{2})				Protamine Collodion Membrane ($\rho^* = 1250\ \Omega$ cm.^{2})			
Solution 1	Solution 2	Bi-Ionic Potential	$\tau_{B^+}^{(2)} / \tau_{K^+}^{(1)}$	Solution 1	Solution 2	Bi-Ionic Potential	$\tau_{Y^-}^{(2)} / \tau_{Cl^-}^{(1)}$
0.0100 N	0.0100 N	mv.		0.0250 N	0.0250 N	mv.	
KCl	CsCl	−8.7	1.41	NaCl	NaCNS	+32.0	3.48
KI	NH$_4$I	−6.8	1.30	NaCl	NaNO$_3$	+23.1	2.46
KCl	RbCl	−5.6	1.25	NaCl	NaI	+12.2	1.61
KCl	KCl	±0.0	1.00	NaCl	NaBr	+7.2	1.32
KI	NaI	+35.4	0.252	NaCl	NaCl	±0.0	1.00
KCl	NaCl	+35.5	0.251	NaCl	NaBrO$_3$	−2.2	0.918
KCl	LiCl	+63.7	0.084	NaCl	Na formate	−7.6	0.744
KI	(CH$_3$)$_4$NI	+81.6	0.042	NaCl	Na salicyl.	−12.3	0.619
KI	(C$_2$H$_5$)$_4$NI	+110.0	0.014	NaCl	Na benzoate	−38.6	0.222
				NaCl	NaIO$_3$	−45.1	0.173
				NaCl	Na acetate	−46.2	0.165
				NaCl	Na propion.	−59.3	0.099
				NaCl	Na butyrate	−65.9	0.077
				NaCl	Na lactate	−68.6	0.069

gives some representative b.i.p. data obtained with some permselective membranes of fairly high standard resistance (in 0.1 N KCl), ρ^*; columns 1–3, and 5–7 are self-explanatory; columns 4 and 8 should be disregarded for the time being.

The various critical cations and anions can be arranged into two consistent and characteristic sequences according to the relative magnitude of the bi-ionic potentials that are caused by their presence (as was done in Table 4). These two ionic sequences are the so-called Hofmeister series.

From the formal electrochemical point of view, as was pointed out by Michaelis, the sign and the magnitude of the b.i.p. must depend on the relative ease with which the two species of critical ions can penetrate across the membrane.[25] The more readily permeable critical ions impress a potential on the other solution that is identical in sign with that of their own charge.

In order to obtain quantitative information concerning the relative ionic "mobilities" of the two critical cations in the membranes, Michaelis [25] employed—not without misgivings—the Planck-Henderson equation for the liquid junction potential as applicable to the simplest possible case, namely, two solutions of uni-univalent electrolytes of equal concentration having two different cations and a common anion:

$$E = \pm \frac{RT}{F} \ln \frac{u_{A^+} + u_{X^-}}{u_{B^+} + u_{X^-}} \tag{5}$$

where E is the experimentally determined potential; u_{A^+} and u_{B^+}, the "mobilities" of the two cations; and u_{X^-}, the "mobility" of the common anion within the membrane. If the membrane is impermeable to anions, u_{X^-} is zero, and the equation for an ideally cation selective membrane becomes

$$E = \pm \frac{RT}{F} \ln \frac{u_{A^+}}{u_{B^+}} \tag{6}$$

where E is now the bi-ionic potential.

The concept of ionic "mobilities" in the membrane, if understood in analogy with the concept of ionic mobilities in free solution, embodies of necessity several rather specific assumptions that are not likely to be adequate for the particular situation within a membrane of porous character.

The magnitude of a b.i.p. is quite obviously a function of the relative contributions of the different species of ions in the system toward the (virtual) transportation of current across the membrane. For this reason Gregor and Sollner suggested that the quantitative evaluation of the b.i.p. be based on the more basic and more general concept of the transference numbers that permits the quantitative interpretation of the experimental b.i.p. values in terms of molecular (ionic) processes with a minimum of hypothetical assumptions.[26, 27]

In order to evaluate quantitatively, from the magnitude of the b.i.p., the true relative contributions of the different ions to the virtual transportation of current across the membrane, it is necessary only to express the above equation in terms of transference [26] instead of Michaelis' "ionic mobilities," and equation 6 becomes the expression

$$E = \frac{+RT}{F} \ln \frac{\tau_{A^+}^{(1)}}{\tau_{B^+}^{(2)}} \tag{7a}$$

the sign referring to the charge of solution 2.

For electropositive membranes (of ideal ionic selectivity) equation 6 is changed to the expression:

$$E = \frac{-RT}{F} \ln \frac{\tau_{X^-}^{(1)}}{\tau_{Y^-}^{(2)}} \tag{7b}$$

In order to visualize in a quantitative way the differences in the behavior of various ions in the experimental chains referred to in Table 4 the ratios $\tau_{B^+}^{(2)}/\tau_{K^+}^{(1)}$ and $\tau_{Y^-}^{(2)}/\tau_{Cl^-}^{(1)}$ were calculated from equations 7a and 7b, and are given in columns 4 and 8 of Table 4.

A reasonably satisfactory physical picture that can explain the data of Table 4 can be based on the consideration of the membranes as ion exchange bodies according to the fixed-charge theory.[26] The two exchangeable (critical) species of ions compete for positions as counter ions of the fixed dissociable groups of the membrane. Concerning the general phenomenon of competitive ion exchange, it is well known from extensive studies in ion exchange that the various competing ions are taken up by ion exchangers to a very different extent. The sequences of the relative adsorbabilities of the various ions are roughly the two Hofmeister series of cations and of anions unless steric hindrance and related factors come into play as complicating factors. The adsorbed critical ions are dissociated off in the pores according to their nature and the nature of the fixed ionic wall groups. The assumption of complete dissociation is undoubtedly justified in many instances, e.g., the majority of the systems shown in Table 4.

The relative abundance of the two species of critical ions in the pores multiplied by their relative diffusion velocities (and valencies) determine their relative contributions toward the virtual transportation of electricity across the membrane and thus the sign and the magnitude of the b.i.p.

Figure 6 represents the situation pictorially. The small, continuous circles around the plus or minus signs in this figure represent the size of the ions including their effective shell of hydration. The large dashed circles indicate the effective range of electrical repulsion between the fixed charges situated on the pore walls and ions of identical signs in

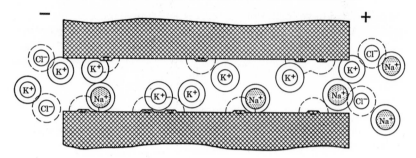

$$D_{K^+} > D_{Na^+}$$

Fig. 6. The origin of the bi-ionic potential KCl||NaCl in a pore; the Na+ ion is larger and less adsorbable than the K+ ion.

the solutions and between such ions; the solid-line large circles surrounding the critical ions indicate the spheres of their mutual repulsion.

Of the nine anionic wall groups of the pore shown in Fig. 6, six are compensated for electrically by the more strongly adsorbable (and smaller) K^+ ions, the other three by the less strongly adsorbable (and larger) Na^+ ions. Complete dissociation is assumed. If the ratio of the diffusion velocities of K^+ to Na^+ in the pore is taken as 76 to 52, the ratio of their ionic mobilities in free solution, then the ratio of their transference numbers is: $\tau_{K^+}/\tau_{Na^+} = (6 \times 76):(3 \times 52)$. The magnitude of the b.i.p. according to equation 11 would (at 25.0° C.) amount to $E = +59.1 \log 456/156 = +28.6$ mv.

The elucidation of the mechanism of the origin of the bi-ionic potential leads directly to an insight into the mechanisms of the *dynamics of polyionic membrane systems* in general, which involve membranes of ideal or nearly ideal ionic selectivity.

As *polycationic potentials* we denote the membrane potentials that arise across ideally cation selective membranes in systems with two or more species of cations that may be present at the two sides of the membrane in pure or mixed solutions at the same or at different activities. *Polyanionic potentials* involve analogous anion-selective membranes and two or more species of anions. Thus one may refer to a two-cationic potential, a three-anionic potential, etc. Making a slight change in definition by switching from concentrations to activities, the bi-ionic potential can be redefined as the special case of a two-ionic potential, cationic or anionic, in which the two critical ions are present at the same activity in single-electrolyte solutions.

From the experimental point of view one may consider as polycationic and polyanionic systems all systems that involve membranes of sufficiently high degree of ionic selectivity under the conditions of the particular experiment so that the contribution of the non-critical ions towards the virtual transportation of electricity may be neglected.

The essential problem in dealing with polyionic systems is to find the quantitative correlation of the potentials that arise with any ratio of activities of two or more species of critical ions in the two outside solutions and the potential in some standard system.

The theoretical treatment of polyionic systems in general can be based on the Planck and Henderson equations in a manner similar to the treatment of the bi-ionic potential. Marshall has investigated the electromotive behavior of clay membranes in polycationic systems primarily from the point of view of the use of these membranes as membrane electrodes in solutions containing two or more species of cations.[11] Following the example of Michaelis, he bases his considerations on a concept of ionic "mobilities" within the membrane; but this concept is beset with numerous difficulties, some of which have been outlined above. As in the case of the bi-ionic potential, a more satisfactory physical picture can be arrived at on the basis of the concept of transference, the mode of presentation that is chosen here.[30] To simplify the theoretical discussion, we shall treat explicitly in subsequent paragraphs electronegative, cation-permeable membranes only, since the electropositive membranes represent a strictly parallel case.

The simplest case of a polyionic potential across a membrane of ideal selectivity, next to the bi-ionic potential, is the situation in which each of the two solutions separated by the membrane contains only one of two species of critical ions but at *different* activities. The Planck-Henderson equation may be applied to the system of the type, a_1 KCl|membrane|a_2 LiCl; introducing transference numbers, we may write

$$E = \frac{+RT}{F} \ln \frac{\tau_{K^+}}{\tau_{Li^+}} \qquad (8)$$

where τ_{K^+} and τ_{Li^+} are the transference numbers of the critical ions in the membrane in the particular two-cationic system under consideration.

Equation 8 assumes its true, full meaning only if the transference numbers of a pair of critical ions for any particular system can be correlated quantitatively to the transference numbers of an appropriate reference system on the basis of clear-cut, simple assumptions.

The simplest possible assumptions are that the bi-ionic potentials and the relative adsorbabilities of the two species of critical ions are independent of concentration and that the relative adsorbed quantities of the two ions are a linear function of the ratio of their activities in the two solutions. On the basis of these assumptions, it must be anticipated that the ratio of the transference numbers of the two critical ions within the membrane, τ_{K^+}/τ_{Li^+}, in the system, a_1 KCl | membrane | a_2 LiCl, is directly proportional to the ratio of the transference numbers of the two critical ions within the same membrane in the corresponding bi-ionic potential system (when the ratio of the two activities is unity) and to the ratio of the activities of the two critical ions in the two external solutions of the particular system under discussion. If the transference numbers pertaining to the bi-ionic reference system are denoted as $\tau_{K^+}{}^{\circ}$ and $\tau_{Li^+}{}^{\circ}$, the ratio of the transference numbers in the general two-cationic system above can be expressed as

$$\frac{\tau_{K^+}}{\tau_{Li^+}} = \frac{a_{K^+}{}^{(1)} \tau_{K^+}{}^{\circ}}{a_{Li^+}{}^{(2)} \tau_{Li^+}{}^{\circ}} \tag{9}$$

and the two-cationic potential as

$$E = \frac{+RT}{F} \ln \frac{a_{K^+}{}^{(1)} \tau_{K^+}{}^{\circ}}{a_{Li^+}{}^{(2)} \tau_{Li^+}{}^{\circ}} \tag{10}$$

To test equation 10 and its analog for positive membranes, a number of systems of various concentration ratios, with cation- as well as with anion-selective permselective membranes, were studied. Representative calculated and experimental potential data are shown in Table 5. The calculated values are based on standard transference numbers derived from bi-ionic potentials measured at 0.050 N and on

TABLE 5. A COMPARISON OF SEVERAL CALCULATED AND EXPERIMENTAL TWO-IONIC POTENTIALS WITH SINGLE ELECTROLYTE SOLUTIONS AT DIFFERENT CONCENTRATIONS ACROSS THREE REPRESENTATIVE PERMSELECTIVE MEMBRANES ($T = 25.0 \pm 0.1°$ C.)

Membrane	Solution 1	Solution 2	Two-Ionic Potential	
			Calculated	Experimental
			mv.	mv.
Sulfonated polystyrene collodion $\rho^* = 1325\ \Omega\ cm.^2$ $\dfrac{\tau_{K^+}{}^{\circ}}{\tau_{Li^+}{}^{\circ}} = 6.27$	0.0100 N KCl	0.0500 N LiCl	$+8.2$	$+8.0$
	0.0100 N KCl	0.200 N LiCl	-25.5	-25.0
	0.0100 N KCl	0.500 N LiCl	-48.2	-49.3
Protamine collodion $\rho^* = 5450\ \Omega\ cm.^2$ $\dfrac{\tau_{CNS^-}{}^{\circ}}{\tau_{Cl^-}{}^{\circ}} = 5.30$	0.200 N KCNS	0.0100 N KCl	-113.8	-109.7
	0.200 N KCNS	0.0500 N KCl	-74.6	-74.2
	0.200 N KCNS	0.500 N KCl	-21.8	-24.4
Protamine collodion $\rho^* = 1400\ \Omega\ cm.^2$ $\dfrac{\tau_{CNS^-}{}^{\circ}}{\tau_{Cl^-}{}^{\circ}} = 4.42$	0.500 N KCNS	0.0100 N KCl	-130.0	-124.7
	0.500 N KCNS	0.0500 N KCl	-91.2	-87.9
	0.500 N KCNS	0.200 N KCl	-58.9	-56.8

ionic activities that were computed according to the Guggenheim assumption. No attempt has been made to correct for the asymmetry of the two liquid junction potentials that arises when saturated KCl-agar bridges are inserted into the two solutions of different composition and different concentration.

The data of Table 5 show that the calculated and experimental potential values agree in all instances within a few millivolts.

A further extension of the use of the Planck-Henderson equation combined with the concept of transference numbers within the membrane leads to an equation useful for the most generalized type of two-ionic potential system in which both species of critical ions are present in any arbitrary combination of concentrations on each side of the permselective membrane. The system a_1 KCl, a_2 LiCl | membrane | a_3 KCl, a_4 LiCl represents this general case.

The equation for the two-cationic potential can be expressed quantitatively by introducing transference numbers in the Planck-Henderson equation:

$$E = \frac{+RT}{F} \ln \frac{\tau_{K^{+}}^{(1)} + \tau_{Li^{+}}^{(1)}}{\tau_{K^{+}}^{(2)} + \tau_{Li^{+}}^{(2)}} \tag{11}$$

$\tau_{K^{+}}^{(1)}$ and $\tau_{K^{+}}^{(2)}$, and $\tau_{Li^{+}}^{(1)}$ and $\tau_{Li^{+}}^{(2)}$ represent the contribution of the K^{+} and Li^{+} ions originating in solutions 1 and 2, respectively, to the virtual transportation of current within the membrane. Thus, the quantity $\tau_{K^{+}}^{(1)}$ is analogous to $\dfrac{c_{K^{+}}^{(1)} u_{K^{+}}}{\Sigma c_i u_i}$ in the Planck or Henderson terminology for a liquid junction potential, and similarly $\tau_{K^{+}}^{(2)}$ corresponds to $\dfrac{c_{K^{+}}^{(2)} u_{K^{+}}}{\Sigma c_i u_i}$, $\tau_{Li^{+}}^{(1)}$ to $\dfrac{c_{Li^{+}}^{(1)} u_{Li^{+}}}{\Sigma c_i u_i}$, and $\tau_{Li^{+}}^{(2)}$ to $\dfrac{c_{Li^{+}}^{(2)} u_{Li^{+}}}{\Sigma c_i u_i}$.

According to the previously stated assumptions we may write for the transference numbers within the membrane, $\tau_{K^{+}}$ and $\tau_{Li^{+}}$:

$$\tau_{K^{+}} = \frac{(a_{K^{+}}^{(1)} + a_{K^{+}}^{(2)})\tau_{K^{+}}^{\circ}}{(a_{K^{+}}^{(1)} + a_{K^{+}}^{(2)})\tau_{K^{+}}^{\circ} + (a_{Li^{+}}^{(1)} + a_{Li^{+}}^{(2)})\tau_{Li^{+}}^{\circ}} \tag{12a}$$

and

$$\tau_{Li^{+}} = \frac{(a_{Li^{+}}^{(1)} + a_{Li^{+}}^{(2)})\tau_{Li^{+}}^{\circ}}{(a_{K^{+}}^{(1)} + a_{K^{+}}^{(2)})\tau_{K^{+}}^{\circ} + (a_{Li^{+}}^{(1)} + a_{Li^{+}}^{(2)})\tau_{Li^{+}}^{\circ}} \tag{12b}$$

The transference numbers within the membrane can be split up into terms analogous to quantities in the Planck and Henderson equations and the two-cationic potential E in any system can be expressed as:

$$E = \frac{+RT}{F} \ln \frac{a_{K^+}^{(1)} \tau_{K^{+\circ}} + a_{Li^+}^{(1)} \tau_{Li^{+\circ}}}{a_{K^+}^{(2)} \tau_{K^{+\circ}} + a_{Li^+}^{(2)} \tau_{Li^{+\circ}}} \qquad (13)$$

Table 6 compares in a few representative systems the values of the measured potentials with the values of the potentials calculated from equation 13 and its analog for anionic systems.

TABLE 6. A COMPARISON OF SEVERAL CALCULATED AND EXPERIMENTAL TWO-IONIC POTENTIALS WITH MIXED ELECTROLYTE SOLUTIONS AT VARIOUS CONCENTRATIONS ACROSS TWO REPRESENTATIVE PERMSELECTIVE MEMBRANES ($T = 25.0 \pm 0.1°$ C.)

Membrane	Solution 1	Solution 2	Two-Ionic Potential Calculated mv.	Experimental mv.
Sulfonated polystyrene collodion $\rho^* = 260\ \Omega$ cm.^{2}	0.01250 N NaCl 0.0375 N HCl	0.0500 N NaCl	+99.8	+100.0
$\dfrac{\tau_{H^{+\circ}}}{\tau_{Na^{+\circ}}} = 64.5$	0.01485 N NaCl 0.0352 N HCl	0.0477 N NaCl 0.00234 N HCl	+62.6	+59.0
	0.01719 N NaCl 0.0328 N HCl	0.0453 N NaCl 0.00469 N HCl	+46.4	+44.5
	0.02188 N NaCl 0.02812 N HCl	0.0406 N NaCl 0.00938 N HCl	+26.8	+25.4
	0.02656 N NaCl 0.02344 N HCl	0.0360 N NaCl 0.01406 N HCl	+12.6	+11.6
Protamine collodion $\rho^* = 5450\ \Omega$ cm.^{2}	0.1497 N KCNS 0.000275 N KCl	0.000275 N KCNS 0.00911 N KCl	−106.1	−104.5
$\dfrac{\tau_{CNS^{-\circ}}}{\tau_{Cl^{-\circ}}} = 5.36$	0.1489 N KCNS 0.001103 N KCl	0.001103 N KCNS 0.00827 N KCl	−98.2	−99.0
	0.1478 N KCNS 0.00220 N KCl	0.00220 N KCNS 0.00717 N KCl	−90.7	−93.1
	0.1456 N KCNS 0.00440 N KCl	0.00440 N KCNS 0.00497 N KCl	−80.0	−81.8
	0.1434 N KCNS 0.00662 N KCl	0.00662 N KCNS 0.00276 N KCl	−72.2	−73.3

The agreement in Table 6 between the calculated and the experimental data seems most satisfactory. By a single measurement of the bi-ionic potential with a pair of critical ions across a particular permselective membrane, it becomes possible to calculate the potentials that arise across the same membrane if the two critical ions are distributed in the two solutions in any arbitrary combination of concentrations.

Two-ionic potentials, as shown by Marshall with clay membranes, may be used for the determination, with a fair degree of accuracy, of the activities of two coexisting species of ions of the same sign of charge in solution.[11] For this purpose it is necessary to determine the potentials that arise across two membranes of different, known $\tau_A{}^{+\circ}/\tau_B{}^{+\circ}$ ratios, which separate the "unknown" solution from a known reference solution, or to use the same membrane with two different reference solutions. The rapidly responding, low-resistance permselective membranes, as is indicated by the data of Tables 5 and 6, should turn out to be rather useful as membrane electrodes both in mixed cationic and mixed anionic systems.

The use of membranes of well-defined and highly characteristic electrochemical properties in physicochemical investigations and in model studies of specific biological interest is still in its infancy. However, we may look forward with confidence to a rich harvest of answers to at least some of the questions that have motivated the old masters —Traube, Pfeffer, Höber, Haber, Donnan, Loeb, Michaelis, and Osterhout—to whom we owe so much in the electrochemistry of membranes.

Acknowledgments. The authors wish to thank the editors of the *Journal of General Physiology,* the *Journal of Physical (and Colloid) Chemistry,* and the *Journal of the American Chemical Society* for permission to quote freely from earlier papers and to reproduce a number of graphs. We are particularly indebted to the Electrochemical Society, the editors of the *Journal of the Electrochemical Society,* and the editors of the *Annals of the New York Academy of Sciences* for kind permission to utilize verbatim lengthy sections of earlier reviews by one of us.

REFERENCES

1. E. Grim, Ph.D. Thesis, Univ. Minn., Minneapolis, 1950.
2. E. Grim and K. Sollner, in preparation.
3. K. Sollner, Z. *Elektrochem., 36,* 36, 234 (1930).
4. M. B. Visscher, E. S. Fetcher, C. W. Carr, H. P. Gregor, M. S. Bushey, and D. E. Barker, *Am. J. Physiol., 142,* 550 (1944).
5. K. Sollner, *J. Electrochem Soc., 97,* 139C (1950).
6. K. Sollner, *J. Am. Chem. Soc., 65,* 2260 (1943).
7. H. P. Gregor and K. Sollner, *J. Phys. Chem., 58,* 409 (1954).
8. F. Haber, *Ann. Physik* (4), *26,* 927 (1908); F. Haber and Z. Klemensiewicz, *Z. physik. Chem., 67,* 385 (1909).
9. W. Nernst and E. H. Riesenfeld, *Ann. Physik* (4), *8,* 600 (1902).
10. K. Horowitz, *Z. Physik, 15,* 369 (1923); *Z. physik. Chem., 115,* 424 (1925).
11. C. E. Marshall, *J. Phys. Chem., 43,* 1155 (1939); *48,* 67 (1944); *Soil Sci. Soc. Amer. Proc., 7,* 182 (1942); C. E. Marshall and W. E. Bergman, *J. Am. Chem. Soc., 63,* 1911 (1941); *J. Phys. Chem., 46,* 52, 325 (1942); C. E. Marshall and C. A. Krinbill, *J. Am. Chem. Soc., 64,* 1814 (1942); C. E. Marshall and A. D. Ayers, *J. Am. Chem. Soc., 70,* 1297 (1948); C. E. Marshall and L. O. Eime, *J. Am. Chem. Soc., 70,* 1302 (1948), etc.
12. G. Scatchard, *J. Am. Chem. Soc., 75,* 2883 (1953).
13. R. Neihof, *J. Phys. Chem., 58,* 916 (1954).
14. K. Sollner and R. Neihof, *Arch. Biochem. and Biophys., 33,* 166 (1951).

15. C. W. Carr, *Arch. Biochem. and Biophys.*, *40*, 286 (1952); *43*, 147 (1953); *46*, 417, 424 (1953); C. W. Carr and L. Topol, *J. Phys. & Colloid Chem.*, *54*, 176 (1950).
16. T. R. Bolam, *The Donnan Equilibria and Their Application to Chemical, Physiological and Technical Processes*, G. Bell & Sons, Ltd., London, 1932.
17. F. G. Donnan, *Z. Elektrochem.*, *17*, 572 (1911); *Chem. Revs.*, *1*, 73 (1924); *Z. physik. Chem.*, *(A) 168*, 369 (1934); F. G. Donnan and A. B. Harris, *J. Chem. Soc.*, *99*, 1554 (1911); F. G. Donnan and A. J. Allmand, *J. Chem. Soc.*, *105*, 1941 (1914); F. G. Donnan and W. E. Garner, *J. Chem. Soc.*, *115*, 1313 (1919).
18. K. Sollner and H. P. Gregor, *J. Am. Chem. Soc.*, *67*, 346 (1945).
19. H. P. Gregor, Ph.D. Thesis, Univ. Minn., Minneapolis, 1945.
20. K. Sollner, *J. Am. Chem. Soc.*, *68*, 156 (1946).
21. K. Sollner, *Biochem. Z.*, *244*, 370 (1932).
22. R. Höber, *Physical Chemistry of Cells and Tissues*, Blakiston Company, Philadelphia, 1945.
23. R. Neihof, Ph.D. Thesis, Univ. Minn., Minneapolis, 1950.
24. R. Neihof and K. Sollner, *J. Phys. & Colloid Chem.*, *54*, 157 (1950).
25. L. Michaelis and A. Fujita, *Biochem. Z.*, *161*, 47 (1925); L. Michaelis, *Bull. Natl. Research Council (U. S.)*, *69*, 119 (1929); *Kolloid-Z.*, *62*, 2 (1933).
26. K. Sollner, *J. Phys. & Colloid Chem.*, *53*, 1211, 1226 (1949).
27. H. P. Gregor and K. Sollner, *J. Phys. Chem.*, *50*, 53, 88 (1946).
28. R. Höber, *J. Cellular Comp. Physiol.*, *7*, 367 (1936).
29. R. Mond and F. Hoffmann, *Pflügers Arch. ges. Physiol.*, *220*, 194 (1928).
30. S. Dray and K. Sollner, in preparation; S. Dray, Ph.D. Thesis, Univ. Minn. (1954).

6.

Dynamic Negative Admittance Components in Statically Stable Membranes

OTTO H. SCHMITT *

This symposium is most unusual in that it brings together a group of research-minded specialists who share a common interest in biologically important aspects of electrochemistry without including more than one or two who would be thought of primarily as electrochemists. The symposium, therefore, offers a unique opportunity to stand off at a little distance from our individual technical research problems and to ask whether we individually and collectively are making important progress toward understanding the electrochemistry of biological processes and systems. With this objective in mind, I would like to examine some new and some old ideas about electrobiology that I have been trying to coordinate and reconcile.

Thinking primarily in terms of the electrically excitable biological tissues in which even the most elementary electrochemical processes have yet to be explained on an intuitively satisfying basis, I cannot escape the conclusion that simple underlying principles are being overlooked in the search for sophisticated explanations of the abundantly available experimental data. We have advanced rapidly in instrumentation in the past 25 years with the coming of age of electronics so that our experiments are elegant and decisive, but our explanations are framed in the electrochemical language of Nernst, Hermann, Bernstein, and Helmholtz. Lack of progress is not for lack of effort or for lack of talent; for highly distinguished investigators have spent years of time on the subject; yet the progress is meager in comparison with the corresponding advances in biochemistry or biological ultrastructure analysis.

In seeking an explanation for this anomalous retardation of progress in a field of biophysics that seems so promising, I am struck by the

* From the Departments of Physics and Zoology, University of Minnesota, Minneapolis, Minn.

close analogy between this problem and the one central to the organization of biophysics itself as a new and growing area of biological science. Biophysics is currently defined as an area of biological science that utilizes the theoretical approaches and techniques of physics. As such, it has no language of its own but draws upon the concepts of standard biology and physics with a little chemistry thrown in for good measure. Until biophysics formulates concepts of its own distinct from those of its parent areas, it is unlikely that any major advances will come from the field that could not equally well come from simple cooperation of biologists and physicists. When biophysical formulations are developed, we may expect to have progress comparable to that currently being displayed in other vigorous young fields of science like biochemistry, nuclear physics, and the science of the solid state.

We as biophysicists should not be simply applying the thinking of physics and physical chemistry to biological problems; we should be busily modifying and adapting the concepts that have proved useful in physics to theoretical forms that fit biological phenomena without undue twisting, qualification, or limitation. In short, we should be inventing symbolisms that adequately represent biological phenomena over wide ranges of variation, not twisting established physical representations until they empirically fit the phenomena in special narrow ranges.

Obviously, mere recognition of the need for adequate symbolism does not make such new language available. We can, however, make conscious efforts to create new quantitative treatments whenever we feel that conventional approach yields solutions that are formal only and not intuitively appealing or where we feel that theory rather than experiment limits our progress.

In the light of these ideas, I would like to reexamine somewhat searchingly the operational concepts of electrical capacitance and resistance as they enter into various analyses of biological membrane behavior. Perhaps these classical concepts can be extrapolated into forms that will be effective in providing more understandable explanations of electrical membrane phenomena.

There are at least four substantially different sets of definitions for resistance and capacitance in common use, but under ideal conditions all of them merge into a single self-consistent concept. Many actual physical impedances as found in electrical systems are built up of available resistors and capacitors that approach quite closely to the theoretical ideal; therefore, it is customary to think of the several different definitions as representing merely a variety of handy mathematical formulations for the same thing.

Actually, resistance and capacitance even in the physical cases do often deviate appreciably and in an only partially understood way from the ideal. Consequently, it is often found that only by using the "right" formulation can we avoid seeing too obviously the inadequacy of these nice clean physical concepts.

In order to have these ideas clearly in mind, let me review some of these definitions side by side. In the simplest form, resistance is defined from Ohm's law as $R = E/I$, that is, the ratio of total voltage across an element to the current through it in the steady state. This implicitly assumes time independence and functional linearity. Comparable to this and also implying linearity and time independence is the condenser equation $C = q/E$, capacitance being defined as the steady state ratio of electric charge to voltage.

Now, these two basic equations represent straight-line relationships, whereas in actual cases the relationships are generally somewhat curved. If the curve is gentle and the region of interest limited, it is customary to substitute the ratio of finite changes for the total values of variable yielding the relationships $R = \Delta E/\Delta i$ and $C = \Delta q/\Delta E$, which represent a kind of average resistance and capacitance over a working range. Notice that unless otherwise specified it is assumed that these ratios are still time independent and independent of the *direction* in which a change is made. This last assumption is often valid in electrical capacitors and resistors but is notably invalid in biological cases.

Carrying this restriction of range to the limit, one obtains a third set of ratios, $R = dE/di$ and $C = dq/dE$, which are often called dynamic characteristics in contrast to the static values first mentioned. These last equations are at least meaningful for any continuous functional relationship between the independent variables, but it must be clearly specified whether any time dependence or a path dependence is implied by use of partial derivative notation with appropriate subscripts.

The quantity q that enters the condenser equation is very difficult to measure; and, consequently, in most capacitance measurements current, which is the time derivative of charge, is actually measured, and then capacitance is deduced through some kind of time integration, time independence of capacitance being implicitly assumed. It is of interest at this point to realize that dynamic capacitance thus defined disregards accumulated initial charge and that similarly dynamic resistance ignores steady state potential generation in a system and steady currents that persist.

A fourth formulation of the resistance-capacitance laws combines them with the aid of complex notation into a single lump concept called impedance Z or its reciprocal Y, which is called admittance. These forms implicitly force a sinusoidal time variation upon the system and requires voltage-amplitude independence of both of the constituents. It is furthermore improper to think of impedance in terms of simple Fourier series components for a non-sinusoidal wave form unless specific arrangements are made to take care of frequency dependence of C and R, as these variations are usually finite. Impedance or admittance analysis does, however, frequently permit identification of physiologically inert structural components of biological systems, for these components usually tend to behave like simple physical components in contrast to the highly non-linear active processes. Complex notation also allows a convenient hiding place for the persistent tendency of capacitors to act a bit like resistors without actually leaking. This effect is achieved by letting the dielectric constant become partly imaginary, thus letting part of the condenser current become real and resistive.

In passing, I would like to remark that, although impedance and admittance analysis are formally interchangeable, they do subtly force a set of equivalent circuits upon the analysis and are likely to influence the end results in that way. It is for this reason that I have advocated the use of the admittance terms for describing most membrane phenomena in preference to the more common impedance analysis.

The impedance concept (Fig. 1a) is built up around the idea of a structure in which each element of charge must successively pass through the resistive or "lossy" elements R and through the reactive or condenserlike elements X. Potential gradients in these two elements need not be even similar. Admittance analysis (Fig. 1b) presumes the reactive element now called a susceptance B to be in parallel with the

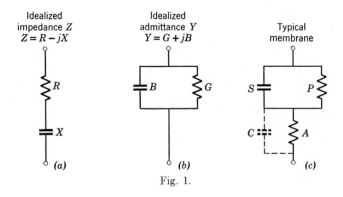

Fig. 1.

resistive element or conductance G. Here the voltage across both elements is the same, but the total charge which moves is the *sum* of the charges flowing in the two elements.

In a typical biological membrane the reactive element S will for the most part include polarization phenomena, the physical capacitance of the membrane, and some of the active processes. The resistive element P will include primarily the membrane's ionic permeability, which is obviously influenced by the active processes, but it will also include energy dissipative terms representing viscous ionic friction in the membrane's capacitance when ionic balances are quickly upset. The element A is the access resistance representing the purely physical resistance of the inert ionic environment surrounding the membrane and must have the dotted capacitor C only in non-biological high-frequency ranges where the dielectric of the water actually carries appreciable displacement current.

It will be seen that for study of active processes the admittance concept permits the membrane permeability to span the polarized region as it is actually believed to exist. The impedance notion would require them formally to be in series. One cannot safely neglect to ask whether membrane components are being quoted in impedance or admittance terms, for it is not unusual to have impedance components quoted in admittance units or vice versa.

Consider as a specific example that a simple membrane were quoted as having a capacitance of 1 μf./cm.^{2} and a conductance equivalent to 1000 ohms for a square centimeter. Calculated on the assumption that these are intended as impedance units and that Fig. 1a applies, the over-all impedance magnitude at 1000 c.p.s. will be 1013 ohms, whereas the impedance would be 157 ohms if the components quoted were admittance components.

In substance, the impedance analyses can nicely handle system behavior in response to sine wave excitation, dividing it as it does into a resistive part that represents energy expended and a reactive part that represents energy stored elastically as potential energy in the case of capacitance, kinetically in the case of inductance. As biologists we should be on the lookout, however, for chemical and physical hysteresis. Any phenomenon that speeds up or delays a current process with respect to a voltage in a system under impedance analysis will cause a shift between the real or resistance terms and the imaginary or capacitance-inductance terms even though the formally implied energy storing is actually absent.

Finally there are transient analyses which analyze current-voltage relationships over a specified cycle not necessarily simple harmonic.

These analyses can be made to yield results either on an instant by instant basis or on an integrated basis around a closed cycle. The technique is very powerful because it permits all "constants" such as R and C to be *variable* and even *non-linear* with time and path if desired, but it is obviously so general as to be nearly useless unless applied to cases that happen to separate out into recognizable parts.

I shall try to illustrate from experimental results obtained in our laboratories † how each of these different approaches yields useful biological information in its own zone and how these analyses lead me to suggest application to biophysical excitation theory of certain extensions of the usual electrical concepts into regions that must formally at least be called negative capacitance, negative resistance, and negative conductance.

Consider first the analysis of nerve membrane impedance and admittance in the classical cases of bullfrog sciatic nerve and squid giant axon.‡ In these tissues it is impossible to insert internal electrodes without fear for the welfare of the adjacent membrane even though several investigators have succeeded in introducing such electrodes without destroying excitability and others have been able to obtain valuable information regarding the membrane by studying the distribution of current between fiber and surrounding fluid as a function of frequency.

In our approach (see Appendix 1) we have presumed that the electrical coaxial cable equations apply to nerve, and we deduce that, for any applied frequency and amplitude of sinusoidal signal current fed to the nerve through two external electrodes, the sinusoidal potential in the extrapolar region referred to an infinitely remote locus will vary linearly in phase and exponentially with amplitude irrespective of the electrical constants of the fiber so long as it is "linear." This leads to the concept of a uniform logarithmic spiral complex plane voltage vector locus along the length of the fiber (Fig. 2) which characterizes completely the membrane admittance of the membrane at any one frequency and which by its uniformity characterizes the uniformity of the preparation. Knowing the pitch and taper of the spiral and one numerical parameter such as the specific longitudinal loop impedance which can be measured directly, it is possible to characterize the mem-

† Most of the work described in this paper was supported in part by grants from the Office of Naval Research and from the Graduate School of the University of Minnesota.

‡ The illustrated results represent the cooperative efforts of several investigators working in the University of Minnesota biophysics group and include especially Peter A. Stewart, Margaret J. Watkins, Viola E. Schmitt, and Helen Gellhorn.

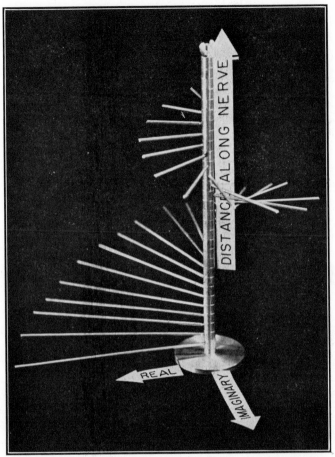

Fig. 2. Logarithmic spiral vector model illustrating distribution of real and imaginary components of complex electrotonic potential along axon in extra-polar regions.

brane completely in impedance or admittance terms at the measuring frequency.

But what are we implicitly reading into the picture by using this analysis? In the first place we are implying *several* different kinds of linearity. We imply that the average admittance of the membrane is independent of signal amplitude both in magnitude and in phase angle. This is an assumption that I certainly considered most questionable in the early stages of this work; indeed I expected the membrane admittance to change drastically as threshold levels were even remotely approached. Figure 3 illustrates how wrong this guess was. For squid

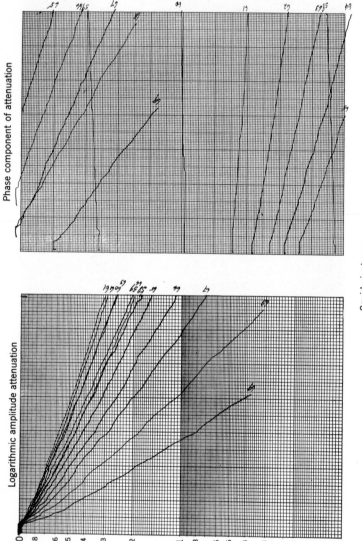

Phase component of attenuation

Logarithmic amplitude attenuation

Squid giant axon

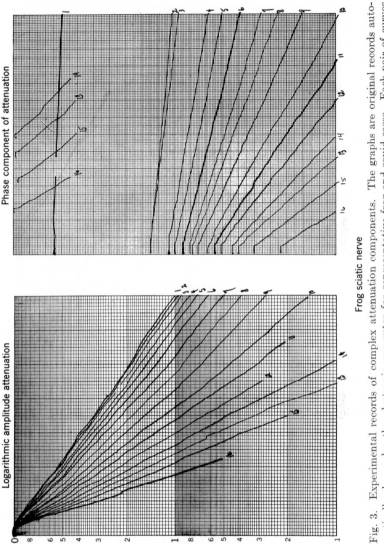

Fig. 3. Experimental records of complex attenuation components. The graphs are original records automatically drawn by the electronic computer for representative frog and squid cases. Each pair of curves represents one set of measurements of α and β at a chosen frequency in the range 40–50,000 c.p.s. and permits independent determination of membrane capacitance and conductance at that frequency.

and for frog, for log amplitude and for phase, both tissues give remarkably straight lines at all frequencies from levels of a few microvolts up to near threshold levels of several millivolts. In the event of excitation this analysis is, of course, worthless as its derivation implies that there shall be no sources or at least no non-linear energy sources in the axon.

Another linearity is implied by the analysis—harmonic linearity. The fiber is assumed to produce only voltages of the frequency applied

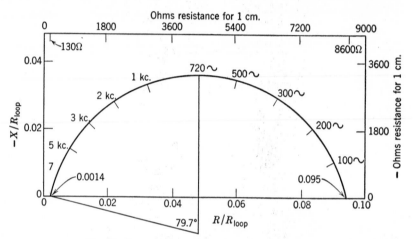

Fig. 4. Average impedance loop for frog sciatic.

and not harmonic overtones or the even more unthinkable subharmonics. Actually the fibers produce modest amounts of overtone harmonics by the "rectification" process, which will be discussed later, but only in special circumstances do they produce subharmonics. This occurs mainly when the fiber is hyperexcitable and at low safety factor.

In the case of frog nerve the transmission line attenuation analysis yields a near-ideal circle diagram (Fig. 4), which shows little evidence of any active process at subthreshold signal levels. The membrane might well be a slightly leaky tube of dielectric material with high electric losses. The membrane is responsive to a few agents like potassium which change the conductance markedly, but otherwise it seems an unresponsive system that could easily be imitated by a structure of physical components.

Squid nerve contrasts rather sharply with frog nerve, for its membrane characteristic responds actively to environmental changes. This change cannot be blamed on the axoplasm, for separate measurements (Fig. 5) demonstrate the axoplasm to be a practically ideal amplitude-

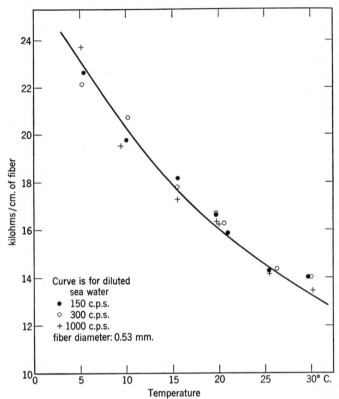

Fig. 5. Temperature characteristic of axoplasmic resistance. The transmission line admittance computer supplies enough data to permit direct calculation on a single axon of axoplasmic resistance per unit length at each of a variety of frequencies. A set of these values for frequencies 150, 300, and 1000 c.p.s. is plotted here for various nerve temperatures in the physiological range. For a group of thirteen sets of measurements on ten different axons the axoplasmic conductivity averaged 51.2% ± 0.8% that of the sea water in which the squid were kept. The curve drawn through the points is not an empirically chosen one but is the calculated resistance curve for sea water diluted to match average axoplasmic resistivity. Note that axoplasmic resistance appears to have no significant frequency dependence at low frequencies.

and frequency-independent ohmic conductor with the temperature characteristics of sea water diluted to 51% of normal conductivity.

Displayed as a set of admittance component curves, plotted against frequency (Fig. 6), the normal squid membrane acts like a simple leaky physical condenser of high capacitance per unit area; but superimposed upon this background are highly characteristic low-frequency components both in conductance and susceptance, which are very re-

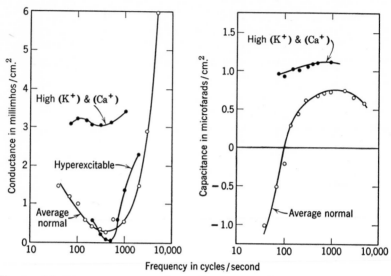

Fig. 6. Admittance components in squid nerve membrane. The subthreshold admittance of squid axon membrane is measured as a function of frequency with the aid of the transmission line attenuation computer and is presented in terms of parallel conductance and capacitance. Excitable nerve shows a marked conductance minimum in the 500 c.p.s. region that can approach negative values in certain hyperexcitable states. Capacitance is fairly constant at high frequencies but plunges into the negative region at a low frequency that is sensitive to physiological influences. Nerves blocked with potassium, etc., lose the characteristic conductance dip, and the negative capacitance shift disappears or moves to a frequency too low to measure.

sponsive to physiological variables and which disappear when the fiber is physiologically incapacitated by aging or other influences that disturb the dynamic integrity of the membrane.

As there is no a priori reason to suppose that the passive ionic membrane permeability is frequency dependent, the dip in conductance in the frequency range, where action potential Fourier components are prominent, suggests that this phenomenon can be ascribed to a dynamic frequency sensitive *negative* conductance component that represents the energy contribution of the active physiological process. Notice, however, that this component is present at all measurable amplitudes and does not have a sharp threshold. The magnitude of the negative conductance term is profoundly influenced by agents that tend to make the nerve unstable, and in fibers nearly in spontaneous activity as in Fig. 6, the conductance is nearly zero in the steady state, the active process having nearly overcome the lossy term.

It should not be presumed that an axon with zero membrane conductance will necessarily go into spontaneous impulse-transmitting activity. The membrane, besides making up its own energy loss, must provide energy for electrical losses in the axoplasm if an impulse is to propagate. An axon with steady state negative conductance at low frequency could be capable of other modes of activity besides the familiar axonal impulse and more like some of the postulated neuron cell body reactions.

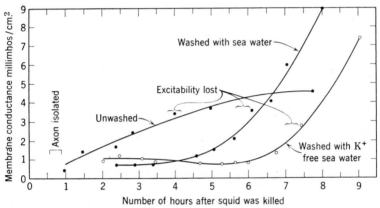

Fig. 7.   Progressive low-frequency conductance changes, squid axon. Failure of non-decremental conduction frequently occurs as nerve membrane conductance rises above 3 millimhos/cm.[2] This form of failure is typical with aging for dissected fibers and occurs in roughly 6 hours if no special precautions are taken. The active life of a fiber after dissection can be extended several hours by frequent washing with low-potassium sea water and can be shortened drastically by washing with high-potassium saline or by failure to wash.

In squid axon there is a striking correlation between the quiescent conductance and impulse propagation failure (Fig. 7). Whether the nerve is brought to the verge of failure by simple aging under optimal conditions, by application of excess K^+, by failure to wash, by heating, or by excessive stimulation, fibers in some dozen experiments all failed at a conductance value of about 3.5–4 mmhos/cm.[2], thus suggesting this as a maximal limit that can be overcome dynamically by the negative conductance term during active propagation.

The sharp downward sweep of the susceptance into the negative region must surely be representable as an active, time-dependent dynamic component that overcomes the static structural capacitance term during low frequency periodic shifts. It is, in my opinion, not profitable to think of this term as inductive, for there is no known momental term to store energy kinetically and this idea is at the root of the inductance concept.

Although it may be profitable to look for kinetic energy processes, it is in my opinion more profitable to call the phenomenon negative susceptance or negative capacitance and to look for its explanation in energy-yielding processes that contain a time delay and thus formally can be equivalent to negative susceptance. Such energy processes can

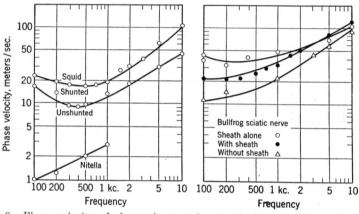

Fig. 8. Phase velocity of electronic wave in unexcited nerve. From the pitch of the logarithmic complex attenuation spiral (Fig. 2) it is easy to calculate a "phase velocity" that represents the constant speed with which any chosen electrical sinusoidal phase advances into the electrotonic region. This phase velocity is fundamentally related to the velocity of nerve impulse propagation.

be manifested as negative susceptance or as negative resistance varying as a function of the testing frequency and the time constants of the process. We can thus explain the regularly observed close correlation between shifts in the conductance dip and the susceptance plunge into the negative region. Quantitatively the observed change requires more than a naive fixed time-delay phase shift.

Regarded as a standing-wave analysis, the foregoing transmission line interpretation has proved useful in enabling us to determine the "phase velocity" in a core conductor; namely the speed at which any particular electric phase proceeds into the electrotonic region (Fig. 8). It becomes obvious, for example, that the electric constants of a nerve, rather than some biochemical process rate, primarily determine the speed of impulse propagation when it is seen that phase velocity directly comparable with measurable action potential velocity can be calculated from electric data taken on a nerve that has never been excited above threshold. The evidence becomes even more convincing when it is shown that reasonably appropriate phase velocities are obtained for such different excitable tissues as squid nerve, frog nerve, and nitella, and that squid nerve shows a correct increase in phase velocity when externally shunted.

It is an interesting sidelight that the perineural sheath of bullfrog nerve can be stripped off and filled with Ringer fluid to make an imitation giant fiber that exhibits a phase velocity only a little higher than that of frog nerve and is actively altered by typical physiologically active reagents. As the sheath never exhibits negative conductance, it will never generate an impulse but it has constants admirably designed to confuse the electrotonic pattern of whole nerve.

Turning now to the action potential aspects of the active membrane process, it is obvious that impedance-admittance analysis is of little value. For frequencies far above physiological range in which the active nerve response can be considered as a slow variation, impedance analysis in the hands of Cole and Curtis and subsequent users of the method has clearly revealed the wide-band conductance variation associated with excitation and has confirmed the hypothesis that the structural capacitance remains substantially inert. These observations nearly exhaust the method, for it is quite meaningless to ask about the 400-c.p.s. impedance variations accompanying the action potential; for, without very elaborate and artificial redefinition, impedance terms are meaningless in a time and amplitude non-linear system varying at a rate approximating that of the measurement signal. New formulations are therefore in order.

It is pertinent, therefore, to determine which of the electrical concepts still have meaning in such highly non-linear cases. Four of the ordinary electrical quantities remain accurately defined for such transient conditions; potential difference, current, quantity of electricity transferred, and energy released or absorbed. Resistance or conductance and capacitance still have meaning if one is careful to state which of the three defining equations is in use and is careful to perform no mathematical operations that violate these restrictions.

Surprisingly, it is possible to derive a whole family of useful simple relationships between these fundamental quantities in an excited nerve through recognition of a single relationship imposed by the constancy of propagation velocity and wave form in any uniform nerve. This constancy permits application of the one-dimensional wave equation that at once relates all the spatial and temporal derivatives of the wave function through simple measurable constants.

Utilizing a few simple mathematical procedures summarized in Appendix 2, it is possible to identify several important components of the action potential that at first glance seem hopelessly obscured or inaccessible (Fig. 9a). The monophasic action potential as synthesized purely from external measurements is identified as a fixed fraction of the transmembrane potential plus an integrating constant that turns out to be the resting potential. This "monophasic" wave form also turns out to represent with different scale constants the quantity of electric charge moved along the axon during the impulse. It can thus be used to test hypotheses involving axonal electrokinetic transport.

The first derivative (diphasic) curve, which can be closely approximated by measuring the potential difference between closely adjacent external leads on the nerve, measures directly the longitudinal current down the axon but can also be shown to represent with different scale constants the time course of net charge deposition and removal at the membrane during the impulse. Although this curve does not distinguish between displacement current and conduction current, and therefore cannot separate charge variations representing redistribution of double-layer charge and concentration cell current, it does measure the sum of these variations and thus permits interesting speculation on the distribution between them with an intuitive sense seldom obtained from impedance or steady state analysis.

The second derivative (triphasic) curve is easily identified with the divergence of axonal current and hence with membrane current density, the term most often used to set up theories of excitation.

Finally, the product of membrane current divided by membrane voltage is identified as membrane power and hence as the instantaneous rate at which the membrane does work or has work done upon it. It should be realized that during part of the action potential cycle the membrane yields energy and during another part absorbs it; but it must, over the cycle, deliver an energy excess large enough to compensate for electrical power loss in the resistance of the axon.

As it turns out, this energy analysis, although accurate and reliable when integrated over a whole cycle of action, is strongly sensitive to resting potential value and so may be misleading on an instant-by-instant basis. Another mathematically equivalent formulation for the energy released during an entire action potential cycle states that this energy is equal to the line integral evaluated by measuring the area of the loop formed when electrical membrane charge is plotted against transmembrane potential (Fig. 9b). This loop is easily plotted on an oscilloscope and is fortunately independent in area of initial charge and resting potential and so gives an immediate measure of membrane energy release.

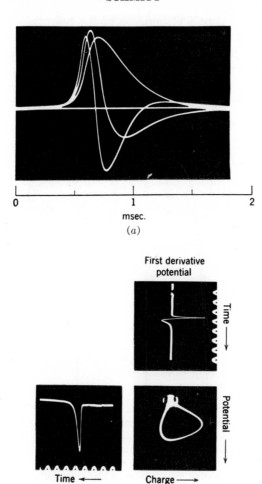

Fig. 9. (a) Monophasic action potential with approximate first and second time derivatives. (Single-fiber nerve preparation from Carcinus, *Electronic Differentiation.*) (b) Parametric components of action potential energy diagram. By electronic processes of integration and differentiation it is possible to obtain simultaneously accurate instantaneous values for the transmembrane potential and its first two derivatives (a). Appropriate combinations of these components can be quantitatively identified (Appendix 2) with important electrical nerve constants including membrane charge shift, membrane current, longitudinal axonal current, and membrane energy release (b). The method is experimentally unique because it does not require internal nerve electrodes.

Space does not permit elaboration of the potentialities inherent in this method, but one example will serve to illustrate the approach. In Fig. 10 are shown values of membrane incremental charge and current plotted against time during the action potential. As a positive product

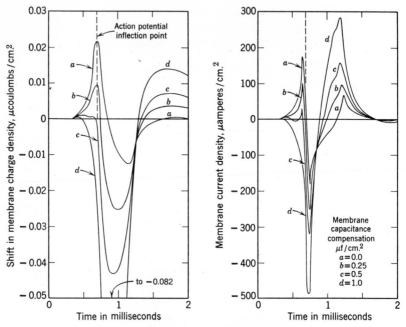

Fig. 10. Active and passive electrical components at squid axon membrane. The excitatory phenomena in nerve are usually associated with the radially directed component of action current that penetrates the axon membrane. At the rapid rates of charge accompanying spread of excitation, a substantial portion of the total current goes to charge the membrane electrostatically and therefore need not represent ionic penetration of the membrane. Assuming successively larger values for the structural membrane capacitance, a value around ½ μf./cm.² is found where the passive capacitance accounts for essentially all the membrane current and charge accumulation until exactly the inflection point of the action potential when active processes set in very suddenly and reach full activity in about 60 μsec.

of current and voltage implies positive work, it will be seen that the membrane initially, *before* it is excited, supplies energy to the action potential and later recaptures some of it. If we now assume that there exists a quiescent membrane capacitance of varying relative magnitude, a value can be found in which practically all the membrane energy comes from this static reservoir until excitation sets in, whereupon a sudden burst of energy is provided to pay back the condenser and to supply external losses. The accompanying curves show the corresponding active and passive charge shifts. Carried out with postulated reactive and resistive components, this method forms a useful and easy method for evaluating otherwise difficult variable and non-linear admittance components.

This analytic method just described suggests a final and very promising method of investigation and analysis involving creation of artificial electrical components to be tested experimentally. In effect the method suggests that electronically generated functions of theoretically appropriate form be combined with naturally occurring biological components or with artificial arrays that might behave like excitable systems.

One application of this technique involves subtraction of known electrical components from a complex system to reveal the underlying active processes in clearer detail; another suggests supplementing imperfect approximations to a synthetic excitable physical-chemical system with artificially added components so that the problem of synthesis need not be solved all at once.

Space permits only one illustration of this approach. As outlined in Appendix 3, it is a simple matter electronically to generate positive or negative resistances, conductances, capacitances, or inductances. It is also possible to provide combinations of these in any proportion.

Using insect cuticle § as a membrane (isolated cuticles of blowfly larvae) in a specially constructed cell (Fig. 11), it is possible to make ordinary impedance measurements and to discover a conventional membrane capacitance (about 0.4 μf./cm.^{2}) and a small variable conductance that together give a completely conventional circle diagram,

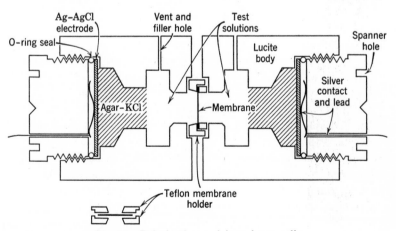

Fig. 11. Polarization and impedance cell.

§ This work was done in collaboration with A. Glenn Richards.

the diameter of which is variable according to ionic conditions at the membrane and membrane past history.

In the instrument illustrated in Fig. 12 it is possible to feed into the membrane an artificial negative static capacitance equal to the membrane's normal static structural capacitance and thus unveil the

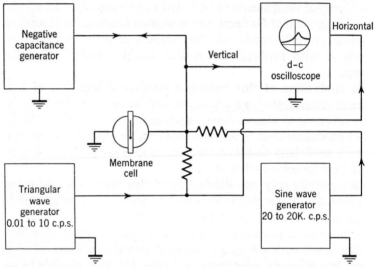

Fig. 12. Polarized membrane resistance plotter. Electronically generated negative capacitance, connected across a biological membrane, can be made to cancel out the static structural capacitance of the membrane, thus revealing the dynamic changes in membrane conductance produced by mild polarization and normally swamped by susceptance. The method is more fully explained in Appendix 3.

dynamic changes normally hidden by the capacitance at high frequency and by polarization and conductance at low frequency.

The three oscilloscopes plot respectively: (1) the phase ellipse at a fixed test frequency to detect susceptance variation, (2) the d-c. or static-current-voltage characteristic to show static non-linearity, and (3) the membrane resistance for a small test a-c. signal as the membrane is polarized by a direct current that sweeps slowly from negative through zero to positive and back in a 20-sec. cycle.

It is evident from the four pictures shown in Fig. 13 that membrane conductance in even such a biologically secreted but non-living membrane can have a sharp minimum at zero or at a finite polarization value, a flat character, a strongly rectifying character as has been reported for squid, or a bimodal character implying transient energy release.

(a)

(b)

Fig. 13.

[Legend on page 113

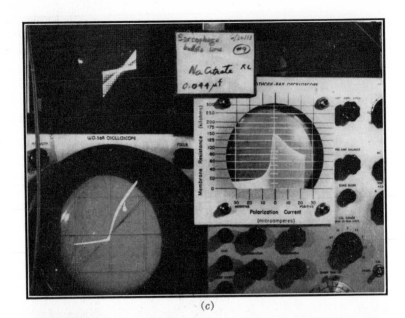

(c)

(d)

Fig. 13.—(Continued)

This last method promises to be an enormous aid in testing detailed characteristics of excitable systems whether totally biological or partly biological and partly synthetic.

I will now summarize some tentative conclusions that are at least suggested by these investigations.

1. The excitatory process is not intrinsically an all-or-none phenomenon but is one that can be evoked more or less completely around electrical cycles of increasing size and appropriate timing. The normal threshold may on this basis be considered merely as a level at which energy safety factor becomes unity.

2. The excitatory process can be usefully described in terms of a variable, negative, time-dependent "conductance."

3. The negative conductance energy cycle appears to be charge limited rather than potential limited and hence is not normally bistable.

4. The notion of a charge sheet invading the potential gradient region of the membrane and thus providing membrane current part by convection, part by conventional capacitance discharge, and part by displacement current associated with redistributed coefficients of capacitance seems tenable.

5. It is possible to duplicate many of the nerve membrane properties including rectification, conductance variation, and negative resistance in metabolically dead non-nerve membranes.

Fig. 13. Non-linear admittance variations of polarized membranes. Cancellation of membrane capacitance by electronically generated negative capacitance reveals many dramatic and varied changes in membrane conductance in response to mild electrical polarization. In the patterns shown, the membrane used is cuticle of the blowfly larva. The patterns are selected to illustrate four quite different types of variation often found. On the upper-left-hand oscilloscope is shown a trace of the alternating-current-voltage ellipse, which remains a straight line if all capacitance is balanced out but tilts to an angle representing the arc tangent of the membrane parallel a-c. resistance. The lower-left-hand oscilloscope plots the static-current-voltage curve (current is abscissa). The right-hand oscilloscope plots magnitude of membrane dynamic parallel resistance vertically against polarizing current. As high membrane resistance implies impermeability, this presentation is of considerable interest. Patterns of the type given in (a) represent nearly linear, somewhat permeable membranes that approach ideal physical-chemical behavior. They constitute a small minority of experimentally tested cases. Patterns given in (b) imply rapid increase of permeability with electric stress of either polarity, whereas the membranes in (c) are unidirectional and hence "rectify" strongly as squid membrane has been shown to rectify. Membranes of the type given in (d) show anomalous multiple permeability minima and therefore are of interest because they can theoretically give rise to dynamic negative resistance phenomena that are statically stable. The special interest in this type is occasioned by its similarity to the characteristics that are found in nerve.

APPENDIX 1

TRANSMISSION LINE ATTENUATION THEORY AS ADAPTED FOR ANALYSIS OF NERVE ADMITTANCE AND IMPEDANCE COMPONENTS IN TERMS OF EXTRA-POLAR ELECTROTONIC POTENTIAL DISTRIBUTION FOR SUBTHRESHOLD SINUSOIDAL STIMULATION

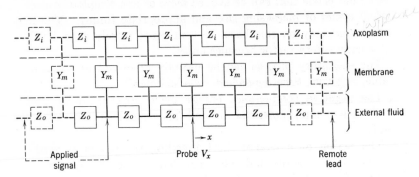

The fiber is supposed to be representable by a uniform distribution of longitudinal impedance inside the fiber Z_i and outside it Z_o connected by a uniformly distributed membrane admittance Y_m. Z and Y units are understood to be in complex ohms and mhos, respectively, per unit length of fiber. It is assumed that Z and Y are unknown functions of frequency unless otherwise specified, but they are assumed independent of signal amplitude. Z_l is the sum of Z_i and Z_o and represents the unit loop impedance.

It is easily demonstrated that the pertinent solutions of the complex transmission line equations for this case will be of the form

$$V_x = A_1 e^{-\lambda x} + A_2 e^{+\lambda x}$$

where A_1, A_2, and λ are constants. As the electrotonic voltages quickly diminish to zero with even modest finite values of x, A_2 must be zero. Therefore $V_x = A_1 e^{-\lambda x}$. Because the constants are in general complex numbers, the equations take the form

$$V_{x,t} = A e^{-\alpha x \epsilon j(\omega t - \beta x + \phi)}$$

where A is an amplitude constant representing the intensity of stimulation, α is the exponential decay constant describing the rate of decay of electronic signal with distance along the fiber, β is a phase constant describing the rate of change of *relative time phase* with distance in the electrotonic region, and ϕ is an initial phase.

The real part of $V_{x,t}$ actually measured is

$$V_{x,t} = A e^{-\alpha x} \cos(\omega t - \beta x + \phi)$$

so that regardless of the electrical complexity of Z_i, Z_o, and Y_m, the logarithm of the measured voltage amplitude, i.e.,

$$\log |V_{x,t}| = \log A e^{-\alpha x} = \log A - \alpha x$$

will vary linearly with αx and with a slope ratio $-\alpha$.

For any slow changes of x, it is evident that $V_{x,t}$ can be thought of as varying cosinusoidally with time, i.e., $V_x = \text{kcos}\,(\omega t + \psi)$ at the angular frequency ω. For any fixed value of ψ then, it is evident that $\beta x = \omega t + \phi'$, so that a "phase wave" propagates with a velocity $x/t = \omega/\beta$ and so β can be measured by noting the linear relationship between ψ and βx for a given time phase $\omega t - 2n\pi + \theta$.

In the usual coaxial line form α and β can be shown to take the forms

$$\alpha = \sqrt{\tfrac{1}{2}\{\sqrt{(R^2 + L^2\omega^2)(G^2 + \omega^2C^2)} + (RG - LC\omega^2)\}}$$

$$\beta = \sqrt{\tfrac{1}{2}\{\sqrt{(R^2 + L^2\omega^2)(G^2 + \omega^2C^2)} - (RG - LC\omega^2)\}}$$

but for nerve fibers longitudinal ωL is always negligible and Z can be adequately represented by pure resistance R so the expressions simplify so that they can be rearranged to read $\alpha^2 - \beta^2 = R_l G$ and $2\alpha\beta = R_l C\omega - R_l B$ where R_l is the loop longitudinal resistance/unit length, G is the membrane conductance/unit length, and C is the capacitance/unit length. This implies that, knowing only the easily measurable phase and log amplitude constants β and α, it is possible to evaluate the membrane conductance G and susceptance ωC in terms of loop resistance, and to evaluate them absolutely if R_l is known. R_l in turn can be evaluated if multiple measurements with varied R_o are made. The phase velocity ω/β is of course readily available without *any* electrical data except β.

As no specific assumptions about Y require it to be capacitive, negative β slopes are readily described in negative C or negative B terms, or even in inductance terms if desired. Negative α implies an excitable fiber and hence is not evaluated by this method.

APPENDIX 2

TRANSIENT ANALYSIS OF UNIFORMLY PROPAGATING ACTION POTENTIAL WAVE

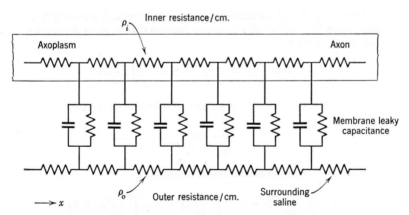

$V = V_{xt}$ = voltage difference between inside and outside of fiber at time t, place x. All components are assumed uniformly distributed lengthwise. For a linear wave phenomenon

$$V_{xt} = f(x - ut) \tag{1}$$

where u is the velocity of propagation.

$$\frac{\partial V}{\partial x} = f'(x - ut) \tag{2}$$

$$\frac{\partial V}{\partial t} = -uf'(x - ut) \tag{3}$$

$$\frac{\partial V}{\partial t} = -u\frac{\partial V}{\partial x} \tag{4}$$

The inner current at any position x must be equal and opposite to the outer current at that point. The lengthwise rate of change of V in an infinitesimal length dx due to the longitudinal current i_l is

$$\frac{\partial V}{\partial x} = i_l(\rho_i + \rho_o) \tag{5}$$

The ratio of $(\rho_i + \rho_o)/\rho_o$ can be measured separately and can be called α, therefore,

$$\frac{\partial V}{\partial x} = i_l \rho_o \alpha \tag{6}$$

The quantity $\dfrac{\partial V_o}{\partial x}$ can be measured experimentally by the approximation

$$\frac{\partial V_o}{\partial x} \approx \frac{\Delta V_o}{\Delta x}$$

$$\Delta V_o = i_l \rho_o \, \Delta x \qquad i_l = \frac{1}{\rho_o}\frac{\Delta V_o}{\Delta x} \tag{7}$$

where ΔV_o is the voltage measured between two closely adjacent points separated by Δx. This permits direct measurement of the longitudinal current flow as a function of time.

As we can integrate and differentiate electrical voltages with respect to time, but can measure spatial potential differences as a function of time, let us change variables with the aid of equation 4.

$$V = \int \frac{\partial V}{\partial t}\,dt = -u\int \frac{\partial V}{\partial x}\,dt \approx -u\int \frac{\Delta V}{\Delta x}\,dt \tag{8}$$

As $\dfrac{\partial V}{\partial x}$ is experimentally available to a good approximation as in equation 7 and has a value

$$\frac{\partial V}{\partial x} = \frac{\partial V_o}{\partial x}\alpha \tag{9}$$

we can evaluate V from external measurements only as

$$V = \int \frac{\alpha \, \partial V_o}{\partial x}\,dx = -u\alpha \int \frac{\partial V_o}{\partial x}\,dt = -u\alpha \int_0^t \frac{\partial V_o}{\partial x}\,dt + V_R$$

$$\approx -u\alpha \int_0^t \frac{\Delta V_o}{\Delta x}\,dt + V_R \tag{10}$$

Note that the resting potential V_R appears as a constant of integration and cannot be evaluated in this manner. Now note that the current i_r, which diverges, is given by

$$i_r = \frac{\partial i_l}{\partial x} = \frac{\partial}{\partial x} \left(\frac{\partial V_o}{\partial x} \right) \frac{1}{\rho_o} = \frac{1}{\rho_o} \frac{\partial}{\partial x} \frac{\partial V_o}{\partial x} \tag{11}$$

which becomes

$$i_r = \frac{1}{\rho_o} \left(\frac{-1}{u} \right) \frac{\partial}{\partial t} \frac{\partial V_o}{\partial x} \tag{12}$$

The radial current density i_r, defined as the membrane current per unit length, is thus obtainable from measured quantities.

$$i_r = \frac{-1}{\rho_o u} \frac{\partial}{\partial t} \left(\frac{\partial V_o}{\partial x} \right) \approx \frac{-1}{\rho_o u} \frac{\partial}{\partial t} \left(\frac{\Delta V_o}{\Delta x} \right) \tag{13}$$

and can be related to the action potential form as follows:

$$i_r = \frac{\partial}{\partial x} i_l = \frac{\partial}{\partial x} \left(\frac{1}{(\rho_i + \rho_o)} \frac{\partial V}{\partial x} \right) = \frac{1}{\alpha \rho_o u^2} \frac{\partial^2 V}{\partial t^2} \tag{14}$$

The penetrating, hence the stimulating, component of an action potential is proportional to its second derivative.

The charge density transferred at the membrane q_r can be easily identified as $\int i_r \, dt$, therefore,

$$q_r = \int i_r \, dt = \int \frac{1}{\alpha \rho_o u^2} \frac{\partial^2 V}{\partial t^2} dt = \frac{1}{\alpha \rho_o u^2} \frac{\partial V}{\partial t} + q_o \tag{15}$$

In terms of the potential from differential leads ΔV_o, the radial charge transfer can be formulated as

$$q_r = \int i_r \, dt = \int \frac{-1}{\rho_o u} \frac{\partial}{\partial t} \frac{\partial V_o}{\partial x} dt \approx \frac{-1}{\rho_o u} \frac{\Delta V_o}{\Delta x} + q_o \tag{16}$$

Note that an integration constant must appear despite the fact that we want the integral of the derivative with respect to time and hence the original functional form.

In order to analyze for membrane energy exchange W, we must examine a product function. The most obvious one is

$$W = \int V i_r \, dt \tag{17}$$

Substituting from equation 14 to get energy in terms of membrane potential,

$$W = \int V \left(\frac{1}{\alpha \rho_o u^2} \frac{\partial^2 V}{\partial t^2} \right) dt = \frac{1}{\alpha \rho_o u^2} \int_0^t V \frac{\partial^2 V}{\partial t^2} dt + W_o$$

This W_o can be set equal to zero at the start of a cycle of activity. Alternatively, using equations 10 and 13,

$$W \approx \int_0^t \left(-u\alpha \int \frac{\Delta V_o}{\Delta x} dt + V_r \right) \left(\frac{-1}{\rho_o u} \frac{\partial}{\partial t} \frac{\Delta V_o}{\Delta x} \right) dt + W_o \tag{18}$$

This can be simplified somewhat to yield

$$W \approx \frac{\alpha}{(\Delta x)^2 \rho_o} \int_0^t \left(\int \Delta V_o \, dt + C \right) \left(\frac{\partial}{\partial t} \Delta V_o \right) dt + W_o \tag{19}$$

Another approach to energy measurement which does not require instant-by-instant knowledge of a product relies upon the "engine indicator" integration procedure.

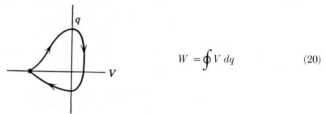

$$W = \oint V \, dq \qquad (20)$$

V and q are available from equations 8 and 16 or from equations 1 and 15 and may be recorded oscillographically for measurement by planimeter. Note that shifts of either axis may be introduced without affecting the area and consequently initial membrane charge and resting potential need not be known.

Membrane energy over the entire action potential cycle but *not* instant by instant can also be determined without knowledge of initial charge or membrane potential by equating the total energy released by the membrane to the total energy absorbed by the axoplasm and surrounding fluid.

$$W_{\text{cycle}} = \int_{\text{cycle}} V i_r \, dt = \int_{\text{cycle}} i_l^2 (\rho_i + \rho_o) \, dt = \alpha \rho_o \int_{\text{cycle}} i_l^2 \, dt \qquad (21)$$

but,

$$i_l = \frac{1}{\rho_o} \frac{\partial V_o}{\partial x}$$

from equation 7; therefore,

$$W_{\text{cycle}} = \alpha \rho_o \int_{\text{cycle}} \left(\frac{1}{\rho_o} \right)^2 \left(\frac{\partial V_o}{\partial x} \right)^2 dt = \frac{\alpha}{\rho_o} \int_{\text{cycle}} \left(\frac{\partial V_o}{\partial x} \right)^2 dt \approx \frac{\alpha}{\rho_o (\Delta x)^2} \int_{\text{cycle}} (\Delta V_o)^2 \, dt \qquad (22)$$

The last approximate form can be evaluated electronically but requires an inconvenient instantaneous squaring process.

APPENDIX 3

MEMBRANE POLARIZATION AND ADMITTANCE COMPENSATION SYSTEM

A membrane in an admittance measurement cell is to be subjected to combined polarization by two currents: (1) a slowly swept direct current proportional to the output of a triangle wave generator and (2) a superimposed a-c. sine wave admittance measuring current proportional to the output of a sine wave signal generator. It is required that these two currents be strictly proportional to their respective generator voltages, non-interactive, and independent of the load admittance presented by the measurement cell combined with the fed-back admittance of several compensating circuits.

Electronic feedback compensation is to be provided (1) to neutralize the capacitance of shielded leads to the membrane vessel, (2) to compensate specified values of membrane susceptance with decade magnified negative capacitance, (3) to provide corresponding decade magnified conductance specified in equivalent shunt ohms/10, and (4) to provide decade preamplification for recording oscilloscopes with the attendant load isolation.

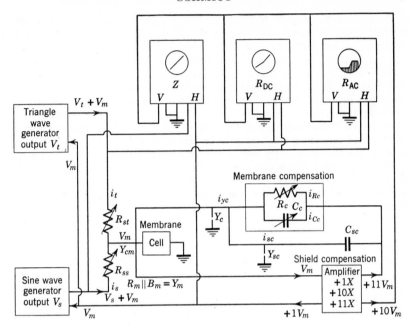

Proper signals, all in the form of voltages, are to be provided to three oscilloscopes to enable oscilloscope Z to plot an a-c. impedance ellipse directly, oscilloscope R_{DC} to plot a static current-voltage curve, and oscilloscope R_{AC} to plot magnitude of membrane conductance in equivalent ohms against d-c. polarizing current.

The triangle wave generator supplies a current

$$i_t = \frac{(V_t + V_m) - V_m}{R_{st}} = \frac{V_t}{R_{st}}$$

It therefore supplies a constant current adjustable by R_{st} but independent of the voltage at V_m, whether due to the membrane, the compensating circuits, or the sine wave generator. By an identical argument it can be shown that the sine wave generator supplies an independently controllable signal current

$$i_s = \frac{(V_s + V_m) - V_m}{R_{ss}} = \frac{V_s}{R_{ss}}$$

The membrane compensating circuit presents to the measurement cell an admittance

$$Y_c \equiv \frac{i_{yc}}{V_m} = \frac{i_{Rc} + ji_{Cc}}{V_m} = \frac{(V_m - 11V_m)(G_{Rc} + jB_{Cc})}{V_m} = -10(G_{Rc} + jB_{Cc})$$

Y_{sc} is by identical reasoning $-10jB_{sc}$; i.e., C_{sc} compensates accurately for the shields when it has a value one-tenth the shield capacitance. Thus the desired negative admittance components are created.

The oscilloscopes contain high-pass or low-pass filters where necessary to discriminate between sweep and a-c. test signals; therefore, it is only necessary to supply the correct horizontal and vertical component magnitudes. Oscilloscope Z requires $10V_m$ vertically and signal proportional to i_s horizontally. $10V_m$ is directly available from the amplifier and $V_s = (V_s + V_m) - V_m = i_sR_{ss}$ supplies the current proportional voltage. Oscilloscope R_{DC} requires $10V_m$ vertically and a horizontal component proportional to V_t. The vertical component is already available and the horizontal is obtained as $V_t = (V_t + V_m) - V_m = i_tR_{ss}$. The R_{AC} oscilloscope requires vertically the magnitude of the reciprocal of the conductance component of compensated membrane admittance to be plotted against the same horizontal V_t used on the R_{DC} scope. By setting the compensation C_c correctly, Y_{cm} for the whole compensated membrane circuit $= G_m - G_c + jB_m - jB_c = G_m - 10G_{Rc}$ if $B_m = B_c$. The oscilloscope will thus receive an a-c. signal through its high-pass vertical filter of magnitude $i_s/Y_{cm} = i_sR_m \sim R_m$ because i_s is constant as proved above.

7·

Ions, Potentials,
and the Nerve Impulse

KENNETH S. COLE *

The process by which nerves transmit information has long been an intriguing puzzle. Since the work of Galvani, the electrical side of this puzzle has been attacked with ever-increasing power as new instruments and techniques have become available. It has, however, required a novel and unique biological approach—coupled with keen insight and prodigious effort—to provide new information and a new analysis that do much to correlate and unify the results of a century and a half. The ancient history will be dealt with in rather cursory fashion. The many facts of nerve behavior that have come from a vast amount of careful experiment and analysis, along with the numerous attempted generalizations, will be passed over or shown with a simplicity not originally possible. The renaissance, beginning in the middle 1930s, will be scanned only as an orientation towards the problems and as a stage setting for the development of the past few years.

CABLE VERSUS NERVE

The analogy between the conduction in nerve and in the submarine cable is obvious and has been used almost continually since the theory of the cable was developed by Lord Kelvin.[1] In this analogy we now know that the copper wire is replaced by the electrolyte in the interior of the fiber, which is a comparatively poor conductor of some 50 ohm cm. specific resistance. The insulation found in the membrane at the surface of the fiber would have a tremendous ability to store electrical energy in its capacity of 1 μf./cm.[2] except that it is also very leaky, as

From the Naval Medical Research Institute, Bethesda, Md. The opinions stated are those of the author and are not necessarily the views of the Navy Department.

cable insulation goes, with a resistance of only a few thousand ohm square centimeters. The calculation of the performance of such a simple cable is straightforward and shows that a short pulse becomes smaller and longer and moves more slowly as it travels and that a few millimeters of a nerve fiber are comparable to several miles of the San Francisco-Honolulu cable. Such a nerve fiber would perhaps have to be stimulated with kilovolts at the spine to produce millivolts at a toe, and this small signal would only appear some seconds later. Yet

Fig. 1. Changes of potential of a single fiber at a short distance from a stimulating electrode. The first potential in each record is the passively propagated stimulus, whereas the additional potentials of the second and third are active response or nerve impulse for slightly and highly superthreshold stimuli. Time marks, 1 msec. apart.

a nerve does behave in this thoroughly useless manner, delivering the first signal in each record of Fig. 1 [2] which depends upon the size, shape, and sign of an applied pulse of only a few millivolts.

The nerve can also respond in the totally different manner shown in the second and third records of Fig. 1. The later response—of about 100 mv. across the membrane—is an integral part of the usable nerve impulse, and it is only triggered by the rapid application of about 10^{-8} coulombs/cm.^{2} in the right direction. Once started in a uniform nerve, this impulse travels with a constant velocity and wave form, depending only upon the local conditions and independently of how or where it originated. It is obvious that such a phenomenon is only possible if energy is available for propagation and is released point by point as the impulse proceeds. Thus a simple cable cannot serve as a model for nerve propagation. Other models, such as the falling dominoes and the burning fuse, propagate satisfactorily but do not recover rapidly, whereas the passive iron wire is not yet known to be any simpler than a living nerve.

SQUID AXON

A new path was opened by J. Z. Young [3] in 1936 when he rediscovered the giant nerve system in the squid and introduced the fibers into nerve physiology. The squid are beautiful, opalescent beasts and, in the North Atlantic, about a foot long, Fig. 2.[4] They are not only

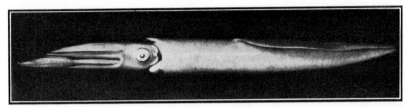

Fig. 2. Model of the North Atlantic squid.

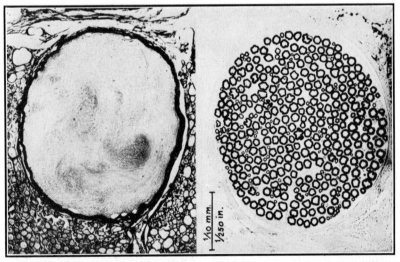

Fig. 3. Microphotographs of a squid giant axon, with surrounding small fibers, and of the small fibers composing a rabbit leg nerve of about the same size.

jet-propelled but use this propulsion to travel rapidly either ahead or astern. Their squirting is controlled by nerves of a kind shown in Fig. 3 [5] where a single squid fiber a half millimeter in diameter is compared with the several hundred small fibers in a rabbit leg nerve of about the same diameter. A couple of inches of such a fiber, or axon as it is often called, can be isolated and kept alive for a fair number of hours—if treated reasonably.

Of course, the first physiological experiments used readily available techniques to measure conventional properties of this axon and led to rather conventional results. But as the potentialities were increasingly exploited a number of characteristics previously only suspected were found and measured, and some new, or previously overlooked,

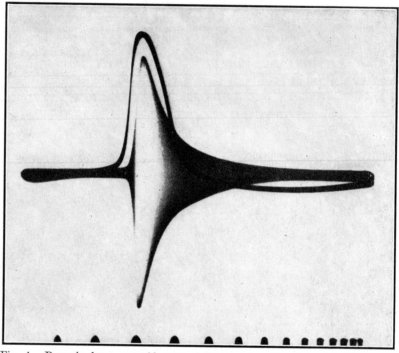

Fig. 4.   Records from a squid axon that are proportional to the increase of membrane conductance (band) and membrane potential (line) during the passage of an impulse. Time marks, 1 msec. apart.

phenomena were brought to light. An example of a verified suspicion is the increased ease with which ions cross the membrane during the passage of an impulse. In Fig. 4 the electrical pulse or action potential is superposed on the increase of electrical conductance.[6] During the impulse the resistance falls to a minimum of some 25 ohm square centimeters from the value of several thousand ohm square centimeters at rest, although the electrical capacity does not change much.

The most startling of the new phenomena came to light when a group on each side of the Atlantic ventured into the unknown and put an electrode into the inviting vast open space inside the axon.[7, 8] It had long been known by measurements with external electrodes that a

resting potential difference of some tens of millivolts was considerably
decreased at the peak of the impulse. The potential recorded by the
inside electrode was about 60 mv. at rest and did not merely meekly
decline during the impulse but vigorously went through zero and actu-

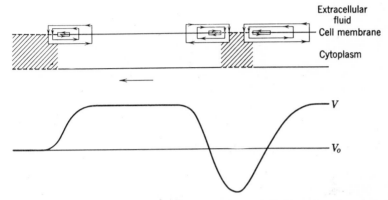

Fig. 5. Diagrams of the local currents of a killed end (left) and an impulse and
of the corresponding potential difference across the membrane.

ally reversed in direction before recovering. This unexpected state
of affairs is shown diagrammatically [9] in Fig. 5 where we see the increase of potential as the internal electrode is run through the injured
end and the reversal of potential in a hypothetical, halted impulse.[9]

Very intensive investigations and thousands of records of the initiation of an impulse demonstrated little but a frustrating inability to deal
with the local circuits that make propagation possible. In the equivalent electrical circuit of Fig. 6 the external and internal electrolytes are

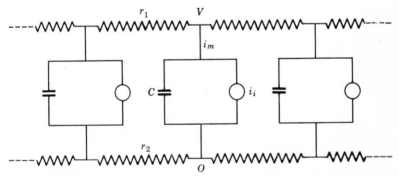

Fig. 6. Electrical circuit with "lumped" elements to represent a short length of
an axon.

represented by resistances and the membrane capacity by a condenser. The total membrane current i_m is that of the condenser $C\dfrac{\partial V}{\partial t}$ added to that carried by ions i_i. As is the case for a cable, this membrane current is also given by the second partial derivative $\partial^2 V/\partial x^2$ of the potential along the axon,

$$i_m = C\,\frac{\partial V}{\partial t} + i_i = \frac{1}{r_1 + r_2}\cdot\frac{\partial^2 V}{\partial x^2}\qquad(1)$$

The term at the right, which arises from the local circuits, makes an analysis of data practically impossible when the membrane ionic permeability is not only complicated but also of an unknown complexity.

CONTROL OF CURRENT

When we meet a limit to our powers of analysis of an involved situation, the only thing to do is to simplify the situation. The first step,

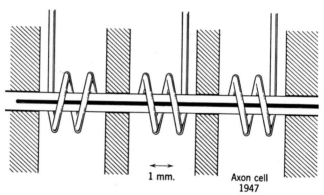

1 mm.   Axon cell
1947

Fig. 7. Diagram of a squid axon with the internal electrode along its axis and the external, measuring electrode, with a guard electrode on each side.

taken after the war, was to eliminate the difficult derivative—and so to deny all impulse propagation to the axon. The axon was threaded through an external measuring electrode and its flanking guard electrodes and then a long internal electrode was inserted along the axis of the axon, as shown in Fig. 7. The membrane potential and current density were then the same at all points in the central measuring region.[10]

Figure 8 demonstrates that a small current, in or out, changes the potential as it starts to charge the capacity of 1 μf./cm.^{2} and that when the current is cut off the capacity discharges through the

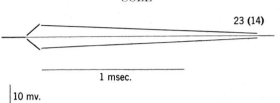

23 (14)

1 msec.

10 mv.

Fig. 8. The membrane potential during and after a small, short pulse of constant current in each direction.

few thousand ohms per square centimeter of the membrane. The potential starts similarly with larger currents,[11] Fig. 9, but later develops an asymmetry with a low steady state potential under the cathode and a high value under the anode, which indicates the rather

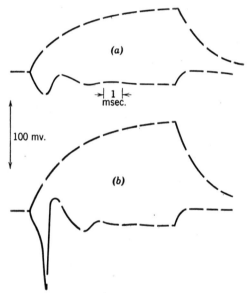

(a)

1 msec.

100 mv.

(b)

Fig. 9. The membrane potential for long-duration constant currents in both directions: (a) below threshold; (b) above threshold. The upward deflections are under the anode.

good rectification characteristics of the membrane. The oscillations, Fig. 9a, under the cathode further complicate the membrane circuit by requiring the addition of an equivalent inductance, and an added and large equivalent capacity is needed under the anode. Only a slight increase of current, Fig. 9b, turns the first cathode minimum into a dramatic drop of potential qualitatively the same as the nerve impulse and widely known as the all-or-none response. Similarly, a larger short-current pulse can be found that may evoke either a slight 10-20 mv. or an explosive 100 mv. response, and the relationship between the current and its duration at this threshold is shown in Fig. 10. The critical transfer of charge is here about one ion for a square 300 A. on a side with a corresponding potential change of some 10 mv.

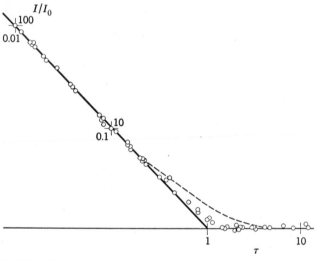

Fig. 10. Relationship between the threshold constant current I and its duration τ for six axons. I_0 is the threshold current of long duration and τ is a time constant of the membrane. The dashed line would be obtained for a system with a single time constant.

CONTROL OF POTENTIAL

Many other and interesting experiments of this type were carried out, but the hoped-for indications of the energy source and its mode of release were still so complicated by the all-or-none response as to be inaccessible. However, it became apparent that the electrostatic energy stored in the capacity of the membrane stood ready to discharge itself into the unknown mechanism in this useful but very puzzling way.

The next step was to force the capacity out of action. This was done by applying and maintaining a sudden change of potential to the membrane with the result that, after the initial short surge, the capacity current $C\dfrac{dV}{dt}$ remained zero and left only the ionic current by itself,[11] Fig. 11. Under these conditions the current flow for a membrane potential

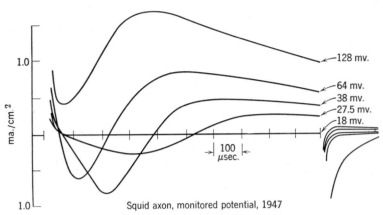

Fig. 11. The membrane current density during the indicated sudden decreases of the potential difference between the internal and external electrodes, of 1 msec. duration.

reduction of 18 mv. is very small and undramatic; but at 27.5, 38, and 64 mv. a reverse current appears before the naively-expected current takes over. Yet, for a change of 128 mv. the current does not reverse. The reversal is not only necessary and sufficient for an all-or-none response of between 64 mv. and 128 mv. to take place after a rapid change of more than 18 mv. but also for a propagated impulse within these limits.

SODIUM AND POTASSIUM ANALYSIS

We now have the direct and unclouded view of our problem which Hodgkin, Huxley, and Katz have extended and interpreted in a most dramatic and convincing manner in the past few years. In their first experiments after the war [12] they found that the change of potential during an impulse was proportional to the logarithm of the external sodium ion concentration. Some of our own data, shown in Fig. 12, not only confirmed but somewhat improved the original observations— perhaps because they were uncomplicated by propagation. These results clearly implicated the sodium ion in addition to the potassium ion, which had long received almost exclusive attention.

A section of the membrane may now be thought of as shown in Fig. 13 with its capacity C, electromotive forces, and ion permeabilities.[13] The potentials E_K and E_{Na} are given by the thermodynamic equilibrium function of the inside and outside ion concentrations; and, since the concentration ratio for the sodium ion is approximately the reciprocal of that for the potassium ion, E_{Na} and E_K are of opposite sign. An ion

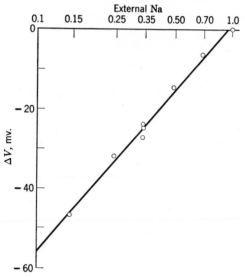

Fig. 12. The effect of the external sodium concentration on the action potential, without external current flow. The changes of the resting potential are not included.

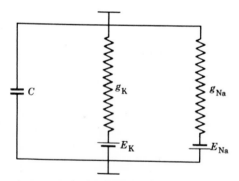

Fig. 13. The more important ionic components of the axon activity. The conductances g_K and g_{Na} depend upon both potential and time.

permeability of a unit area is given as its conductance, which is the rate of net ion transport i_K or i_{Na} per unit of net potential across it

$$g_K = i_K/(E - E_K), \quad g_{Na} = i_{Na}/(E - E_{Na})$$

where E is the total potential difference across the membrane. At rest, the sodium ion permeability is so small as to allow the potassium potential largely to determine the membrane potential, but as the sodium permeability becomes large at the height of activity the potential may reverse to near the sodium potential.

Thus, for the trussed-up axon, which can neither propagate nor give an all-or-none response, it was reasonable to expect that the reverse current of Fig. 11 was a short burst of sodium ions crossing whereas the later current was a steady flow of potassium ions. This was indeed shown to be true.[14] When the membrane potential was made equal to the sodium potential, there was no sodium current flow and the only current was that of potassium ions no matter how the external sodium ion concentration was varied. Then, by subtraction of this potassium current, the sodium current for normal or another external sodium concentration could be found, as shown [15] in Fig. 14 for a potential decrease of 56 mv. A very laborious and ingenious analysis gave the complete time course of the permeabilities after sudden changes of the potential difference across the membrane. As shown in Fig. 15, the increases of permeability are progressively more rapid and larger for the larger potential changes.[15] In this figure the simple ohmic resistors of Fig. 13 would each be represented by a single horizontal line independently of the applied potential. The comparatively slow rise of the potassium conductances requires the presence of an inductance-like mechanism, as does the decline of the sodium conductance, whereas the rather faster onset of sodium is controlled by a capacity analog.

These and other data suggest strongly that, within a time scale of milliseconds:

1. Only the energies inherent in the sodium and potassium ionic ratios are drawn upon for the transport of these ions across the squid axon membrane. Thus—as expressed in electrical terms—these electromotive forces remain constant, independent of applied potential, current, non-linearity, or excitation of the membrane, so long as the concentrations and temperature are constant.

2. The mechanisms by which these ions are allowed to move are controlled primarily by the membrane potential and the temperature.

3. The dependencies of the permeabilities—or conductances—of these two ions on time, temperature, and potential constitute an array of

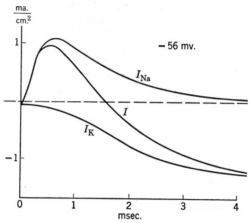

Fig. 14. Ionic currents after a sudden 56 mv. decrease of the membrane potential. The total current I was measured in sea water, the potassium current, I_K was obtained with sodium so reduced that the sodium current was negligible, and the sodium current in sea water, I_{Na} was obtained by difference.

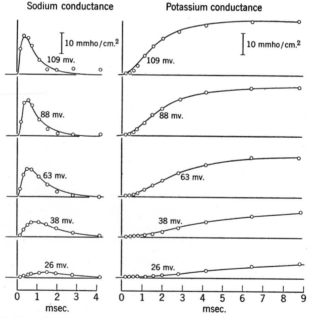

Fig. 15. Sodium (left) and potassium (right) conductances after sudden decreases of membrane potentials as indicated.

experimental facts that contain the core of the dramatic, as well as the fundamental, of classical nerve physiology.

SYNTHESIS

The conductance data could be used directly to predict and analyze the phenomena of varying potentials, currents, and their distributions that had to be eliminated in order to arrive at such a relatively simple picture. But analytical expressions are much more inspiring to work with than are graphical or tabular data. So, in the absence of any information as to how the membrane can perform its tasks, Hodgkin and Huxley [13] designed a mechanism that it might use—if it so chose.

If n is a probability of some event occurring and four of these events in a small region of the membrane provide a path for K^+ ions then the potassium conductance $g_K = \bar{g}_K n^4$, where $\bar{g}_K$ is the maximum conductance. When it is further supposed that

$$dn/dt = \alpha_n(1 - n) - \beta_n n$$

where α_n and β_n are backward and forward rate constants depending only upon the electric field and temperature, the data can be expressed very well. If three events, of probability m, provide a path for Na^+ ions but another, h, alone, blocks it,

$$g_{Na} = \bar{g}_{Na} m^3 h$$

with m and h given by expressions of the same form as for n, these data are also adequately represented.

The complete expression for the membrane current density is then

$$I = C\,\frac{dV}{dt} + \bar{g}_K n^4 (V - V_K) + \bar{g}_{Na} m^3 h (V - V_{Na}) + \bar{g}_L (V - V_L)$$

where V, V_K, V_{Na}, V_L are measured from the resting potential, and $\bar{g}_L$ and V_L are a conductance and potential that may arise from the less important ions. The information now available in this relatively handy form is quite obviously a description of some properties of the squid axon membrane, but it has been obtained under considerable duress and might not be pertinent and of interest for other and more usual situations. The formulation must therefore be compared with the many results of easier but less revealing experiments such as subthreshold characteristics, all-or-none response and impulse propagation.

LINEAR PHENOMENA

A considerable amount of data is available on the membrane capacity by a variety of techniques, and it is in substantial agreement with the potential step results of about 1 μf./cm.^{2}

The d-c resistance of the squid axon membrane was first measured at about 1000 ohm cm.² with the suspicion, later confirmed, that it might be several times this value. The equations give this resistance as largely a result of potassium ion movement and in the neighborhood of 800 ohm cm.² which seems low but is certainly acceptable.

As Hodgkin and Huxley [13] have shown, their equations can be reduced to a single fourth-order linear differential equation that can be used when the potential variations are small—probably of the order of

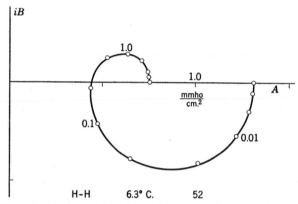

Fig. 16.   The calculated complex alternating-current ionic conductance locus of the membrane. A is the dissipative component and B the conservative component.   Frequencies are in kilocycles.

a millivolt. At the resting potential $V = 0$, the rise of potassium conductance has a time constant τ_n of about 5.5 msec. at 6.3° C. and the equivalent potassium circuit contains an inductance. The sodium conductance decay is also inductive with $\tau_h = 8.5$ msec.; and it can be combined with the potassium rise, with the average of the two time constants as a good approximation. The sodium rise is faster with $\tau_m = 0.24$ msec. and is capacitative. These elements combine to give an oscillatory transient agreeing with experiment. The corresponding complex ionic conductance locus is shown in Fig. 16. A calculated equivalent inductance of 0.4 henry/cm.² corresponds to an experimental value of about 0.2 henry/cm.² Some of our old data on the a-c. characteristics in the frequency range of these ionic effects are similar, but they are not as consistent as desirable. The locus is calculated to enlarge and extend into the negative half plane for a constant cathodal polarization. This expansion into the negative half-plane has been

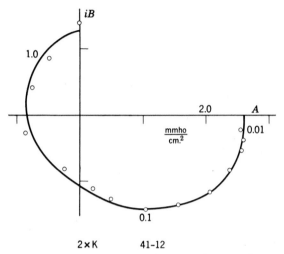

Fig. 17. The complex alternating-current ionic conductance locus of the membrane in twice sea-water-potassium concentration as calculated from longitudinal impedance measurements of a squid axon.

found experimentally to appear similarly for decrease of external calcium or, as shown in Fig. 17, for excess potassium.

MEMBRANE EXCITATION

Turning now to the non-linear situation with larger potential changes but still with uniform membrane potentials and current densities so that a spread of activity and propagation are still denied to the axon, the threshold and all-or-none response of membrane potential may be investigated. Although still not a partial differential equation, the necessary ordinary differential equation is so extremely non-linear as to show no hope of an analytical solution and can only be solved by tedious step-by-step numerical methods. In this way Hodgkin and Huxley [13] showed that a sudden potential displacement of 6 mv. did not give an active response whereas 7 mv. gave a full-blown action potential of 100 mv. They also demonstrated the excitation upon release of an anode polarization and investigated the initiation of a second impulse at various times after an initial response—both in good agreement with experiments. With the aid of the Bureau of Standards digital computer, SEAC, the relation between the duration and the current density just necessary to excite with the results given in Fig. 18 has been computed. For a duration of 0.01 msec. a current of 637.51 μa./cm.^{2} gave only an alteration of potential of 8 mv. whereas 637.52 μa./cm.^{2} gave almost 100 mv. The threshold conditions are not as yet defined analytically, but the calculations indicate a critical point at about 8.4 mv., and the results, Fig. 18, are certainly in as good agreement with experiment, Fig. 10, as are simpler and earlier attempts, such as the two-factor formulations. Multiple responses have also been calculated for currents a few times that required for a single response.

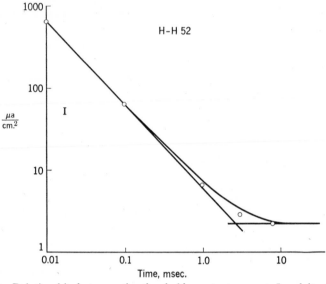

Fig. 18. Relationship between the threshold constant current I and its duration as calculated. The curve would be obtained for a system with a single time constant.

PROPAGATED ACTIVITY

The calculations appropriate to an actual, normally functioning nerve fiber are even more difficult and have not yet been attempted in their complete form. As a consequence, there is no information as to the conditions necessary to initiate a propagated impulse or to block it and there is no prediction of the velocity of propagation. But with the assumption of a constant velocity of propagation, Hodgkin and Huxley have solved the still ordinary differential equations for a series of velocities until they found one to give an action potential that returned to the starting value and remained there for a reasonable period of time. This grueling procedure produced the potential forms that are shown in Fig. 19 along with a comparable oscillogram.[13] The velocity required to give this potential was 18.8 meters/sec., whereas

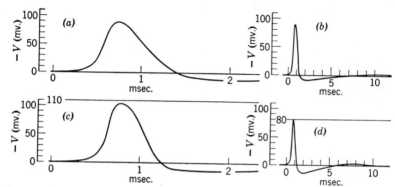

Fig. 19. Calculated (a, b) and measured (c, d) action potentials of a propagated nerve impulse.

the velocity of the similar nerve was found experimentally to be 21.2 meters/sec.—in essential agreement with many other observations.

In the process of calculating the form of the propagated action potential, the conductances of the sodium and potassium ions were computed [13] as shown in Fig. 20, and, when it is remembered that these are the high-frequency conductances, their sum can be compared with the early measurements of the impedance change (at frequencies of 10 kc. or more) during the passage of an impulse, Fig. 4. The calculated peak increases of conductance were in the range 31 to 53 mmho/cm.[2], whereas the mean of the observed increases was 40 mmho/cm.[2]

The time course of the current flow of both sodium and potassium is then also available [13] as shown in Fig. 21, where it is seen that the membrane current is first entirely that of sodium whereas the later rise

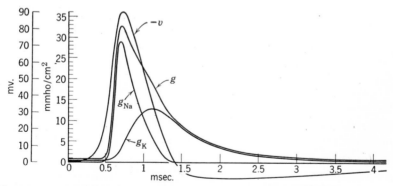

Fig. 20.   Calculated action potential V and ionic conductances g_K potassium, g_{Na} sodium, g total of a propagated nerve impulse.

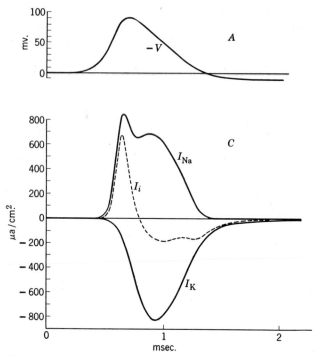

Fig. 21. Calculated action potential A and ionic currents C of a propagated nerve impulse. I_K and I_{Na} are the potassium and sodium ion currents, and I_i is the total ionic current.

of the potassium current cancels the sodium near the maximum of potential and becomes the only current during the later stages of the recovery process. The total amount of sodium ion moving into such an axon during the passage of an impulse then integrated to 4.3 $\mu\mu$mol/cm.^{2} and the corresponding loss of potassium came to 4.26 $\mu\mu$mol/cm.^{2} Although one might wish for more complete experimental data, the available results from work with radioactive isotope tracers give 3.5 and 3.0 $\mu\mu$mol/cm.^{2} impulse for the sodium and potassium transports respectively.

DISCUSSION

The virtually complete separation of the potassium and sodium ion movements across the squid axon membrane and the detailed information of their dependence on time, potential, and concentration have given a general, compact, and quantitative description of the membrane characteristics, which seems likely to form an adequate basis for all the phenomena in its province—both known and yet to be observed!

Quite apart from the difficulty of calculating the answers to numerous interesting questions, many may be appalled and discouraged by the formidable empiricism of the formulation. There are a dozen analytical functions and more than as many constants whose forms and values have little more rigorous justification than that they state the facts. Nonetheless the formulation is not only far simpler than an equally accurate statement of all the phenomena that it includes but sets useful, stringent conditions upon any theory of the underlying mechanisms. We may now be amazed that such things as the one- and two-factor theories of threshold [16] and the several suggested nonlinear mechanisms of excitation should have so complicated a basis—but we can also be more tolerant of their deficiencies!

Perhaps the electrical and ionic events of excitation and conduction might yet have been achieved by direct study of these phenomena, but one doubts that the picture could have been so clear and so convincing. Yet Hodgkin and Huxley have explained these fundamental nerve properties on the basis of measurements in which there was no longitudinal current—preventing the propagation—and no capacity current—eliminating the all-or-none response.

It should be quite apparent that this work is also an extremely stimulating point of departure. Many squid axon data—including some under controlled-current conditions—should be examined from this point of view. The mechanisms of the underlying sodium and potassium transports, which are only hinted at so far, must be sought out by every possible means. The characteristics of these processes in other excitable tissues need to be found and the differences understood.

If it is found that similar sodium and potassium transports are not confined to the squid axon, it becomes that much more important to find the underlying mechanisms by which such transports can take place and in the manner so well described for the squid axon. Further, to the extent that these ion movements—which are of the nature of leaks—are important, we are faced with the vital question of the mechanisms by which the ion gradients are created and maintained across the membrane in the face of such losses. Therefore, some of the questions of the maintenance of the electrochemical energy upon which these processes of excitation are drawing become more specific and more important.

SUMMARY

The recent powerful exploitation of the squid giant nerve fiber has given an explanation of the propagation of the nerve impulse in terms of sodium and potassium ions crossing the membrane at the surface of the fiber under the control of the membrane potential difference. The relations between the potential and the ion movements allow a rapid reversal and recovery of the potential to be propagated at the cost of an initial intake of sodium ions and a later loss of potassium ions by the fiber. The mechanisms of the ion flow controls and the ultimate re-exchange of the ions are yet to be explained.

REFERENCES

1. Lord Kelvin (Sir William Thomson), *Phil. Mag.*, (4) *11*, 146 (1856).
2. F. Brink, Jr., in: *Handbook of Experimental Psychology*, John Wiley & Sons, New York, p. 72, 1951.
3. J. Z. Young, *Cold Spring Harbor Symposia Quant. Biol.*, *4*, 1 (1936).
4. L. W. Williams, *The Anatomy of the Common Squid*, Loligo pealii, Leseur, Leiden, 1909.
5. J. Z. Young, *Doubt and Certainty in Science*, Clarendon Press, Oxford, 1951.
6. K. S. Cole and H. J. Curtis, *J. Gen. Physiol.*, *22*, 649 (1939).
7. A. L. Hodgkin and A. Huxley, *Nature*, *144*, 710 (1939).
8. H. J. Curtis and K. S. Cole, *J. Cellular Comp. Physiol.*, *15*, 147 (1940).
9. H. J. Curtis and K. S. Cole, *Medical Physics*, p. 584, Year Book Publishers, Chicago, 1950.
10. G. Marmont, *J. Cellular Comp. Physiol.*, *34*, 351 (1949).
11. K. S. Cole, *Arch. sci. physiol.*, *3*, 253 (1949).
12. A. L. Hodgkin and B. Katz, *J. Physiol. (London)*, *108*, 37 (1949).
13. A. L. Hodgkin and A. F. Huxley, *J. Physiol. (London)*, *117*, 500 (1952).
14. A. L. Hodgkin and A. F. Huxley, *J. Physiol. (London)*, *116*, 449 (1952).
15. A. L. Hodgkin and A. F. Huxley, *Cold Spring Harbor Symposia Quant. Biol.*, *17*, 43 (1952).
16. B. Katz, *Electric Excitation of Nerve*, Oxford Univ. Press, London, 1939.

8·

The Nature of the Electrochemical
Potentials of Bioelectric Tissues

HARRY GRUNDFEST *

The study of bioelectric phenomena has been a particularly fortunate subdiscipline of physiology. The electrophysiologist finds a wealth of material in the electrogenic cells of various excitable tissues. They can usually survive for long periods of time after isolation from the animal. Many of these cells present special modifications, analysis of which serves to illuminate the general problem of bioelectric mechanisms. Added to these advantages of biological character, is the fact that accurate electrical measurements have long been relatively easy to make. Indeed, since the advent of electronic devices, they can be made under many special conditions encountered in or experimentally imposed on living material. Finally, electrochemistry, to the birth of which electrophysiology contributed materially, has in turn furnished the electrophysiologist with a body of general theory regarding possible mechanisms of bioelectric generators. Unfortunately, this old liaison has become extremely tenuous. The electrochemist deals with relatively simple, essentially static systems. The electrophysiologist, on the other hand, is delving more and more deeply into the dynamic living generator and finding richer and more exciting complications.

THEORIES OF BIOELECTRIC MECHANISMS

Up to about 15 years ago the generally accepted theory of bioelectric phenomena was based on the concept of concentration cells adapted [1-5] to the special conditions of a living system. According to this theory the resting potential reflects the marked difference between intracellu-

* From the Department of Neurology, College of Physicians and Surgeons, Columbia University, New York, and Marine Biological Laboratory, Woods Hole, Mass.

lar and extracellular potassium, K_i^+/K_o^+, which exists probably in all cells and which in bioelectric tissues was supposed in turn to reflect impermeability of the cell surface (or membrane) to all cations but K^+. The response of excitable cells was supposed to represent a temporary, local breakdown of this impermeability and a consequent electrical depolarization of the active region. The flow of current caused by this new condition could in turn initiate similar changes in nearby regions and thereby cause propagation of the response in the form of a brief electrical pulse, known as the spike. As electrochemistry disclosed the existence of more complex systems, such as the Donnan equilibrium, these findings were incorporated as improvements on the earlier theory.[6]

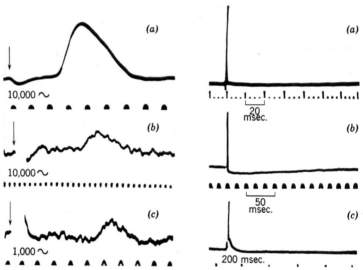

Fig. 1. Characteristic differences in the action potentials of mammalian A, B, and C nerve fibers, shown respectively in (a), (b), and (c). Left: The spikes of single nerve fibers of the three groups differ in time scale, the duration being about 0.5 msec., 1.2 msec., and 2.0 msec. The arrows indicate the onset of the stimulus. Right: The responses of a large number of fibers of the respective groups were elicited by a strong stimulus, the amplification was adjusted so that the amplitudes of the summated spikes in each case were in the same range. The after-potential sequence, which follows the spike, differs in the three groups not only in time scale but also in relative magnitudes. The A fibers have relatively small negative and positive after-potentials; B fibers lack the negative and have a large, prolonged positive after-potential; autonomic C fibers have large, long-lasting negative and positive after-potentials. (From H. Grundfest, "Mechanisms and Properties of Bioelectric Potentials," in: *Modern Trends in Physiology and Biochemistry*, Academic Press, New York (1952), where sources are given.)

Electrophysiological discoveries of recent years, aided especially by newer technical means and new experimental material, are superseding the rather static and entirely too general concepts of the early theory. Specification of chemical as well as physical properties of the bioelectric generator are needed. Indeed, older data showing the existence of differences among different tissues in respect to a number of functions would seem to demand such specific differences (Fig. 1).

Furthermore, in the course of recent years, and particularly since the availability of isotopic tracer methods, it was also found that the concept of a static membrane, at rest selectively permeable to K^+ and perhaps also to Cl^- but temporarily capable of becoming permeable non-selectively, had to give way to a more dynamic concept.[7] Although the membrane at rest apparently acts as a barrier to certain substances, it is in reality also permeable to other ions.[8-10] Additional mechanisms, such as a metabolically driven "sodium pump,"[11,12] have been invoked to explain the existence of asymmetry in inside-outside ionic distribution.

A devastating challenge to one aspect of the classical theory arose from the observations[13-15] that the spike of the giant axon of squid is not merely the manifestation of a temporary depolarization of a semi-permeable, excitable membrane negatively charged at its interior. Rather, the membrane appears to repolarize in the opposite sense during the spike so that the potential overshoots the reference (zero) level of the surrounding solution by a considerable amount. This overshoot has been found in a wide variety of bioelectric tissues (Fig. 2).

Hodgkin and Katz[16] suggested that the reversal of charge of the active membrane causing the overshoot of the spike is associated with a temporary change in the ionic transport, specifically an increase for Na^+. That ion is driven inward in the direction of its electrochemical gradient, and K^+ moves outward as required by the new electrical conditions. The reality of such ionic shifts, about 3-4 $\mu\mu m./cm.^2$ of membrane per impulse, was demonstrated by a number of investigators[8,9,17-20] using radioisotopic techniques (Fig. 3).

A more elaborate theory has been recently proposed by Hodgkin and Huxley.[21] In the briefest outline, this theory also assumes that the resting potential is maintained at, or close to, the potassium potential by a dynamic type of Donnan system, itself brought into existence by operation of a sodium pump. Decrease of the membrane potential by a critical amount sets off a series of events led by an increase in effective sodium transport. The resultant flow of this ion along its

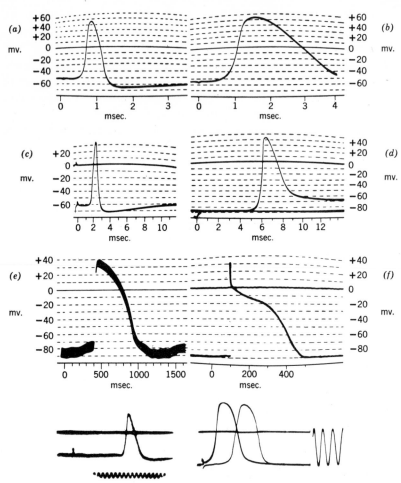

Fig. 2. Overshoot of the spike above the level of the resting potential, equivalent to temporary repolarization of the membrane in the reverse sense from that at rest, is exhibited by many excitable tissues. (a) and (b) represent the spikes of the giant axon of the squid *Loligo* at 18.5° C. and 5° C. respectively; (c), the spike of the giant axon in another cephalopod, *Sepia;* (d), the response of a frog skeletal muscle fiber; (e), the response of frog heart muscle; and (f), the response of a dog Purkinje fiber. Amplitudes of the resting potentials (inside negative) and of the spikes as shown in the calibrations. (From Hodgkin.[20]) Below, (*left*) is the response of a tissue-cultured chick dorsal root ganglion cell. (From S. Crain, this laboratory, to be published.) The resting potential was 44 mv., and the spike height 75 mv.; time is msec. On the *right* is the propagated spike of the electroplaque of the electric eel, recorded simultaneously at two points in the same cell.[32] Calibration, 100 mv. and msec.

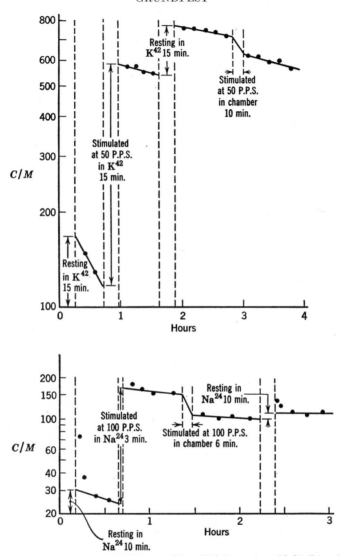

Fig. 3. A giant axon of *Sepia* takes up either K^{42} (upper) or Na^{24} (lower) when immersed in a solution containing one of these isotopes and loses this when re-immersed in isotope-free sea water. The ordinates represent counts per min.; $1 \ C/M \equiv 4.8 \times 10^{-12}$ mols $K+$ or 4.0×10^{-11} mols $Na+$ per cm. of nerve. When the nerve is stimulated while in the isotope-containing solution, the rate of accumulation of the tracer in the axon is higher than when at rest. Also, when the isotope-containing nerve is stimulated while in sea water, the rate of loss of the tracer is higher than when the nerve is at rest. (From Keynes.[9])

electrochemical gradient (inward in the normal condition) further reduces the membrane potential by virtue of the alteration of charge across the capacity of the membrane, which has a value of 1 μf./cm.^{2} of membrane in the squid axon. The Na$^+$ inflow is thereby enhanced, and the charge further altered. The interplay of sodium movement and change of charge is therefore regenerative and explosive in character. It becomes limited at the approach toward a new electrochemical gradient (the sodium potential) and is dissipated by two new, late events—"inactivation" of the heightened sodium mobility and enhanced outflow of K$^+$. The latter process, also proceeding as directed by the new electrochemical gradient, eventually returns the membrane potential to the original resting level.

The quantitative aspects of this theory, though stochastic in nature and therefore involving a number of semiempirical formulations,[22] are a contribution of the greatest importance since they encompass a number of bioelectric phenomena not hitherto unified in a quantitative manner.

Although still in their initial stages, three series of studies, carried on since 1950 by the writer and a number of collaborators, afford some experimental tests of this far-reaching and important theory. Measurements of the change in membrane conductance during activity, under the conditions of altered external Na$^+$ or K$^+$, to a considerable extent appear to provide confirmation of the Hodgkin and Huxley theory.[23–25] These experiments among other things demonstrated the existence of a late, small decrease of the membrane conductance below the resting level (Fig. 4). A change of this type, though smaller in magnitude, was predicted in the calculations of Hodgkin and Huxley, but not mentioned in their paper.[18]

However, other types of experimental results appear to indicate that the Hodgkin and Huxley theory requires further elaboration as to underlying mechanisms. This elaboration affects the concept of the mechanisms of the resting potential, the relation between these mechanisms and the generator of the spike, and the nature of the events that determine the ability of excitable tissues to propagate activity. These problems have come to light primarily from two new series of electrophysiological studies. The first employs a new technique, that of recording bioelectric changes when the internal environment of the giant axon of squid is altered by microinjection.[26–30] The second utilizes the special properties of new material, the electroplaque of the electric eel.[31, 32] However, various data also indicate the need for such reexamination and will be drawn upon as needed.

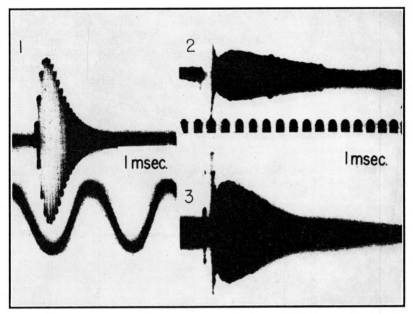

Fig. 4. The membrane conductance increases during the spike (record 1) as seen
by the temporary imbalance of a 30-kc. bridge signal. In the later portion of
the action potential the resistance bridge is again unbalanced (seen at a slower
sweep and higher gain in record 2), but in the opposite direction, indicating that
conductance is lowered below the resting level ("initial after-impedance" [25]).
The terminal phases of the increase of the spike conductance and the initial after-
impedance are greatly modified by alteration of external K^+ demonstrating that
the latter event is a property of the tissue. Record 3 shows the increase caused
by removing all K^+ from the external fluid.

THE ELECTROCHEMICAL SYSTEM OF THE RESTING POTENTIAL

A number of reasons for suspecting that the resting potential must
involve a mechanism other than some type of Donnan potential derive
from several varieties of experimental data. Columns 2–4 of Table 1
show that in four types of tissue widely studied electrophysiologically and
chemically the ratio $K_i/K_o \neq Na_o/Na_i \neq Cl_o/Cl_i$.

Hodgkin [20] has suggested that the chemical measurements are insuffi-
ciently accurate. These measurements, however, have been made by a
number of investigators with a number of techniques (cf. Hodgkin,[20]
Table 1). The likelihood of the data being consistently wrong therefore
appears to be remote and particularly so when the measured ratio of
Na_o/Na_i is seen always to be too low in relation to K_i/K_o and also
always lower than Cl_o/Cl_i.

TABLE 1 *

| Tissue | Approximate Ratio, Inside:Outside | | | Resting Potential | |
| | Na | K | Cl | Obs. | Calc. K_i/K_o |
(1)	(2)	(3)	(4)	(5)	(6)
Loligo axon	1:9	19:1	1:14	50–60	74
Sepia axon	1:10	21:1	....	62	77
Carcinus nerve	1:10	34:1	1:21	82	89
Frog muscle	1:7	48:1	1:64	88	98

* From J. C. Eccles, *The Neurophysiological Basis of Mind*, Oxford, Clarendon, 1953, after Hodgkin [20] and Keynes.[19]

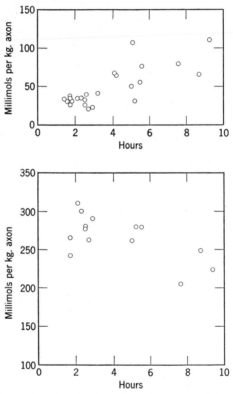

Fig. 5. Sodium (upper) and potassium (lower) content of *Sepia* giant axons as a function of their time of survival. The determinations were made by analyzing the radioactivity of nerves "activated" by neutron bombardment. During the first 4 hours of survival no significant ionic shifts seem to occur. The data are from Keynes and Lewis [10] (their Figs. 7 and 8, excluding the values for axons 2 cm. and less in length).

It has also been suggested that the excised nerves rapidly undergo changes in ionic composition, thereby falsifying the chemical determinations.[19, 20] However, examination of data Keynes and Lewis [10] obtained with an elegant isotopic technique does not support this view (Fig. 5). For the first 4 hours after death of the animal, Na_i^+ and K_i^+ concentrations of the giant axon remain nearly steady. Shanes (personal communication) using a different method also finds that the leakage of K^+ from the 3-to-4-hour-old giant axon at 25° C. is not greater than 2% per hour. Crab nerves, having a higher surface to volume ratio than do squid axons, in late summer lose less than 3% K^+ per hour.[33] In early summer, these crab nerves lose even less, whereas frog nerves and desheathed nerves of the toad retain the original levels of potassium for at least 24 hours (Shanes, personal communication).

It is also possible, of course, that the differences in inside-outside ionic ratios derive from the complex manner in which the electrical and chemical gradients enter into the determination of the electrochemical poising of a dynamic system.[20, 34-37] However, a number of types of data now available indicate that the resting potential is itself not primarily determined on the basis of these ratios or of the ratio of the "dominant" K^+. These data will now be discussed briefly.

1. Examination of columns 5 and 6 of Table 1 shows that the resting potential is consistently lower than might be expected on the basis of the Donnan ratio $(K^+)_i/(K^+)_o$.

2. There appears to be no significant correlation between the resting potential and prolonged survival of the isolated nerve. Even after 10–18 hours when it might be expected that the axon had lost considerable K^+ and gained Na^+, the resting potential may still be between 50 and 60 mv. (Table 2).[38]

TABLE 2. RESTING POTENTIAL AND SPIKE HEIGHT IN SQUID AXONS KEPT IN SEA WATER FOR VARIOUS TIMES AFTER REMOVAL FROM ANIMAL

Nerve Number (Series D, 1953)	Time	Resting Potential mv.	Spike Height mv.
176 ⎫ paired 177 ⎭	1 hr. 18 hr.	48 46	95.5 87.6
198 ⎫ paired 199 ⎭	30 min. 12 hr.	49 54	97 97
202	5 hr., 10 min.	47	108
165	5 hr., 10 min.	45.5	98.5
166	5 hr., 40 min.	53	99
150	12 hr.	44	94
195	12 hr.	52.5	103.5
151	13 hr., 25 min.	54	98
152	13 hr., 38 min.	61	104
187	14 hr.	46	88.6

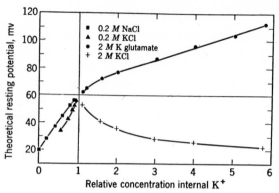

Fig. 6. Changes expected in the resting potential of the squid giant axon on changing the internal concentration of K^+ by different means. Injection of 2 M glutamate (or aspartate) would increase only K^+_i; injection of 2 M KCl would at the same time increase Cl^-_i. Injection of 0.2 M KCl would decrease K^+_i and increase Cl^-_i. These changes would be accentuated on injecting 0.2 M NaCl. The calculations are based on the equation: [16]

$$\text{Resting potential} = 59 \text{ mv.} \log_{10} \frac{K^+_i + 0.04\,(Na^+_i) + 0.45 \times 540}{10 + 0.04 \times 455 + 0.45\,(Cl^-_i)}$$

(From Grundfest, et al.[38])

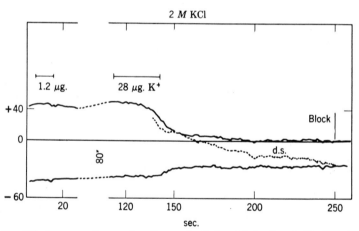

Fig. 7. Effects on resting and action potentials of injecting 2 M KCl into a squid giant axon (experiment 163-52; $T = 25.5°$ C.; 350 micron fiber; ordinate represents millivolts). The lower solid line shows the internal negativity of the resting potential. The uppermost line represents the spike height. The first injection introduced 0.016 mm.³ containing 1.2 μg. K^+ with no effect. The second injection, nearly 2 min. later, lasted 30 sec., introduced 0.35 mm.³ of fluid containing 53 μg. of KCl or 28 μg. K^+. The spike began to decline during the eighteenth second of the injection, but the resting potential remained unchanged for another 13 sec. Block occurred as shown. The discontinuous line (labeled d.s.) represents the height of the delayed spike (shown in Fig. 11, records 7 and 8), which occurs before block. Note the interruption on the time scale.[38]

150

3. Similarly, Stephenson [39] finds that violent changes in $K_i{}^+$ and $Na_i{}^+$ take place in crab muscle fibers without parallel alteration of the resting potential.

4. Large alterations of $K_i{}^+$ or Cl_i have been produced experimentally by means of microinjection into giant axons of squid.[28, 29, 38] The changes in resting potential should be approximately ±30 mv. (Fig. 6), but the experiments reveal no such changes (Figs. 7, 8), except for a decrease when the spike is seriously decreased and propagation block is incipient.

5. Measurements of resting potentials have been made in the course of the above experiments with a wide variety of liquid junctions.[38] The nature of these junctions does not seem to affect the measured values, though this should play a role if the resting potential were due to a Donnan system.

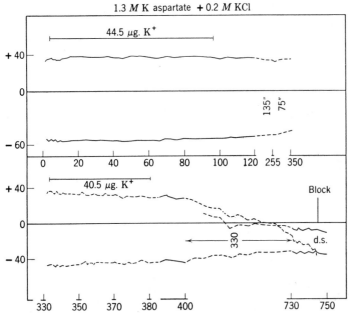

Fig. 8. Effect of injecting 1.3 M potassium aspartate in 0.2 M KCl (experiment 189-52; $T = 27.5°$ C.; $D = 460$ microns; ordinates in mv.). During the first injection of 0.75 mm.³ containing 44.5 μg. K+ the spike increased by 4 mv. The resting potential remained unchanged but after 3 min. had elapsed it diminished by 10 mv. Small progressive decrease in both spike and resting potential occurred during the second injection of 0.5 mm.³ or 40.5 μg. K+ (shown in the lower part of the figure). Block occurred 6 min. after the end of the second injection. Note interruptions of the time sequence for varying intervals.[38]

6. A resting potential can be measured in the axon with reversible Ag-AgCl microelectrodes.[40] The magnitude is nearly that recorded simultaneously with a liquid-filled microcapillary electrode system.[41] In a Donnan equilibrium involving Cl^- the Ag-AgCl electrode should not, of course, record a potential.[42]

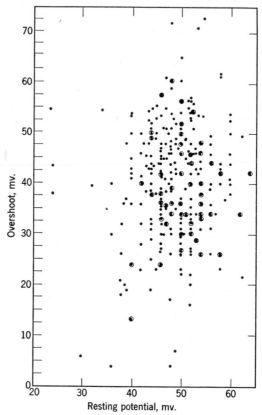

Fig. 9. Relation between resting potential and overshoot in nearly five hundred squid giant axons.[38] Large dots represent five or more axons. Temperatures ranged from 22 to 28° C.

7. Measurements on about 500 axons, in all states of physiological condition but all capable of producing an overshoot in the spike and propagation along the axon, show a wide distribution of resting potentials [38] (Fig. 9). It is unlikely that these differences can be ascribed to differences in ionic composition (cf. 2, 3, 4, above).

8. Table 3 shows that microinjection of very small quantities of divalent cations can cause block. This is accompanied by a large de-

TABLE 3. EFFECTIVENESS OF DIFFERENT CATIONS IN CAUSING PROPAGATION
BLOCK IN SQUID GIANT AXONS [38]

Cation	Substance	Number of Experiments	Average Blocking Quantity of Cation (μg.)	
K^+	KCl	7	35.6	
	$KHCO_3$	3	29	
	KNO_3	2	42.6	33.0
	K_2SO_4	4	71.5	
	K glutamate	11	23.4	
	K aspartate	8	23.8	
Rb^+	RbCl	3	66	
Na^+	NaCl	12	5.9	
	Na glutamate	10	9.7	7.8
	Na aspartate	6	8.6	
Li^+	LiCl	4	4.0	
Ba^{++}	$BaCl_2$	10	0.5	
Ca^{++}	$CaCl_2$	13	0.3	
Mg^{++}	$MgCl_2$	6	1.0	
Sr^{++}	$SrCl_2$	6	5.0	

crease in resting potential, which is largest in the region of injection.

The eight types of data enumerated above indicate that the resting potential is not primarily determined by differences in inside-outside concentrations of various ions; that it cannot be evaluated by means of these ratios; and that it can be recorded with an electrode system which should be insensitive to a Donnan potential involving Cl^-. Other experiments also show that injection of various other ions (Na^+, Rb^+, Li^+, NO_3^-, $SO_4^=$) are without primary effect on the resting potential. Therefore, another and perhaps primary factor must be involved in producing the resting potential. The nature of this factor may be disclosed by detailed examination of the bioelectric effects produced by microinjection.

THE NATURE OF BIOELECTRIC CHANGES PRODUCED BY MICROINJECTION OF IONS

Examination of Figs. 7 and 8 shows that the resting potential is not affected by rather massive injections of potassium chloride or aspartate. However, when the amount of injected K^+ attains approximately 50 μg., the spike height decreases, after which the resting potential falls, though never to complete depolarization even when propagation is blocked. The sensitivity of the axonal interior to Rb^+, an ion similar in many physiological properties to K^+, is also similar to K^+ (Table

3). On the other hand, injections of much smaller amounts of Na^+ or Li^+ cause essentially the same sequence of events (Fig. 10 and Table 3). As already mentioned, divalent cations (Ba^{++}, Ca^{++}, Mg^{++} and Sr^{++}) act in even smaller concentrations (Table 3) and also can produce greater depolarization.

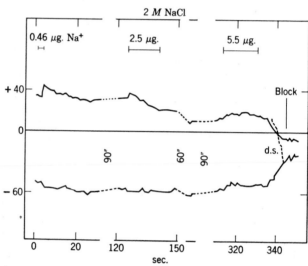

Fig. 10. Effects of injecting 2 M NaCl (experiment 170-52; $T = 25.5°$ C.; $D = 40$ microns; ordinates in millivolts). At the first two injections spike height increased somewhat (10 mv. and 6 mv. respectively). The first brief injection (0.01 mm.³ containing 0.46 μg. Na^+) also caused an increase in the resting potential. The larger second injection (0.06 mm.³, containing 2.5 μg. Na^+) caused a decline of the spike after the initial increase but no change in the resting potential. A third injection of 0.12 mm.³ (5.5 μg. Na^+) eventually caused propagation block. The resting potential, which had returned to the value, rapidly decreased to a very low level as block developed. Note interruptions in the time sequence.[38]

When a number of sites in the nerve are simultaneously examined for changes in resting potentials, the values obtained may be quite different, the depolarization that occurs at the site of injection always being larger than it is even a few millimeters away (Fig. 11). Examination of the spike during the course of injection also shows that this may be differently affected in different regions. The records of Fig. 11 were from an experiment in which three electrodes were inserted at separations of 4.9 and 2.9 mm. The centrally placed recording electrode was also a micropipette filled with 0.5 M Na^+. Within a few seconds after injection of Na^+ into the axon began, the spike at the

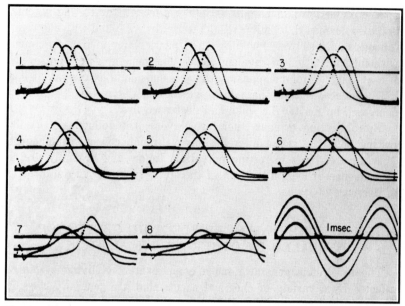

Fig. 11. Three microelectrodes were inserted into a squid axon at separations of
4.9 and 2.9 msec. The spike at electrode 1 is the earliest, because it was recorded
nearest the site of stimulation. The middle spike is that recorded by electrode
2, which was also a pipette used for injecting 0.5 M Na+ into the axon. In the
text, the three spikes recorded at the different loci are referred to the electrodes.
(1) The three responses just before beginning of an injection. (2) Seventeen seconds after beginning of the injection. (3) Thirteen seconds later. (4) Twelve
seconds later, 3 sec. before the end of a 45-sec. injection. A pause of 1 min. then
ensued, relatively little change taking place in the responses. (5) At end of the
pause. (6) Twenty-third sec. of another injection. (7) End of the 1-min. second
injection. (8) Thirty seconds later. Elapsed time in these records is about 3
min., 30 sec. Cal. 100 mv. Further description in text.[38]

injection site decreased in amplitude and broadened (record 2). However, after 30 sec. of continuous injection neither of the responses at
the adjacent electrodes had yet been altered (record 3). Still later
(record 4) the spike at electrode 1 had also broadened and decreased
in amplitude only slightly, that at 3 still remaining unchanged. During a 1-min. pause in the injection, spike 2 had further broadened
(record 5). This and the subsequent record (6), during a second injection, show that the electrical activity at electrode 2 (the pipette)
outlasted that recorded by electrode 3. It may be also seen from
records 6–8 that when the spike at electrode 2 had decreased considerably, the resting potential at that site had also become smaller than
at either electrode 1 or 3. Thus, when the spike generator at the site

of microinjection had become seriously affected, the resting potential had also decreased. Similar results were always found with the simultaneous multielectrode recordings and particularly in the experiments with microinjection of divalent ions. The generators of the bioelectric activity therefore appear to have a considerable amount of local independence, but in these local variations the resting potential is decreased only after the spike had decreased first.

Microinjection of ions, therefore, reveals the following: (a) The resting potential is not altered simply through concentration effects. (b) Local changes in resting potentials follow and probably are the consequence of local alteration of the spike generator in the direction of decrease of its e.m.f.

THE NATURE OF THE BIOELECTRIC GENERATOR AS REVEALED BY OTHER CHEMICAL AGENTS

The bioelectric generator, as a component of a living system, is affected by a variety of chemical agents that are generally classified under the category of "drugs" because the mode of action of most of them is at present unknown. These actions are impressive, however, in view of the very small concentrations of drugs that are effective. Exposure of a giant axon of squid for a few minutes to one of the veratrum alkaloids in a concentration of one part in one million brings out a large, prolonged negative after-potential.[43] The veratrum alkaloids act similarly on vertebrate nerve fibers including those that do not normally have a negative after-potential.[44, 45] The magnitude and time course of the negative after-potential are determined by the specific alkaloid [43] as are the magnitude and time course of the associated increased membrane conductance.[25] The mode of action of the veratrum alkaloids is at present unknown, although there is some evidence [25] that they increase outflow of Cl^- during the response.

Other substances such as eserine, diisopropyl fluorophosphate (DFP) appear to act in correlation with their properties as inhibitors of acetylcholinesterase (cf. Nachmansohn, this book), whereas the actions of CO, fluorides, azides, cyanides, arsenicals, and anoxia appear to be elicited by virtue of effects on other enzyme systems.[46] These actions are gross in that the obvious effect is to decrease and eventually to abolish the spike.[47]

The anticholinesterases eserine and DFP, applied to the exterior of frog nerve, cause block without depolarizing [48] as does cocaine.[49] These findings were confirmed on the squid giant axon and on crab nerves.[50] The nerve fiber, however, is a limited type of material for extensive studies of this kind. Many substances do not penetrate the permeability barriers of that cell and therefore cannot act on the bio-electric generator.[51] When this barrier is bypassed, as by microinjection, a number of such "inactive" substances also cause bioelectric changes. Thus, curare, acetylcholine and its analogs, and prostigmine when injected in very small concentration act to change the spike and eventually cause propagation block.[26, 30, 52]

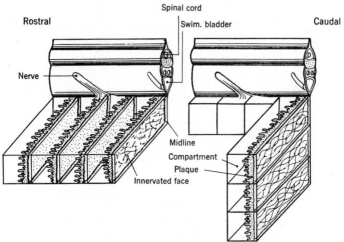

Fig. 12. Diagrammatic representation of the electroplaques of the electric eel. A spike such as seen in Fig. 2b occurs only at the innervated, caudal face of the cell membrane, the rostral, digitated face remaining quiescent. The layer of cells on the left, in the rostro-caudal direction, therefore forms a series circuit, with voltages additive. The stacking of cells in a dorso-ventral direction (*right*) puts them in parallel. The fish is thereby able to emit discharges up to 600 volts high and can deliver currents of 1 amp. or more.[31]

Our most detailed studies of the action of these drugs have been on the electroplaque of the electric eel.[31, 32, 53] This cell is large and can therefore be easily manipulated. It is also permeable to a wide range of substances that do not penetrate the axon or the muscle fiber. The reason for this permeability is as yet unknown but may reside in the fact that only one face of the cell, the innervated caudal surface (Fig. 12), is reactive in the same way as is the excitable membrane of nerve or muscle fibers. The morphologically different anterior face which is neither electrically excitable nor electrogenic [31, 54] and has a low resistance,[54] may therefore constitute a different type of barrier membrane, permeable to substances that cannot enter nerve or muscle fibers.

The application of curare, acetylcholine and its analogs, anticho-

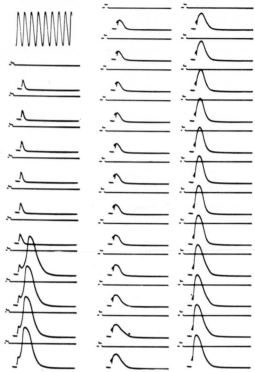

Fig. 13. All-or-nothing and graded responses in the electroplaque of the electric eel. A pair of simultaneous traces is shown for each record. The upper, longer trace is the potential reference zero and also records the amplitude and duration of a stimulus applied to the cell. The lower trace is of the electrical activity recorded with an inserted microelectrode. The downward displacement indicates the resting potential and the upward deflection the response. Left column: From above down, 100 mv. and 1000 c.p.s. calibration. The next six pairs of traces represent the application of weak stimulation to the cell at 5 per sec. The small deflections are the escape of the stimulus into the amplifier, no response of the cell being visible. However, the stimuli produced additive excitatory effects in the cell, for the seventh stimulus evoked a spike of full amplitude, and this response persisted with subsequent stimuli. Right columns: The two columns also represent a continuous sequence from the same experiment, but 88 min. after introducing eserine into the bath fluid. The stimulus (also at 5 per sec.) was increased, as seen in the upper traces, and evoked a small local response. With successive stimuli this response grew, at the end almost equaling in height the spike of the normal cell. Note that the resting potential is unaffected by the drug, but the ability of the cell to respond with an explosive, all-or-nothing spike is lost. The continuously graded response is not propagated.

linesterases, or anesthetics always causes first a decrease in the spike.[32] Subsequently some of these substances (acetylcholine and its analogs, prostigmine) cause profound depolarization. Others, such as curare, eserine, DFP, procaine, do not depolarize the cell. However, with these the cell does not entirely lose its reactive ability for a long time. Electrical stimulation can still cause activity of the bioelectric generator, but this is no longer the explosive, propagated response of the normal cell (Fig. 13). Instead, the response is graded, increasing with the intensity of the stimulus, but still capable of reaching the amplitude of the full spike. This response is confined to the region of stimulation and is not propagated.

Thus two grades of interference with the bioelectric generator are disclosed. In one case the interference is partial, affecting the regenerative and therefore explosive propagating response. This interference does not alter the resting potential. The second grade of interference blocks all activity of the bioelectric generator and when this process has progressed affects the resting potential as well so as to cause depolarization.

DISCUSSION

THE RESTING POTENTIAL

It would appear that the distinction currently made between the mechanisms generating the resting potential (a Donnan system) and the spike (specific ionic transports) is inconsistent with new data. A considerable amount of evidence, presented above, argues against the resting potential as being a consequence of a Donnan system. Most telling in this respect are experiments with alteration of the internal ionic environment of the axon by microinjection. The resting potential then appears to be insensitive to ionic changes. It is altered only when the spike generator is seriously affected. It is noteworthy that alteration of the spike generator by extremely small quantities of divalent cations may cause even more profound depolarization than does the injection of very large amounts of K^+ or Rb^+, and smaller amounts of Na^+ or Li^+. Furthermore, large alterations of anions appear to have no effect.

Additional support derives from the study of the action of drugs applied to the outside of the electroplaque. Substances that have only a partial effect on the spike generator, eliminating its regenerative, explosive, propagated response but still permitting full local, but graded reactivity, do not alter the resting potential. Only those substances that totally inactivate the spike generator, also depolarize, but depolarization is again subsidiary to inactivation.

A theory giving a quantitative description of the resting potential cannot as yet be formulated. However, one may venture a working hypothesis not only as a guide to experimental tests but as a subject for criticism by electrochemists. The view proposed here is based on the existence of a sodium-extruding mechanism [55] in excitable tissues. Whenever the "intrinsic diffusion constants" [56] (i.e., the coefficients of flux inward and outward in the absence of restraints) differ in a steady state system, a diffusion potential must develop to balance ionic transports in the two directions. The existence of a sodium pump implies an inequality in the coefficients. On this basis, then, the resting potential might not be a Donnan potential, owing to unequal distribution of K^+ in the face of a sodium-extruding mechanism, but a diffusion potential set up by the very existence of this mechanism. According to this view, therefore, the origin of the resting potential does not derive from the unequal distribution of ions (primarily K^+) in two media that are delimited by a membrane and caused by the Donnan mechanism. The site of the generator of the potential is rather assumed to be the membrane itself. The potential is assumed to derive from the properties of this living, complex membrane and specifically from the existence of a sodium pump.

MEMBRANE AS GENERATOR

A number of contradictions with the explanation of the resting potential as a Donnan system become explicable on the basis that it is a diffusion potential produced by properties of the membrane itself. Some of these are: the surprising lack of dependence of the magnitudes of the resting potential on the nature of the junction systems; the ability of an inserted Ag-AgCl electrode to detect the resting potential; and the insensitivity of the potential to large changes of internal K^+ and/or Cl^- (Figs. 7, 8). These contradictions are resolved because the source of the potential is viewed as lying within the membrane and not in the ionic asymmetries between the internal and external compartments bounded by the membrane.

At first glance the alteration of resting potential, which has been observed in many bioelectric tissues when the external K^+ concentration is changed [20] and which has been considered as a proof of the Donnan nature of this potential, appears to offer difficulty to the view proposed here. However, the relation between resting potential and external K^+ is not the simple one expected from Donnan consideration. Lowering external K^+ below the level normal in body fluids or raising it some two to three times above that level causes small changes in resting potential.[15, 20] Only when the external K^+ concentration becomes high does the tissue behave as a Donnan system, with the resting potential decreasing approximately 50 mv. for a tenfold increase of K_o^+. However, threefold increase of external K^+ decreases spike height by more than 50 per cent [24] and propagation block usually occurs with a fourfold increase of K_o^+. From these facts it may be concluded that the resting potential remains nearly independent of external K^+ as long as the spike height and propagation of the impulse are not seriously affected. When these functions are depressed by external K^+, the bioelectric generator of the resting potential is also affected and the tissue then behaves as a passive Donnan system. This interpretation, therefore, brings into agreement the effects of altering external K^+ with the results of internal alterations by microinjection (Figs. 7, 8).

On the basis of the view suggested here, the high internal concentration of K^+ of nerve or muscle serves to satisfy conditions of electroneutrality and osmotic pressure as in the Donnan system. The resting potential, however, might or might not attain the value predicted from the potassium distribution. Furthermore, since the resting potential would be determined primarily by the degree of activity of the sodium-extruding mechanism, that potential might be to some extent also independent of the internal sodium concentration (as in Table 2 and Figs. 10, 11), as well as largely independent of the external concentration of that ion.[16, 20] To the extent that the pump is independent of the spike generator, the overshoot of the spike (which is dependent on the sodium distribution [16, 21]) and the resting potential need have no close correlation (as seen in Figs. 9, 13).

This view does not exclude the simultaneous presence of other types of generators, such as those of the Donnan potential. If they were present, all the generators would act in parallel. The resting potential would be determined by the relative internal resistances as well as the e.m.f.'s of the various generators. There is evidence that the squid giant axon has a larger resting potential *in situ* than when it is excised and that it is then also sensitive to the nature of the recording electrodes.[71] This would indicate that the K^+ Donnan generator has a low internal resistance in the intact axon and that this resistance increases markedly under experimental conditions, so that the resting potential is then determined by the membrane generator discussed above. It is noteworthy that under the presumably new conditions the axon survives for a long time (Table 2) and is capable of generating about one million spikes at a rate of more than 300 per sec.[17] The existence of parallel generators of different fundamental types also appears indicated in frog muscle fibers [72] and had been proposed earlier by Shedlovsky.[60] Injection of KCl or NaCl into frog muscle fibers [73] or of Cl$^-$ into cat motoneurons [74] does not affect their resting potential.

In addition to the classical view that the resting potential represents a Donnan mechanism and the view, suggested here, that it resides in the membrane as a diffusion potential determined by the sodium pump, there are a number of other approaches to this problem. Teorell [35] and Meyer and Sievers [57] suggested a complex membrane phenomenon in which participate two Donnan potentials (one at each membrane boundary) and a gradient within the membrane. Teorell [36,58] has recently developed an "extended fixed-charge theory." He has also pointed out the formal relation of this to the "activated-state theory." [36,59] Shedlovsky has suggested [60,61] that the membrane may be a composite of proton transport and ionic diffusion processes acting in parallel.

THE SPIKE

It has been stressed in the foregoing that the resting potential appears to depend upon the ability of the cell to maintain its excitable properties. The experiments involving effects of drugs on the electroplaque demonstrate this relation with particular clarity. Depolarization occurs with those drugs that eliminate the ability of the excitable membrane to react to a stimulus. Those drugs that inactivate the bioelectric generator only partially, eliminating the propagative ability of the cell, but not its local reactivity, cause no depolarization (Fig. 13).

These experiments also reveal that the bioelectric mechanism responsible for the spike is itself complex. One part of this mechanism, that causing the explosive, all-or-nothing, and therefore propagative response, can be eliminated selectively while local reactivity of the excitable membrane remains.[76] It has also been shown (Fig. 11) that on injection of Na$^+$ local alterations in the bioelectric generator can be produced that affect its e.m.f. (as measured by the spike height) and the time course of its changes (as measured by the duration of the spike) in a remarkably restricted region. When the changes are large enough, local depolarization also takes place. At the present time, however, our lack of knowledge of the molecular nature of the reactive complex permits only speculations concerning the nature of the alterations produced under the different experimental conditions (cf. Nachmansohn, this book).

The dependence of the resting potential on the integrity of the spike generator implies further that the sodium pump is in some way also involved in the mechanism of the action potential. Earlier suggestions [62,63,64] that the spike is caused by a stoppage of the pump and a consequent unidirectional (inward) flux of sodium would seem to meet with the difficulty that the conductance of the membrane rises about sixtyfold during activity.[21,65] However, Teorell (reference 37, p. 337) has pointed out that when dealing with a charged membrane (as in biological systems) net flux of an ion species may decrease while the total conductance increases. If the pump transports sodium outward in some combined uncharged form, the situation is further complicated because the countertransport (inward) is presumably by ionic diffusion.

The various alternative views of the bioelectric generators described above can and no doubt will be further tested by experiment. It is important, however, to stress again the data that have been presented here, particularly because it would be helpful to the electrophysiologist if the electrochemists were to view bioelectric generators as a challenge to their own intellectual concepts. A variety of experimental tests indicate that the bioelectric generators for the resting potential and the spike are not passive systems such as is the case in permselective membranes.[66] The excitable cell incorporates a number of specific, dynamic processes into a complex. Although its components are as yet unknown in detail, their actions are measurable. Part of this complex causes the resting potential. Another aspect causes the spike, probably by the mechanism proposed by Hodgkin and his colleagues,[16,21,67-70] but modified to encompass the ability of the membrane to exhibit localized presumably molecular alterations the effects of which have been described here. Both actions appear to be interlocked. The resting potential is only affected when the spike generator is altered reversibly or irreversibly toward the direction of nonreactivity. Further knowledge of this interlocked and undoubtedly complex living system will depend on a greater understanding of the molecular structures that are involved and of their dynamics. The combined forces of many disciplines, of which electrochemistry is not the least important, are needed to attack and overcome the difficulties that confront any individual investigator of these problems.

Acknowledgment. The work on which this paper is based was supported in part by grants from the Atomic Energy Commission, the National Institutes of Health, the United Cerebral Palsy Association, and the Marine Biological Laboratory. I wish to thank particularly my colleagues M. Altamirano and C.-Y. Kao for their help and advice.

REFERENCES AND NOTES

1. L. Hermann, in *Handbuch der Physiologie, 2*, part 1, p. 3, F. C. W. Vogel, Leipzig, 1879.

2. J. Bernstein, *Elektrobiologie*, Braunschweig, Friedrich Vieweg und Sohn, 1912.

3. R. S. Lillie, *Protoplasmic Action and Nervous Action*, University of Chicago Press, Chicago, 1923.

4. M. Cremer, in: Bethe, A., *Handbuch der normalen und pathologischen Physiologie*, Vol. 8, No. 2, p. 999, Julius Springer, Berlin, 1928.

5. R. Lorente de Nó, *A Study of Nerve Physiology, Studies from the Rockefeller Inst. Med. Research*, Nos. 131, 132, 1947.

6. R. Höber, *Physical Chemistry of Cells and Tissues*, Blakiston Co., Philadelphia, 1945.

7. P. J. Boyle and E. J. Conway, *J. Physiol., 100*, 1 (1941).

8. M. A. Rothenberg, *Biochim. et Biophys. Acta, 4*, 96 (1950).

9. R. D. Keynes, *J. Physiol., 114*, 119 (1951).

10. R. D. Keynes and P. R. Lewis, *J. Physiol., 114*, 151 (1951).

11. A. Krogh, *Proc. Roy. Soc. (London), B, 133*, 140 (1946).

12. H. H. Ussing, *Physiol. Revs., 29*, 127 (1949).

13. A. L. Hodgkin and A. F. Huxley, *Nature, 144*, 710 (1939).

14. A. L. Hodgkin and A. F. Huxley, *J. Physiol., 104*, 176 (1945).

15. H. J. Curtis and K. S. Cole, *J. Cellular Comp. Physiol., 19*, 135 (1942).

16. A. L. Hodgkin and B. Katz, *J. Physiol., 108*, 37 (1949).

17. H. Grundfest and D. Nachmansohn, *Federation Proc., 9*, 53 (1950).

18. R. D. Keynes, *J. Physiol., 113*, 99 (1951).

19. R. D. Keynes, *Publ. inst. biofis. (Rio), 9*, 51 (1951).

20. A. L. Hodgkin, *Biol. Revs. Cambridge Philos. Soc., 26*, 339 (1951).

21. A. L. Hodgkin and A. F. Huxley, *J. Physiol., 117*, 500 (1952).

22. A full discussion of this theory will be found in K. S. Cole in this symposium.

23. H. Grundfest, R. Guttman, C. D. Hendley, and I. B. Wilson, *Science, 115*, 522 (1952).

24. H. Grundfest, A. M. Shanes, and W. Freygang, *J. Gen. Physiol., 37*, 25 (1953).

25. A. M. Shanes, H. Grundfest, and W. Freygang, *J. Gen. Physiol., 37*, 39 (1953).

26. H. Grundfest, C.-Y. Kao, D. Nachmansohn, and R. Chambers, *Nature, 169*, 190 (1952).

27. H. Grundfest, C.-Y. Kao, M. Altamirano, and D. Nachmansohn, *Federation Proc., 12*, 58 (1953).

28. H. Grundfest, M. Altamirano, and C.-Y. Kao, *XIX Intern. Physiol. Congress*, p. 420 (1953).

29. H. Grundfest, M. Altamirano, and C.-Y. Kao, *Federation Proc., 13*, 63 (1954).

30. H. Grundfest, *Arch. exp. Pathol. Pharmakol., 220*, 136 (1953).

31. M. Altamirano, C. Coates, H. Grundfest, and D. Nachmansohn, *J. Gen. Physiol., 37*, 91 (1953).

32. M. Altamirano, C. Coates, and H. Grundfest, *J. Gen. Physiol., 38*, 319 (1955).

33. A. M. Shanes, *J. Pharmacol. Exp. Therap., 105*, 216 (1952).

34. H. H. Ussing, *Advances in Enzym., 13*, 21 (1952).

35. T. Teorell, *J. Gen. Physiol., 19*, 917 (1936).

36. T. Teorell, *Ann. Rev. Physiol., 11*, 545 (1949).

37. T. Teorell, *Prog. Biophys. and Biophys. Chem., 3*, 305 (1953).

38. H. Grundfest, C.-Y. Kao, and M. Altamirano, *J. Gen. Physiol., 38,* 254 (1954).
39. W. K. Stephenson, *Biol. Bull., 105,* 368 (1953).
40. A. Mauro, *Biol. Bull., 105,* 378 (1953).
41. I am indebted to Prof. Mauro for permission to mention these results, which were obtained by him in our laboratory. *Federation Proc., 13,* 96 (1954).
42. D. I. Hitchcock, in: *Physical Chemistry of Cells and Tissues* (R. Höber, editor), p. 59, Blakiston Co., Philadelphia, 1945.
43. A. M. Shanes, *J. Gen. Physiol., 34,* 795 (1951).
44. H. S. Gasser, C. H. Richards, and H. Grundfest, *Am. J. Physiol., 123,* 299 (1938).
45. H. Grundfest, *Am. J. Physiol., 127,* 252 (1939).
46. The squid giant axons appear to be rather insensitive to microinjection of sulfhydryl inhibitors (unpublished).
47. An anomalous action of acetylcholine lies in the different effects of low and high concentrations.[30] The blocking action of low concentration of acetylcholine is absent when high concentrations are used. The spike, now maintained at a high amplitude, becomes greatly prolonged. The action may be in some respect similar to that of Na^+ seen in Fig. 11.
48. J. E. P. Toman, J. W. Woodbury, and L. A. Woodbury, *J. Neurophysiol., 10,* 429 (1947).
49. G. H. Bishop, *J. Cellular Comp. Physiol., 1,* 177 (1932).
50. H. Grundfest and R. Guttman, unpublished.
51. M. A. Rothenberg, D. B. Sprinson, and D. Nachmansohn, *J. Neurophysiol., 11,* 111 (1948).
52. Analysis of the effects of microinjected drugs on the bioelectric activity of squid axons will be published elsewhere.
53. M. Altamirano, C. Coates, H. Grundfest, and D. Nachmanson, *XIX Intern. Physiol. Congress,* p. 158 (1953).
54. R. D. Keynes and H. Martins-Ferreira, *J. Physiol., 119,* 315 (1953).
55. The existence of a metabolically driven sodium pump implies membrane components that combine specifically with Na^+ to transport this ion against the concentration gradient, inside to outside. This is probably not a thermodynamically reversible system, but no attempt has been made yet to apply the methods of irreversible thermodynamics.
56. J. F. Danielli, in: *The Permeability of Natural Membranes,* by H. Davson and J. F. Danielli, p. 338, Cambridge, 1943.
57. K. H. Meyer and J. F. Sievers, *Helv. Chim. Acta, 19,* 649 (1936).
58. T. Teorell, *Z. Elektrochem., 55,* 460 (1951).
59. B. J. Zwolinski, H. Eyring, and C. E. Reese, *J. Phys. & Colloid Chem., 53,* 1426 (1949).
60. T. Shedlovsky, *Cold Spring Harbor Symposia on Quantitative Biology, 17,* p. 97 (1952).
61. T. Shedlovsky, *Electrochemical Constants, Natl. Bur. Standards, Circ.* 524 (1953).
62. H. Grundfest, in: *Progress in Neurology and Psychiatry,* Vol. 5 (E. A. Spiegel, editor), p. 16, Grune & Stratton, New York, 1950.
63. H. Grundfest, in: *First Conference on Nerve Impulse,* Josiah Macy, Jr., Foundation, New York, 1950.
64. H. B. Steinbach, in: *First Conference on Nerve Impulse,* Josiah Macy, Jr., Foundation, New York, 1950.

65. K. S. Cole and H. J. Curtis, *J. Gen. Physiol., 22,* 649 (1939).
66. K. Sollner, in this symposium.
67. A. L. Hodgkin, A. F. Huxley, and B. Katz, *J. Physiol., 116,* 424 (1952).
68. A. L. Hodgkin and A. F. Huxley, *J. Physiol., 116,* 449 (1952).
69. A. L. Hodgkin and A. F. Huxley, *J. Physiol., 116,* 473 (1952).
70. A. L. Hodgkin and A. F. Huxley, *J. Physiol., 116,* 497 (1952).
71. K. S. Cole and J. W. Moore, *Biol. Bull., 107,* 295 (1954).
72. G. Ling and R. W. Gerard, *J. Cellular Comp. Physiol., 34,* 413 (1949).
73. G. Falk and R. W. Gerard, *J. Cellular Comp. Physiol., 43,* 393 (1954).
74. J. S. Coombs, J. C. Eccles, and P. Fatt, *Australian J. Sci., 16,* 1 (1953).
75. H. Grundfest, in: *Conf. on Nerve Impulse, Trans. 5th Conf. 1955,* Josiah Macy, Jr., Foundation Publications, Packanack Lake, N. J.
76. The presence of these two components has also been demonstrated in recent experiments on squid giant axons (H. Grundfest and C.-Y. Kao, unpublished). The phenomena ascribable to this complex mechanism are discussed more fully elsewhere.[75]

9·

Molecular Basis for Generation
of Bioelectric Potentials *

DAVID NACHMANSOHN † AND IRWIN B. WILSON †

THE PROBLEM OF PERMEABILITY CHANGE

The electric processes and the movements of ions associated with the conduction of the nerve impulse have been fully discussed in a preceding paper by K. S. Cole.[1] The presently available facts may be briefly summarized as follows: The concentration of sodium ions is much higher in the outside fluid than inside the nerve fiber, and the reverse is true for potassium ions. These ionic concentration gradients are now generally believed to be the primary energy source of the electromotive force of the action potentials propagating the impulse. A sudden increase in sodium permeability allows sodium ions to move from the outside of the fiber to the inside. This movement of charge makes the inside positive and provides a satisfactory explanation for the rising phase of the action potential. The falling phase and the subsequent repolarization depend on the outflow of potassium ions.

The demonstration of these ion movements underlying the bioelectric potentials observed during activity raises the fundamental question: By what mechanism does the potential energy source of electromotive force, inactive in rest, become suddenly effective? What is the process in the membrane responsible for the sudden transient change in resistance and the tremendous increase in permeability to sodium? Knowledge of the trigger process by which the ionic concentration gradient becomes an effective force is fundamental for the understand-

* This article is based on work supported by grants from the United States Public Health Service, Division of Research Grants and Fellowships of the National Institutes of Health, by the Research and Development Division, Office of the Surgeon General, Department of the Army, and by the Atomic Energy Commission. It is dedicated to Otto Loewi's eightieth birthday.

† From the Department of Neurology, College of Physicians and Surgeons, Columbia University, New York, N. Y.

ing of the mechanism of the generation of bioelectric potentials. The first hypothesis concerning the nature of the process responsible for the change in ion permeability required for the generation of bioelectric potentials was proposed by Kurt H. Meyer in 1937.[2] On the basis of his extensive studies of ion permeability across artificial membranes, Meyer postulated that every change in permeability is preceded by a chemical reaction. Membranes are formed by protein chains. Appearance of amino groups will increase anionic permeability, whereas that of carboxyl groups will increase movements of cations. The specific chemical reactions thought to be responsible for the appearance of these groups remained, however, unexplored.

The difficulty of identifying these reactions is readily recognized if two essential features of the process are kept in mind: the high speed and the small amount of energy involved. According to the impedance measurements of Cole and Curtis,[3] the permeability change of the membrane reaches its peak within 100 μsec. A chemical reaction responsible for this change must have a comparable speed. According to the heat measurements of A. V. Hill and his associates, the heat released during nerve activity is of the order of magnitude of 10^{-11} gcal. per cm.[2] per impulse. Therefore, the metabolism of the specific compounds responsible for the permeability change must be exceedingly small.

In 1913, Otto Meyerhof, then a young privatdozent at the University of Kiel, pointed out, in a lecture entitled *Zur Energetik der Zellvorgänge,* that the real problem in the utilization of metabolites is how, step by step, energy is available for function.[4] Knowledge of the sequence of energy transformations is required for the understanding of cellular mechanisms. The muscle, in which relatively large amounts of chemical energy are transformed in mechanical work, seemed to be the most favorable material for such an analysis. Meyerhof's life work was devoted to establishing the sequence of energy transformations associated with the elementary process of muscular contraction. He emphasized (1) the significance of thermodynamics for studying the sequence of reactions in intermediary metabolism, (2) the cyclic character of the reactions taking place, and (3) the necessity of correlating chemical reactions observed in vitro with events in the intact cell. The analysis of cellular function in general must be based upon the same approach.

Early in this century it was discovered that acetylcholine has a powerful pharmacological action and mimics the effects of stimulation of certain nerves. The compound therefore attracted the interest of many physiologists. Studies of the last 15 years, based upon an approach fundamentally similar to that used for the analysis of muscular contraction, have shown that the action of acetylcholine is directly associated with the permeability changes to ions occurring during the passage of the impulse and forms an integral part of the elementary process by which bioelectric potentials are generated.[5-7] Before discussing the picture as it has developed, we shall factually illustrate the way in which this problem has been analyzed.

PERTINENT FEATURES OF ACETYLCHOLINESTERASE IN RELATION TO FUNCTION

SPECIFICITY

The enzyme that inactivates the ester by hydrolysis is called acetylcholinesterase.[8] Esterases are, of course, widely distributed in animal organisms and hydrolyze a great variety of esters, but the type of esterase in conducting tissue has a number of properties by which it may readily be distinguished from other esterases. The enzyme has a rather sharply defined optimum substrate concentration. The activity-substrate concentration relationship shows a typical bell-shaped curve. The hydrolysis rate is about the same when the acyl group of the substrate contains two or three carbons, but in contrast to most other esterases it drops sharply with four carbons.[9,10] The Michaelis constant is small. This type of esterase is present in all types of conducting tissue throughout the animal kingdom. It occurs even in monocellular organisms endowed with ciliar movements (Seaman and Houlihan [11]).

LOCALIZATION

Another physiologically significant feature is the exclusive localization of acetylcholinesterase in the surface membranes of nerve fibers. In experiments with the giant axons of squid all the enzyme activity was found in the sheath whereas no activity was detectable in the axoplasm.[12] Since the active membrane must be in the sheath, this peculiar localization appears pertinent especially in connection with other findings.

SPEED

The outstanding feature of the enzyme from the functional point of view is the high speed at which it is able to hydrolyze the ester. The turnover number is about 20 million per minute.[13] This is a much higher speed than that of all other enzymes tested except the catalase. The figure indicates that the ester may be split in a few microseconds.

The obvious prerequisite for associating a chemical reaction with electric manifestations is a comparable speed. The high speed of the esterase action satisfies this postulate and makes it possible to assume that its action is responsible for the generation of bioelectric current.

ESSENTIALITY

The features described, although suggestive, do not provide evidence that the actions of acetylcholine or cholinesterase are essential in conduction. Such an assumption requires a demonstration of a direct relationship between function and chemical reaction. One method frequently employed for testing the essentiality of an enzyme for a cellular function is to block its activity by specific inhibitors. A famous observation of this kind is Lundsgaard's classical demonstration that lactic acid formation can be blocked with iodoacetate without impairing muscular contraction. Clearly, if the esterase is essential in conduction, this function must be abolished by complete inactivation of the enzyme.

A large amount of evidence has accumulated indicating that it is impossible to dissociate conduction from acetylcholinesterase activity. This was first shown with reversible inhibitors of the enzyme which block conduction reversibly.[14] Still more conclusive evidence was obtained with an irreversible inhibitor, diisopropyl fluorophosphate (DFP), an alkyl phosphate. The famous German "nerve gases," as for instance Tabun, belong to this group; they are the most powerful chemical warfare agents known. These compounds inhibit acetylcholinesterase essentially irreversibly. Inhibitors of this type are in many respects more suitable for such investigation than reversible inhibitors. Extensive studies with a great variety of nerve fibers exposed to DFP have shown that it is impossible to dissociate conduction of the nerve impulse from acetylcholinesterase activity.[15] To illustrate this point, one experiment may be briefly mentioned.[16]

Acetylcholine is a quaternary ammonium salt and unable to penetrate into the nerve fiber, but its tertiary analog dimethylaminoethyl acetate, which also is hydrolyzed by cholinesterase, penetrates readily. This compound permits, therefore, simultaneous measurement of conduction and acetylcholinesterase activity. On exposure to DFP, conduction fails when the enzyme activity has dropped to 20% of the initial value (Fig. 1), which is in agreement with previous data.

The presence of acetylcholinesterase in all types of conducting tissue and the dependence of conduction in all those tissues upon the activity of the enzyme permit the conclusion that the role of acetylcholine in conduction is both general and essential.

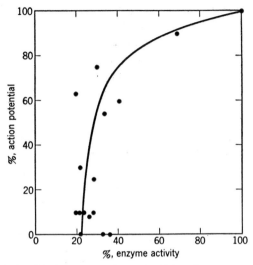

Fig. 1. The relationship between action potential and enzyme activity in nerve subjected to 5–8 mg. of DFP per ml.

SEQUENCE OF ENERGY TRANSFORMATIONS

For a better understanding of the physiological role of acetylcholine it appeared necessary to integrate acetylcholine into the metabolic pathways of the cell and to establish the sequence of energy transformations. For this analysis the electric organ of fish proved to be an invaluable material. The most important feature of these organs is the generally accepted fact that their strong bioelectric potentials are of a nature identical with that of nerve and muscle. The electric organ is formed by compartments, each containing one cell, the electric plate or electroplaque, and arranged in columns. The action potential developed by a single plate is about 0.15 volt, which is of the same order of magnitude as that found in ordinary nerve and muscle fibers. It is the arrangement of these plates in series, as in a Voltaic pile, which makes the electric discharge of these organs so powerful. Indeed, Volta recognized the analogy and called his pile an artificial electric organ. Only one face of the electric plate is innervated, and half a century ago Bernstein suggested that the arrangement in series may be explained by the change of potential at the innervated face only. Recent work on individual cells of *Electrophorus electricus* has shown that Bernstein's hypothesis was correct and that only the innervated face reverses the charge.[17,18] Summation of the voltages developed by the individual cells would be impossible if both faces would reverse their potentials. The great differences in the strength of the discharge in various species do not depend on the units, which show relatively small variations, but on the shape and dimensions of the organs. In the species with the most powerful electric organ known, the *Electrophorus electricus* (Linnaeus), about 5000 to 6000 plates are arranged in series from the head to the caudal end of the organ. The voltage of the discharge is on the average 500 to 600 volts. In the *Torpedo marmorata* the number of elements in series does not exceed 400 to 500. The discharge here is on the average 40 to 50 volts.

In 1937, Nachmansohn utilized for the first time the electric organ for the study of the metabolic relationships of acetylcholine and their connection with the energy transformations involved in the generation of bioelectric currents. The choice of this material was decisive for the later developments.

DIRECT PROPORTIONALITY BETWEEN VOLTAGE AND ACETYLCHOLINESTERASE

The strong electric organs of *Torpedo* and *Electrophorus electricus* have an extraordinarily high concentration of acetylcholinesterase. Two to four grams of acetylcholine are hydrolyzed per gram of (wet weight) tissue per hour. The significance of these figures becomes apparent when compared to those in other tissues (Table 1). The

TABLE 1. ACETYLCHOLINESTERASE CONCENTRATION IN VARIOUS TISSUES COMPARED TO THAT OF ELECTRIC TISSUE OF *Electrophorus electricus* (El. el.)

Tissue		Milligrams ACh Split per Gram-Hour
Mammalian at 37° C.	muscle	5–10
	nerve fibers	10–30
	brain	20–100
Frog at 23° C.	muscle	3–6
	nerve fibers	5–10
	brain	40–80
Electric organ of El. el. at 23° C.		2000–4000
Mammalian kidney		0
Mammalian liver		0

high concentration of enzyme is even more striking in view of the high water and low protein content. The protein content is only about 2%, whereas 92% of the organ is water. The fact that the organs contain enough enzyme capable of hydrolyzing amounts of acetylcholine equivalent to several times their own weight per hour suggests a close relationship to their highly specialized primary function, i.e., the generation of bioelectric potentials. Indeed, a striking parallelism exists between the concentration of the enzyme and the voltage and number of plates per centimeter. The electric organ of *Electrophorus electricus* is particularly suitable for the demonstration of this relationship. The number of electric plates per centimeter varies considerably with the size of the specimen; and, moreover, it decreases markedly from the head to the caudal end of the organ in each specimen. Since the volt-

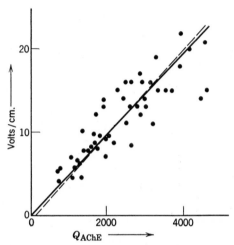

Fig. 2. Direct proportionality between voltage per centimeter and acetylcholinesterase concentration in the electric tissue of *Electrophorus electricus*. Dashed line is calculated from data with the method of least squares; solid line is calculated on assumption that the line goes through the zero point. Q_{AChE} = mg. ACh split per mg. tissue (fresh weight) per hour.

age of each plate is about the same, the voltage per centimeter varies considerably. Figure 2 shows the relationship between voltage and acetylcholinesterase concentration tested on a great number of specimens of *Electrophorus electricus* of various sizes,[19, 20] covering a range of the action potential from 0.5 to 22 volts per centimeter. The voltage per centimeter is plotted against acetylcholinesterase concentration. Calculated by the method of least squares, the resulting line goes through zero, indicating a direct proportionality between voltage per centimeter and enzyme concentration. Such a direct proportionality between physical and chemical processes is rarely found in biological function. The electric organ offers, of course, a particularly favorable case for many reasons. The finding is in rather striking contrast to the even distribution and low concentration of other tested enzymes, for example, respiratory and glycolytic enzymes, adenosine-triphosphatase, and others.

PHOSPHORYLATED COMPOUNDS AS ENERGY SOURCE

From the studies of the intermediary metabolism associated with muscular contraction it became apparent that chemical reactions of some phosphorylated compounds constitute the most readily available source of energy for endergonic processes. The work of Meyerhof and Lohmann suggested that adenosinetriphosphate (ATP) might be the primary source of energy for muscle contraction and that the adeno-sinediphosphate (ADP) formed is rephosphorylated by the breakdown of phosphocreatine, a transfer of phosphate that occurs without loss of energy. Phosphocreatine thus acts as a kind of storehouse for supplying phosphate to ADP for the rapid regeneration of ATP. The energy released by the breakdown of phosphocreatine was found to account adequately for the total electric energy released by the discharge.[21, 22] In addition, there is energy released by the simultaneous formation of lactic acid. It may be assumed that the energy released during lactic acid formation is used as in muscle for rephosphorylating creatine. The sum of the two reactions may therefore be used as indication of the energy supplied by the phosphorylated compounds rich in energy. This amount is more than adequate to account for the total electric energy released, but it is possible and indeed probable that part of the energy released is not used for the immediate process of recovery but for the restoration of the ionic concentration gradient.

It was safe to assume that, as in muscle, the breakdown of ATP during nerve activity precedes that of phosphocreatine. Today it is generally accepted that ATP reacts directly with the structural muscle protein in the elementary process of contraction. However, for many reasons, it was considered most unlikely that ATP was responsible for the change in permeability postulated in the elementary process of conduction. From the available evidence it appeared more likely that the action of acetylcholine was directly responsible for the alterations of the membrane required for the generation of the action potential and that these reactions occurred prior to the breakdown of ATP. The breakdown of ATP would then be a recovery process supplying the energy for the resynthesis of acetylcholine hydrolyzed during activity.

This assumption proved to be correct. In 1943, an enzyme was extracted from brain and electric tissue,[23] which in cell-free solution acetylates choline only in the presence of ATP. The enzyme was referred to as choline acetylase. This was the first demonstration that the energy of ATP may be used outside the glycolytic cycle. Since then, during the last 10 years, a great number of endergonic reactions have been demonstrated to utilize the energy of ATP.

ACETYLATION MECHANISMS

The observation that ATP provides the energy for the acetylation of choline opened the way for a detailed analysis of the mechanisms of acetylation in general. It was the first time that a biological acetylation was obtained in a soluble system. At that time, in the early 1940's, the paramount importance of acetate in intermediary metabolism as a building stone of many essential cell constituents had become apparent, mainly through the application of isotope techniques. During the last 10 years many investigators have studied the mechanisms of acetylation. Today it is well established that the first step is the acetylation of a coenzyme discovered in 1945 simultaneously by Lipmann,[24, 25] by Lipton [26] in Barron's laboratory, and in our laboratory,[27, 28] and later called Coenzyme A (CoA). The formation of acetyl CoA is catalyzed by the enzyme acetylkinase using the energy of ATP hydrolysis. The acetyl group is then transferred to other acceptors through the action of enzymes more or less specific for the acceptor. Choline acetylase transfers the acetyl group from acetyl CoA to choline.[29]

Besides the implications for general biochemistry, the evidence that ATP provides the energy for acetylcholine synthesis supported the view that the action of acetylcholine and its hydrolysis precede the breakdown of ATP in the sequence of energy transformations. It thus became possible to integrate acetylcholine into the metabolic pathways of the cell.

The question remained, however, whether acetylcholine is itself responsible for the permeability change associated with the generation of bioelectric potentials. If this were true, it should have an electrogenic action. This electrogenic action was found.[30] Injection of acetylcholine into the electric organ of Torpedo perfused with eserine generates electric potentials (Fig. 3). This electrogenic effect makes it difficult to assume that acetylcholine is required for recovery and supports the assumption that the action of the ester is responsible for the change in permeability associated with the nerve impulse. It is true that other compounds may produce similar effects, but acetylcholine is the only compound that fulfills all the requirements for such an assumption, and all the known facts are consistent with this conclusion.

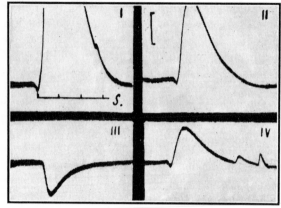

Fig. 3. Electrogenic action of acetylcholine. The potential changes are produced by intra-arterial injection of acetylcholine into the electric organ of *Torpedo marmorata* in the presence of eserine. I, II, and IV correspond to the injection of 10, 5, and 2.5 μg. of acetylcholine; at III only perfusion fluid was injected. At II, 0.5 mv. is indicated. (Time in seconds.)

THE ELEMENTARY PROCESS

The precise action of acetylcholine in the elementary process is still under investigation, but the picture that has emerged on the basis of all the facts available may be briefly outlined. Acetylcholine is, in resting condition, in an inactive and bound form. It may be called tentatively the storage form. It appears likely that the ester is bound to a protein or lipoprotein. No information is at present available about the nature of this storage form. During activity, as is well established experimentally, acetylcholine is released from the bound form. The free acetylcholine acts upon a receptor, and this action upon the receptor is responsible for the change of permeability and, thus, for the generation of the potential.

Although the receptor has not yet been isolated, the most likely assumption appears to be that it is a protein. Some data to be discussed later suggest that the effect of acetylcholine may be a change in configuration of the protein.

To continue the discussion of our picture, the complex between acetylcholine and the receptor is in dynamic equilibrium with the free ester and the receptor. The free ester is susceptible to attack by the esterase, and the hydroloysis permits the receptor to return to its resting condition. The "barrier" for the rapid ion movements is thus established again. This action of the enzyme leads to the immediate recovery and ends the cycle of the elementary process. It is the rapidity of this inactivation process that makes rapid restoration of

the membrane possible and thus permits the nerve to respond to the
next stimulus within a few milliseconds. The further recovery leads to
the resynthesis of acetylcholine in its bound form. Here the cyclic

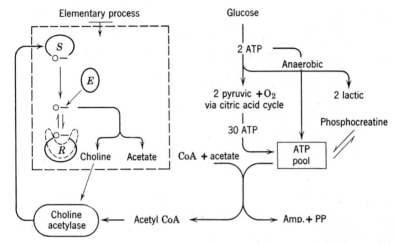

Fig. 4. Sequence of energy transformations associated with conduction and integration of the acetylcholine system into the metabolic pathways of the nerve
cell. The elementary process of conduction may be tentatively pictured as follows:

1. In resting condition acetylcholine ($\bigcirc$—) is bound, presumably, to a storage
protein (S). The membrane is polarized.

2. ACh is released by current flow (possibly hydrogen ion movements) or any
other excitatory agent. The free ester combines with the receptor (R), presumably a protein.

3. The receptor changes its configuration (dashed line). This process increases
the Na ion permeability and permits its rapid influx. This is the trigger action
by which the potential primary source of e.m.f., the ionic concentration gradient,
becomes effective and by which the action current is generated.

4. The ester-receptor complex is in dynamic equilibrium with the free ester
and the receptor; the free ester is open to attack by acetylcholinesterase (E).

5. The hydrolysis of the ester permits the receptor to return to its original
shape. The permeability decreases, and the membrane is again in its original
polarized condition.

processes known from muscle and other cells enter the picture. The
immediate precursor of the acetyl group of the acetyl CoA is not yet
known. It may be acetate, but it may also be another acetyl donor.
Figure 4 shows the sequence of energy transformations associated
with conduction and the integration of acetylcholine into the metabolic
cycle of the nerve cell. It illustrates how the role of acetylcholine
may be tentatively pictured in the elementary process.

THE PROTEINS OF THE ACETYLCHOLINE SYSTEM

We have seen that the acetylcholine system forms an integral part of the metabolic cycle of the neuron and is intrinsically associated with its primary function, the propagation of the nerve impulse. Knowledge of the forces of interaction between acetylcholine and the proteins of the system is evidently necessary for an understanding of the fundamental process. Unfortunately only the two enzymes are available in purified aqueous solution, so that studies with the receptor must be made with intact structures, and nothing is known of the postulated storage protein. Fortunately, knowledge acquired with one of these proteins may aid us in understanding certain processes, involved with the others, which at present can be approached only indirectly. Since acetylcholine has only a limited number of features that may contribute to its binding with proteins, all proteins that combine specifically with the ester must do so through much the same elementary interactions and are presumably similarly constituted at the active site. The consequences of this binding will differ from protein to protein, and small differences may lead to a considerable alteration of function. The esterase is the most suitable for these studies and has been extensively investigated,[31, 32] but only those properties that appear to be important to the group as a whole will be presented.

The interaction of acetylcholine with the esterase falls naturally into two phases; the first is the formation of the enzyme-substrate complex, and the other is the ensuing hydrolytic process.

FORMATION OF THE ENZYME SUBSTRATE COMPLEX

Some of the main results may be given as illustration. The positive electric charge of acetylcholine suggests that the enzyme might contain a suitably located negatively charged region, which would contribute to the attraction, fixation, and orientation of the substrate upon the enzyme surface. The existence of such a negative site has been demonstrated in various ways with suitable substrates as well as with competitive inhibitors. For instance,[33] if the inhibition of the enzyme by prostigmine is compared with that of eserine as a function of pH, the inhibitory strength of prostigmine remains unchanged over a wide range of pH. Prostigmine is a quaternary ammonium compound, and its electric charge is independent of pH. In contrast, eserine is a much stronger inhibitor at acid pH than at higher pH. Eserine exists at pH below 8 predominantly as a cationic conjugate acid, whereas it is an uncharged base at high pH. The increase of about twenty-fold of inhibitory strength can be ascribed to increase of electrostatic or coulombic forces in the binding of the cationic form. Dimethyl-aminoethyl acetate, the tertiary analog of acetylcholine, is hydrolyzed much faster at acid pH, where it accepts a proton and is in a cationic form, than in the alkaline range, where it is a neutral molecule (Fig. 5).

In addition to the coulombic forces, the methyl or alkyl groups of the nitrogen contribute to the binding by Van der Waals or London

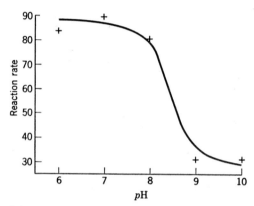

Fig. 5.   Rate of hydrolysis of dimethylaminoethyl acetate relative to acetyl-choline (arbitrary units) as a function of pH.

dispersion forces. This was demonstrated with methylated competitive inhibitors of the ammonium and hydroxyethylammonium series.[34] Except for the fourth alkyl group, each methyl group has binding properties that increase the potency of the inhibitor sevenfold (Table 2). There is little difference in binding between compounds containing three and four alkyl groups. This point will be discussed later.

TABLE 2.   INHIBITORY POTENCY OF METHYLATED AMMONIUM IONS

M = molar concentration to produce 50% inhibition when the acetylcholine concentration is 4×10^{-4} M.

$-\!N\!-$		$-\!N\!-\!C_2H_4OH$	
Number of Methyl Groups	M	Number of Methyl Groups	M
4	0.018	3	0.005
3	0.015	2	0.005
2	0.12	1	0.07
1	0.7	0	0.28

Besides the anionic site attracting the cationic nitrogen, there is also a group in the enzyme surface that reacts with the ester group and is called the esteratic site. The carbonyl group has a marked polar character. The importance of the electrophilic character of the carbon has been demonstrated by using a series of nicotinamide derivatives.[35] The order of increasing electrophilic character of the carbon parallels the observed order of inhibition, suggesting that a covalent bond is formed between the carbon and some basic group in the enzyme. A further clue to the mechanism of enzymic hydrolysis has been

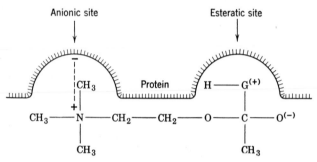

Fig. 6.   Schematic presentation of interaction between the active groups of acetylcholinesterase and its substrate.

obtained from the pH dependence. The activity of the esterase is at a maximum between pH 8 and 9; and, since the constitution of acetylcholine does not vary with pH, changes in enzyme activity must, therefore, be attributed to changes in the protein. These changes may be interpreted in terms of the dissociation of acidic and basic groups. On the basis of this concept a few equilibria and relations may be postulated. Mathematical analysis of these relations led to an equation and predictions that were borne out by experiments. Wilson thus was able to calculate the pK's of the basic and acidic groups.[36]

Figure 6 is a schematic representation of the enzyme substrate complex. Coulombic and Van der Waals forces act at the anionic site. At the esteratic site a covalent bond is formed between the basic group (G) and the carbon atom of the carbonyl group. The acidic group (H) is not involved in the binding.

THE HYDROLYTIC PROCESS

Let us now turn to the mechanism of the hydrolytic process. Wilson proposed the following mechanism:

$$H-\underset{\cdot\cdot}{G} + R-\overset{O}{\overset{\|}{C}}-OR' \rightleftharpoons R'\underset{\cdot\cdot}{O}\underset{\longleftarrow}{}\overset{H\longrightarrow G^{(+)}}{\underset{\underset{(a)}{R}}{\overset{\|}{C}}-O^{(-)}} \rightleftharpoons \overset{G^{(+)}}{\underset{\underset{(b)}{R}}{\overset{\|}{C}}-O^{(-)}} + R'OH$$

$$H-\underset{\cdot\cdot}{O}: + \overset{H\quad G^{(+)}}{\underset{\underset{(b)}{R}}{\overset{\|}{C}}-O^{(-)}} \rightleftharpoons HO-\overset{H-G^{(+)}}{\underset{\underset{(c)}{R}}{\overset{\|}{C}}-O^{(-)}} \rightleftharpoons H-\underset{\cdot\cdot}{G} + R-\overset{O}{\overset{\|}{C}}-OH$$

Again, H symbolizes the acidic group and $\underset{\cdot\cdot}{G}$ the basic group in the esteratic site. The pair of electrons symbolizes the electron-transmitting properties of the group. Acetylcholine forms the Michaelis-Menten complex (a). The first process is the acetylation of the enzyme with simultaneous elimination of choline. (b) shows the acylated enzyme depicted as enolate ion, which is one of the resonance forms. The acyl enzyme reacts with water or other nucleophilic agents, such as hydroxylamine. (c) is an acid enzyme complex similar to the ester enzyme complex and leads to regenerated enzyme and acetic acid. The proposed mechanism has been verified in a variety of ways.[37, 38]

REVERSAL OF ENZYME INHIBITION BY ALKYLPHOSPHATES

The studies of the molecular forces, of which only a very brief outline was given, have already yielded valuable information for the physiology and pharmacology of the nervous system and have opened new ways of approach. Two examples may be given. The proposed mechanism of the hydrolytic process led to an explanation of the action of alkylphosphates to which, as mentioned before, belong the most powerful chemical warfare agents. In splitting ordinary phosphate esters, a C—O bond is broken and the phosphate group is preserved. In splitting alkyl phosphates a group linked to phosphorus is broken. Wilson proposed, in 1950, the following mode of action, by which alkylphosphates inhibit esterases.[39] The esterase attacks the electrophilic phosphorus atom in a nucleophilic substitution reaction, and the phosphoryl group is transferred to the basic group in the active surface. Instead of an acylated enzyme, a phosphorylated enzyme is formed (Fig. 7), but the reaction of this phosphorylated enzyme with water is extremely slow, since this covalent bond is very strong. For this reason these compounds are strong inhibitors instead of substrates. A few years ago it was believed that DFP "destroys" the enzyme. However,

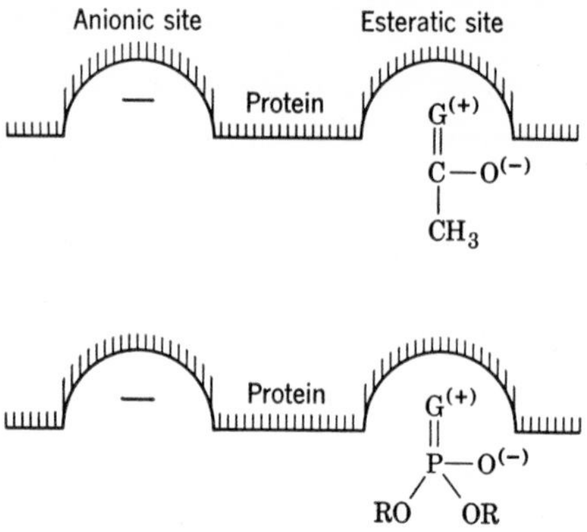

Fig. 7. Schematic presentation of the acetylated enzyme (upper row) compared to the phosphorylated enzyme (lower row).

if the mechanism proposed above is correct, it should be possible to reverse the inhibitory action. This reversal was accomplished. The reaction with water is very ·slow, and the restoration process takes weeks. If, however, stronger nucleophilic agents are used, such as hydroxylamine, reactivation of the enzyme is fast.[40] Recently additional evidence has been obtained to substantiate Wilson's views.[41]

The reversal of the alkylphosphate-inhibited enzyme by hydroxylamine is satisfactory in the case where the alkyl is an ethyl group, but in the case of diisopropyl the reversal was small. Wilson argued that if the hydroxylamine would be attached to a quaternary nitrogen group in the proper distance, the group would be better fixed on the enzyme and direct the hydroxylamine in its attack upon the phosphoryl group. Estelle Meislich in our laboratory synthesized the N-methylnicotin hydroxamic acid methiodide.

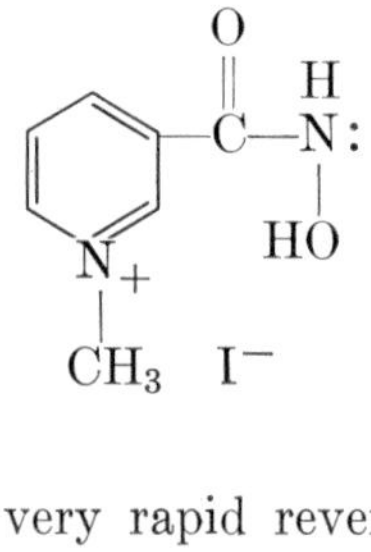

With this compound a very rapid reversal of tetraethylpyrophosphate was obtained, and, for the first time, a complete reversal of the DFP action became possible.[42]

DIFFERENTIAL BEHAVIOR TOWARDS TERTIARY AND QUATERNARY NITROGENS

Another interesting feature resulting from these studies is the differential behavior of the proteins of the acetylcholine system towards tertiary and quaternary nitrogens. The binding forces between the esterase protein and small molecules are not greatly affected by the presence of the fourth alkyl group. But the functional activities are markedly altered. This is also true for choline acetylase and for the receptor protein. For the esterase the difference is relatively small: the tertiary analog of acetylcholine is split at about half the rate of that of acetylcholine itself. The difference is much more pronounced in the case of the acetylase: [43] removal of one methyl group reduces the rate of acetylation by choline acetylase by a factor of 12. Finally, the biological activity of dimethylaminoethyl acetate upon the receptor, measured by assay with the frog's rectus abdominis muscle, is only 1/100 of that of acetylcholine. It has indeed been known for nearly 100 years that the pharmacological action of quaternary compounds is much stronger than that of their tertiary analogs.

The striking effect of the fourth alkyl group towards the three proteins has been observed in many respects. This action is all the more remarkable since the quaternary group is chemically saturated. A clue may be the tetrahedral structure of the quaternary group. Such a structure is more or less spherical, and the only way the protein could be in contact with all methyl groups would be by enveloping the molecule. This implies a change in protein configuration. A change of configuration would be of special interest with regard to the functional properties of the receptor. Rearrangement of acidic and basic groups by folding or unfolding of the protein chains would be one possible way to account for the increased sodium permeability effected by the system.

Studies with the electric organ of *Electrophorus electricus* have been valuable in analyzing interactions with the acetylcholine system. Microelectrodes were introduced into a single cell. A schematic drawing of the preparation used is presented in Fig. 12, Chapter 8. The electrical characteristics of the membrane were studied on exposure to compounds that react specifically with the acetylcholine system.[44] All these compounds, as expected, block the discharge. However, there are striking differences in quality and quantity.

Some of the compounds have a relatively weak action on the esterase but a high affinity to the receptor, and this fact has made it possible to distinguish block of receptor and enzyme inhibition as the cause of conduction failure. Using ethyl chloroacetate as a substrate it is possible to assay the esterase in the intact cell. With certain blocking agents, such as procaine, decamethonium, and carbaminoylcholine, the enzyme is but slightly inhibited under conditions in which propagation has been eliminated. In contrast, eserine, DFP, and prostigmine and its tertiary analog produced block only under conditions in which the enzyme was very strongly inhibited. By these results an experimental distinction has been achieved between the long postulated receptor of acetylcholine and acetylcholinesterase.

These studies have also suggested that interactions with the receptor may involve two phases analogous to the two phases of interaction with the enzymes. Quaternary compounds, for instance, have a much stronger tendency to depolarize than the tertiary analogs. Most of the tertiary compounds do not depolarize at all, even in high concentrations. Possibly they are unable to produce the change in configuration necessary for accelerated ion movements. The local anesthetic procaine, a tertiary structure related to acetylcholine, has long been known to block conduction without depolarization. Applied to the electric cell before carbaminoylcholine, it prevents the depolarizing action of the choline ester; this finding supports the view that both compounds compete for the same receptor.

Thus it appears that we may separate the compounds into two categories, those that show only binding and those that show two aspects of interaction, namely, binding and depolarization caused by attendant changes in the receptor.

The question has been repeatedly raised whether receptor and esterase may not be identical. Although this would be theoretically possible, there are many observations that suggest that at least the active sites, if not the proteins, may be different. We have seen that various compounds like procaine, decamethonium, and others block propagation without interfering with enzyme activity. Another evidence in favor of two different sites of action is provided by observations with DFP. DFP blocked propagation of the electroplaques without depolarization. Similar observations separating block of conduction and depolarization with DFP and eserine in axonal conduction were previously reported by Toman, Woodbury, and Woodbury.[45] The enzyme activity of the electroplaques at that period was very low. Adding a small amount of carbaminoylcholine rapidly produced depolarization. Moreover, in earlier observations it was found that block of conduction in axons by DFP is reversible for periods of 30 min. or even longer. Since we know that the enzyme DFP complex is essentially irreversible, the block must be attributed to the binding of DFP at a site that does not split off the fluoride and therefore permits a readily reversible complex. Such a loose binding between protein and DFP is in agreement with the idea of a readily reversible association between receptor and the active agent.

It may also be mentioned that acetylcholine and butyrylcholine have about the same biological activity, although the first is a very good substrate of the esterase, and the second a very poor one. Dimethyl-aminoethyl acetate, on the other hand, is a substrate not much poorer than acetylcholine (45%), but its biological activity is low. Finally, curare and curare-like compounds are known to be very strong blocking agents, although relatively poor inhibitors of the esterase. In contrast, eserine, a very strong inhibitor of the enzyme, has very poor blocking abilities.

All these observations taken together are a strong support for the assumption of two different sites, although the evidence may not yet be conclusive. As working hypotheses they integrate best our present knowledge.

The study of the molecular forces in the proteins of the acetylcholine system is relatively recent and in full progress. It may eventually lead to an understanding of the generation of bioelectric potentials on a molecular level and thus provide the basis for the understanding of the functioning of the nerve cell in terms of physics and chemistry.

REFERENCES

1. K. S. Cole, this book, chapter 7.
2. K. H. Meyer, *Helv. Chim. Acta, 20,* 634, 1937.
3. K. S. Cole and H. J. Curtis, *J. Gen. Physiol., 22,* 649 (1939).
4. O. Meyerhof, *Zur Energetik der Zellvorgänge,* Vandenhöck u. Ruprecht, *Göttingen,* 1913.
5. D. Nachmansohn, *Biochim. et Biophys. Acta, 4,* 78 (1950).
6. D. Nachmansohn, in: E. S. G. Barron, *Modern Trends of Physiology and Biochemistry,* p. 229, Academic Press, New York, 1952.
7. D. Nachmansohn, *Harvey Lectures,* Academic Press, New York, 1953–1954.
8. K. B. Augustinsson and D. Nachmansohn, *Science, 110,* 98 (1949).
9. D. Nachmansohn and M. A. Rothenberg, *Science, 100,* 454 (1944).
10. D. Nachmansohn and M. A. Rothenberg, *J. Biol. Chem., 158,* 653 (1945).
11. G. R. Seaman and R. K. Houlihan, *J. Cellular Comp. Physiol., 37,* 309 (1951).
12. E. J. Boell and D. Nachmansohn, *Science, 92,* 513 (1940).
13. M. A. Rothenberg and D. Nachmansohn, *J. Biol. Chem., 168,* 223 (1947).
14. T. H. Bullock, D. Nachmansohn, and M. A. Rothenberg, *J. Neurophysiol., 9,* 9 (1946).
15. D. Nachmansohn, *Bull. Johns Hopkins Hosp., 83,* 463 (1948).
16. I. B. Wilson and M. Cohen, *Biochim. et Biophys. Acta, 11,* 147 (1953).
17. M. Altamirano, C. W. Coates, H. Grundfest, and D. Nachmansohn, *J. Gen. Physiol., 37,* 1, 91 (1953).

18. R. D. Keynes and H. Martins-Ferreira, *J. Physiol.*, *119*, 315 (1953).
19. D. Nachmansohn, R. T. Cox, C. W. Coates, and A. L. Machado, *J. Neurophysiol.*, *5*, 499 (1942).
20. D. Nachmansohn, C. W. Coates, and M. A. Rothenberg, *J. Biol. Chem.*, *163*, 39 (1946).
21. D. Nachmansohn, R. T. Cox, C. W. Coates, and A. L. Machado, *J. Neurophysiol.*, *6*, 383 (1943).
22. D. Nachmansohn, C. W. Coates, M. A. Rothenberg, and M. V. Brown, *J. Biol. Chem.*, *165*, 223 (1946).
23. D. Nachmansohn and A. L. Machado, *J. Neurophysiol.*, *6*, 397 (1943).
24. F. Lipmann, *J. Biol. Chem.*, *160*, 173 (1945).
25. F. Lipmann and N. O. Kaplan, *J. Biol. Chem.*, *162*, 743 (1946).
26. M. A. Lipton, *Federation Proc.*, *5*, 145 (1946).
27. D. Nachmansohn, *Ann. N. Y. Acad. Sc.*, *47*, 395 (1946).
28. D. Nachmansohn and M. Berman, *J. Biol. Chem.*, *165*, 551 (1946).
29. S. R. Korey, B. de Braganza, and D. Nachmansohn, *J. Biol. Chem.*, *189*, 705 (1951).
30. W. Feldberg, A. Fessard, and D. Nachmansohn, *J. Physiol.*, *97*, 3 (1940).
31. D. Nachmansohn and I. B. Wilson, in: *Advances in Enzymol.*, *12*, 259 (1951).
32. I. B. Wilson, in: McElroy and Glass, *Enzyme Mechanisms*, Johns Hopkins Press, Baltimore.
33. I. B. Wilson and F. Bergmann, *J. Biol. Chem.*, *185*, 479 (1950).
34. I. B. Wilson, *J. Biol. Chem.*, *197*, 215 (1952).
35. F. Bergmann, I. B. Wilson, and D. Nachmansohn, *J. Biol. Chem.*, *186*, 693 (1950).
36. I. B. Wilson and F. Bergmann, *J. Biol. Chem.*, *186*, 683 (1950).
37. I. B. Wilson, F. Bergmann, and D. Nachmansohn, *J. Biol. Chem.*, *186*, 781 (1950).
38. I. B. Wilson, *Biochim. et Biophys. Acta*, *7*, 520 (1951).
39. I. B. Wilson, *J. Biol. Chem.*, *190*, 111 (1951).
40. I. B. Wilson, *J. Biol. Chem.*, *199*, 113 (1952).
41. W. N. Aldridge and A. N. Davison, *Biochem. J.*, *55*, 763 (1953).
42. I. B. Wilson and E. K. Meislich, *J.A.C.S.*, *75*, 4628 (1953).
43. R. Berman, I. B. Wilson, and D. Nachmansohn, *Biochim. et Biophys. Acta*, *12*, 315 (1953).
44. M. Altamirano, W. Schleyer, C. W. Coates, and D. Nachmansohn (in press).
45. J. E. P. Toman, J. W. Woodbury, and L. A. Woodbury, *J. Neurophysiol.*, *10*, 429 (1947).

10·

Some Electrical Properties
of Large Plant Cells

L. R. Blinks *

Certain very large cells of fresh water and marine algae offer exceptional opportunities for electrochemical studies on biological systems. Both the inner fluid (sap) and outer solutions (sea water or pond water) are well characterized, and easy substitution of the normal environmental fluids can be accomplished. In some cases, the vacuolar sap can also be easily washed away and new solutions substituted (by perfusion). The protoplasm is thin and of definite surface. The cells live well in the laboratory, sometimes for days or weeks under constant experimentation.

Some of the results of these studies are summarized in the chapter by Osterhout,[1] which deals especially with the potassium effects and the calculations of relative mobilities of ions in the protoplasmic surface. The fresh-water plant *Nitella* behaves as an almost perfect potassium electrode, giving nearly the theoretical slope of 58 mv. per tenfold concentration change of KCl. The KCl gradient is here probably responsible for the normal potential. *Halicystis* and *Valonia* cells respond to potassium as well, though transiently; but they can hardly maintain their normal potential, owing to such a gradient. In *Valonia* it is the wrong direction, and in *Halicystis* the gradient can be abolished by perfusion without decreasing the potential. On the other hand, certain anion gradients appear to be important; this has led to a theory of the potential difference (P.D.) across the protoplasm of *Halicystis*, which involves low anion mobilities with a difference in the properties of the outer and vacuolar membranes in this respect. This has been summarized elsewhere.[2]

These properties are not strictly "static," insofar as they involve the diffusion of ions; nevertheless the potentials are very constant and imply a rather steady state in the protoplasm. The present chapter

* From Hopkins Marine Station, Stanford University, Palo Alto, Calif.

is concerned with somewhat more dynamic properties, which are either responsive to changes in the cell's metabolism, or can be studied only by the flow of electric current (such as resistance and capacitance). Capacitance is often not static, but more like a "polarization" capacity. Higher current densities involve directional effects, rectifications, and eventually "stimulations" and conduction, which are of a slow and primitive type in plants but are nevertheless an interesting prototype of the speedy and specialized responses in nerve.

Besides the postulated high organic anion content of the protoplasm and the experimentally demonstrated asymmetry of the two surfaces with respect to such anions, one other factor is necessary to maintain the e.m.f., which is not only large and very constant but able to drive small currents (1 to 10 μa.) for long periods without appreciable fall of the P.D. Since currents must mean actual diffusion of ions, into and out of protoplasm, the gradients should tend to disappear, both by the entrance of chloride and by the loss of organic anions. Obviously, the gradients must be maintained at the expense of energy, which can only be metabolic in origin.

RELATIONS TO METABOLISM

There may be several mechanisms linking metabolism to bioelectric effects. One is the accumulatory process, which concentrates such ions as K and Cl in the vacuole—and possibly in the protoplasm. Much remains to be learned about this, but it is clearly linked to aerobic metabolism. The organic acids of the protoplasm itself also result from metabolic activity. The maintenance of both inorganic and organic ion gradients consequently is an essential step in the production of bioelectric potentials. Should the gradients cease to exist, the P.D. would surely run down and disappear. But there are other effects (of temperature, oxygen tension, poisons, light, etc.) that occur so quickly that alterations in gradients could hardly be fast enough to account for the changes observed. Many of these rapid changes may be due to alterations of the surfaces ("membranes") across which the gradients set up diffusion potentials. This should not be surprising, since the membranes are themselves the products of metabolism, and may remain subject to metabolic influences.

EFFECTS OF LOW OXYGEN TENSION

Different genera of large plant cells differ considerably in this respect. The P.D. in *Nitella* seems scarcely affected by low oxygen:

the cell continues to produce and conduct action currents after many hours in highly purified nitrogen and hydrogen. *Valonia* is somewhat more sensitive, its P.D. falling slowly in sea water freed of oxygen and recovering quickly on aeration if this exposure has not been too long. *Halicystis*, possibly owing to its higher respiratory rate, is quite

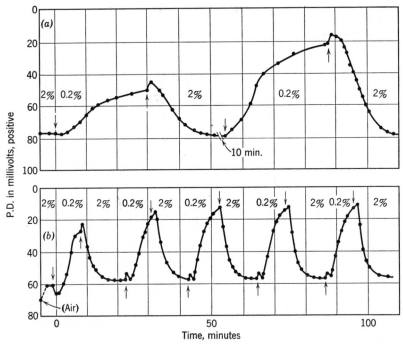

Fig. 1. Graphs showing the fall of potential in impaled cells of *Halicystis* when 0.2% O_2 is substituted for 2% O_2 (in nitrogen) and recovery when 2% O_2 is again bubbled.

sensitive to decrease of oxygen tension.[3] Bubbling sea water with 2% O_2 in N_2 just maintains the P.D. at room temperature; if this bubbling is stopped (or the temperature raised), the high positive P.D. (70–80 mv.) immediately begins to fall, as the cell consumes the remaining oxygen around it. Active bubbling with 0.2% O_2 drives the P.D. down to 5 or 10 mv. positive. Aeration gives prompt recovery, and the cycle may be repeated indefinitely (Fig. 1).

Is this effect due to a change of the *gradients* (e.g., of organic ions) or of the *surfaces* across which these gradients set up potentials? The question has been answered by substituting nitrate, formate, etc., for the chloride of the sea water outside the cells. As the P.D. fell (under low oxygen tension), so also did the response to these anion substitutions. When the P.D. was lowered to its minimum, the effect of such substitutions almost entirely disappeared, but reappeared almost immediately when the cell was aerated (Fig. 2) in proportion to the recovery of P.D. itself. (The responses to increased KCl or to

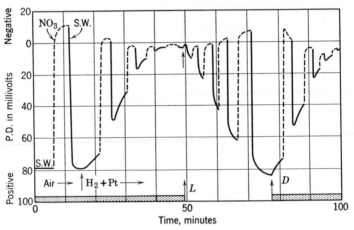

Fig. 2. Effect of substituting nitrate for chloride in an artificial sea water, and restoration of chloride (S.W.), upon the potential of *Halicystis*. The first substitution is made in the presence of air, the next four when hydrogen is bubbled through the sea water (in the presence of platinized asbestos). As O_2 is depleted, the response to the anion substitution is progressively decreased and essentially abolished. When oxygen is restored, in this case by photosynthesis in the light (*L*), the responses rapidly reappear. On darkening (*D*) they disappear again. Solid lines (S.W.), chloride; broken lines, nitrate (NO_3).

dilution of sea water are also changed under low oxygen tension but do not parallel the P.D. change as closely as do the anion responses.)

The low oxygen effect might be regarded as an incipient injury by which the cell becomes temporarily more like a dead cell, with high permeability to all ions—hence, the loss of diffusion potentials. (A dead cell also has a low P.D. and fails to respond to ionic substitutions.) However, instead of *falling* (as in a dead cell), the resistance of the cell *rises* greatly during these low oxygen exposures. The protoplasm apparently loses its ionic discrimination by becoming less instead of more permeable to the ions concerned. (Only very long anaerobic exposures produce irreversible injury, with permanent fall of P.D. and resistance.)

MECHANISM OF THE LOW OXYGEN EFFECTS

Metabolic control over the properties of the surface seems thus established, but its mechanism is not clear. Possibly the surface needs some constituent (like the "R" substance mentioned below) to keep it sensitized to the ions concerned. This may be a product of aerobic metabolism. Or, under anaerobic conditions, some new substance may be produced (e.g., alcohol, aldehyde, lactic acid, etc.) that alters the surface in some manner (cf., the action of guaiacol, hexylresorcinol, nitrobenzene, etc., see below). The effect may be due simply to an increased internal acidity (resulting from anaerobic respiration or fermentation). Rather similar depressions of P.D. (with loss of ionic discriminations) occur on exposure to penetrating weak acids, such as acetic or carbonic acid (strong acids are not as effective).

This control by *internal* acidity may be due to the inward orientation of polar, dissociating groups in the surface layer and to their linkage with the underlying (probably protein) matrix of the cytoplasm. A somewhat similar control of many electrical properties by internal acidity has been found in *Valonia* and may account for the effect of some poisons (HCN, dinitrophenol) and anesthetics. But, whatever the mechanism may be, the experimental findings show clearly why the P.D. falls under low oxygen tension. The external protoplasmic surface loses its sensitivity to external ionic changes and presumably, therefore, its sensitivity to similar ions of the protoplasm itself, whose gradients across that surface are responsible for the normal P.D. under aerobic conditions. It is probably not the gradients themselves that change rapidly but, rather, the surfaces across which they set up diffusion potentials. It seems unnecessary to introduce other hypotheses, e.g., dependence of the P.D. on internal oxidation-reduction levels (see below).

EFFECTS OF OTHER CHEMICAL AGENTS

1. *Ammonia.* Unlike penetrating weak acids (or those presumably produced in metabolism), ammonia penetrates cells readily in the undissociated form (NH_3), raising the internal pH, definitely in the sap and probably also in the cytoplasm, though this must be much better buffered. Its effect upon *Halicystis* is striking. If as little as 0.001 to 0.002 M NH_4Cl is added to sea water at pH 8.0, the original positive P.D. undergoes a characteristic change.[4] The time curve has a small initial cusp, an inflection, a more and more rapid decrease,

and finally a reversal of P.D., which is maintained, rather irregularly, at a negative value for as long as the ammonia is present—up to an hour or more (Fig. 3). When the ammonia is removed, or reduced below a threshold value, the P.D. quickly becomes positive again. This cycle may be repeated almost indefinitely without injury to the cell. The effect can also be produced at a subthreshold NH_4Cl concentration (e.g., 0.0001 M NH_4Cl) by raising the pH, and recovery

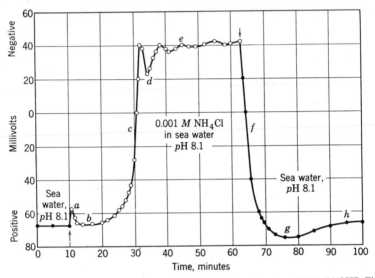

Fig. 3. Time course of potential change in *Halicystis* when 0.001 M NH_4Cl is added to the sea water (at pH 8.1). Cusp (*a*), recovery (*b*), and rapid reversal (*c*), with a characteristic cusp (*d*) and irregular negative potential (*e*) result. There is rapid recovery on restoration of sea water without ammonia.

can be achieved by lowering the pH again, which shows that the effect is due to the undissociated ammonia. (In fairly acid sea water, e.g., at pH 5, 0.1 M NH_4Cl or higher is necessary to cause reversal. Here the ammonium *ion* effect predominates, rather resembling the potassium ion, with a relatively high mobility.)

The ammonia effect may result from saponification of fatty acids in the cell surface brought about by the penetrating weak base, which is able to reach the ionizing, polar groups—presumably inwardly directed toward the protoplasm. If so, the vacuolar surface seems immune, for a large negative potential persists (Fig. 3). (This is contrary to the lowering of potential by low oxygen tension and weak acids, which probably affects both surfaces.) The reversal of P.D. can be produced just as readily by *perfusing* the vacuole with 0.002 M

NH$_4$Cl at pH 8 as by supplying it externally; here the ammonia must strike the vacuolar surface first but seems not to affect it. Under the influence of ammonia, the P.D. responds much less to anion substitutions in the sea water, indicating that the outer surface has been altered. It does, however, retain some response to increased potassium. The resistance also rises, again showing no increase but rather a decrease in ion permeability (solubility, mobility, or both).

Other weak bases (amines, pyridine, aniline, and several alkaloids) act like ammonia on *Halicystis* (including control by pH); and we assume that they all operate by the same mechanism, i.e., by the penetration of a weak base.

Ammonia has little effect upon the P.D. of *Valonia*, slightly raising the already negative P.D.; the effect is increased both by higher pH and by light. The cytoplasm of *Valonia* may be neutral or slightly alkaline so that the entering base cannot greatly change conditions; *weak acids* (as seen below) are more effective. After these have been given, ammonia counteracts their effects.

2. *Guaiacol and Cresols.* On *Valonia*, these substances have an effect opposite to that of ammonia on *Halicystis;* 0.01–0.02 M guaiacol reverses the P.D. from a low negative value to a strongly positive one (which then slowly falls toward normal again). The reason for this change is shown by making dilutions or ionic substitutions in the sea water. In the presence of guaiacol the normal large potassium effect becomes actually reversed in sign, a slightly greater positivity being produced by it instead of the usual large negativity.[5] The sodium concentration effect is also reversed, dilution of sea water producing a more positive instead of more negative P.D. The relative mobility of K (as compared to that of Cl) becomes 0.36 instead of 20; and that of Na, 4.5 instead of 0.3. These effects are reversible, normal P.D. and ionic responses returning after removal of the guaiacol. Cresol, hexylresorcinol, benzene, nitrobenzene, and aniline have also been found to produce somewhat similar effects on *Valonia*.

On *Halicystis*, guaiacol has a different effect,[6] lowering the positive P.D. somewhat, increasing the apparent mobility of Na until it surpasses Cl, but not particularly affecting the mobility of K. The effects of anion substitution have only been slightly studied in the presence of guaiacol but should prove particularly significant in view of their large effect on the P.D. of *Halicystis*. The direct-current resistance of both *Valonia* and *Halicystis* rises under guaiacol treatment, indicating a general decrease of ionic permeability.

In *Nitella*, guaiacol raises the apparent mobilities of Li, Na, Cs, and Ca while not affecting those of K, Rb, NH$_4$, or Mg.[7] The partition coefficients (protoplasm/water) of practically all the ions except K and Rb are raised, so that the "chemical" effect produced when they are substituted for K is decreased. (Thus the calculated partition ratio S_{Na}/S_K is raised from 0.0263 to 0.426 in the presence of guaiacol.) Hexylresorcinol has somewhat similar effects but acts at even lower concentrations. These effects are perhaps too great to be accounted for by altered solubilities and mobilities alone; Osterhout has suggested that charged complexes are involved. In any case, organic substances can markedly alter the response of the cell to inorganic ions.

3. *Other Weak Acids, Poisons, Stimulants, etc.* In studying the guaiacol effect, it is necessary to rule out its action merely as a weak acid; Osterhout found that other weak acids had no comparable effect over the short periods involved. But over longer periods (10–15 min. exposure) many weak acids do slowly lower and then reverse the negative P.D. of *Valonia*. Several respiratory poisons or stimulants (e.g., dinitrophenol, hydroquinone) have similar effects.

Since many of these effects can be promptly overcome by adding a low concentration of a penetrating base like ammonia (or higher concentrations of a less penetrating base such as potassium), it seems possible that they are all due to increased internal acidity. Since some of the substances inducing positivity are not themselves acidic, they may operate by inducing a higher respiratory rate, thereby increasing the CO_2 inside the cell. The respiratory rate of single *Valonia* cells was sometimes increased 50–100% by some of these treatments.

4. *Acidity and Alkalinity; Oxidation-Reduction.* This suggests a simple cause for the anomalous negative P.D. of *Valonia:* The normal respiratory rate of the cell may be too low to maintain the requisite internal acidity; but, when it is increased, the P.D. of *Valonia* becomes positive like that of most of the other plant cells. Is this effect due to the hydrogen ion gradient itself, or to alterations of the surface induced by acidity? Such alterations can be definitely shown in some cases, but the H^+ ion itself may be more important than was formerly suspected. In sea water between pH 6–pH 9.6, it has not much direct effect; but, in more acid sea waters (particularly when well stirred and well buffered), large and reversible effects begin to appear, strong acids greatly increasing the normal negative P.D. before they have time to penetrate the cell and lower or reverse the P.D. Under such treatment, however, the potassium effect and anion substitution effects become decreased, so that it is difficult to separate them from direct H^+ ion mobility effects. Conversely, although high pH has little effect in normal sea water, it increases and stabilizes the potassium effect, doing away with the transient cusps of the time curve and

delaying "desensitization." Large effects of hydroxyl ion have also been reported in *Nitella*.

Obviously, if acidity can considerably affect bioelectric properties (either via H^+ ion mobilities or alterations of the surface response to other ions), it may be an important mediator in metabolic control by factors affecting respiration and photosynthesis. Various anesthetics, as well as oxidants or reductants, may operate via changes of acidity. In *Nitella*, little effect of oxidants or reductants was found [8] when care was taken to keep the solutions well buffered, but greater effects occurred in unbuffered solutions—probably due to acidity changes when the substances were oxidized or reduced at the cell surface. Effects of certain strong oxidants on *Valonia* and *Halicystis* can perhaps be similarly attributed to acidity changes.

DEFICIENCIES

1. *Calcium.* Certain striking effects are produced by deficiencies. Calcium is an example. Salt balance or antagonism is less important in *Nitella* or *Valonia* than in *Halicystis*, where the absence of Ca, as in unbalanced NaCl, depresses the P.D., sometimes carrying it immediately to zero, sometimes to negative values.[9] The temporary reversal of sign is probably due to alteration of the outer surface before the unbalanced solution can affect the vacuolar surface; this leaves the inwardly directed, negative P.D. of the latter to display itself for some minutes before it in turn is affected by low calcium. The vacuolar surface is apparently the more resistant, for perfusion of unbalanced solutions in the vacuole does not induce the expected effect (a temporarily increased positive P.D.).

2. *Potassium.* Short exposures to potassium-free sea water affect the P.D., as might be expected, in the opposite direction to increased K content. But other changes appear later. In *Valonia*, the P.D., after remaining for a while near zero, may then suddenly reverse and become positive, just as with weak acids. The basis may be the same. If metabolic production of acids continues, without a base such as potassium entering to neutralize them, the protoplasm may become acidic. Very low concentrations of ammonia (a still more rapidly penetrating base) can prevent, or overcome, this effect. The "potassium deficiency" effect (reversal of P.D.) can also sometimes be produced by merely returning the cell to normal sea water, after long exposures to potassium-rich sea waters. Here some potassium may move out and leave the protoplasm more acid. Or the entering K

may have stimulated excess acid production, which continues for a time after its removal.

3. *Distilled Water Effects—"Leaching."* *Nitella* cells, exposed for several days to distilled water, behave alike to KCl and NaCl, or may even respond more to NaCl than to KCl.[10] The normal potassium effect is reversed, due to a change both of partition coefficients (S) and relative mobilities (U) in the protoplasmic surface. The relative mobilities become nearly equal, while the former may even be reversed from the usual preferential solubility of K to that of Na. (In normal cells the values were $U_K = 12$, $U_{Na} = 8$, and $S_{KCl}/S_{NaCl} = 60$; in the cells leached with distilled water the values became: $U_K = U_{Na} = 2.2$, and $S_{NaCl}/S_{KCl} = 8$.)

Normal behavior is restored by adding calcium, or by an extract of the distilled water in which the cells have been soaked, suggesting that something (R), which can be replaced, has been lost from the cells in the absence of calcium. This substance R (composition unknown) sensitizes the cells to potassium. R, or a substance with equivalent effect, occurs in a variety of biological materials (egg white, milk, blood, urine); guanidine, adrenalin, ephedrin, ammonia, etc., duplicate its effects. Some such substance, produced in metabolism, might be responsible for the changes produced by low oxygen tension, etc.

PHYSICAL AGENTS

Mechanical Disturbance. The potassium effect, lost through leaching may be restored by pinching the cell. This may injure the membranes enough to permit the diffusion of R from sap to protoplasm. Or it may initiate an action current (see below) that releases the substance. Mechanical disturbance probably opens small breaks in the protoplasmic surface, with loss of P.D. at that point.

Insertion of the capillary salt bridge into *Valonia* and *Halicystis* cells also produces effects. These effects seem to be due not only to the actual opening and healing of the wound around the capillary but also to a stimulation of respiration. The striking effect of hypotonic sea water upon the P.D. and resistance of *Valonia* may also be of this nature, due to the rupture of vacuolar or other surfaces of the protoplasm.

Temperature. The effects of temperature upon the P.D. have often been studied in the hope of diagnosing the controlling processes. In *Halicystic ovalis*, the large positive P.D. is very little altered over the temperature range tolerated by these cells (5–25° C.). The Q_{10} is only 1.1–1.2, indicating that a physical process such as diffusion prob-

ably controls the normal P.D. If so, the organic salt gradients postulated above as the source of P.D. are evidently well maintained over
this temperature range, even though the respiratory rate has its usual
large Q_{10} value of 2.0 or more.

However, larger temperature effects can be induced by several treatments. If the oxygen tension (see above) is lowered toward its critical
value at 15° C., then *raising* the temperature to 25° C. *depresses* the
P.D.; here the Q_{10} is less than 1.0. This is because the oxygen is now
consumed faster by the cell and anaerobic conditions set in with their
effects on P.D., already described.

Low concentrations of ammonia also sensitize *Halicystis* to temperature changes. At close to threshold concentrations of NH_4Cl, warming may cause the P.D. to decrease or reverse, and cooling to recover,
again yielding an apparent Q_{10} of less than 1.0, or even a negative
value.

Increasing the KCl content of sea water *increases* the temperature
coefficient. The Q_{10} value in *Halicystis* may become as large as 2.0 or
more when 0.1–0.2 M KCl is added to the sea water. The reason is
that whereas the potassium effect has its usual cusped time curve at
room temperature, cooling prolongs the initial cusp into a flat plateau.
This is either because KCl enters the surface less readily or the protoplasm is not as quickly desensitized to potassium at low temperatures.
Consequently the K effect endures longer.

The depression of P.D. by KCl is therefore controlled by temperature, and vice versa. The high Q_{10} induced by KCl illustrates the importance of studies with specific agents that affect the P.D. in order
to analyze the mechanism of the temperature control.

Temperature has little effect upon the P.D. changes produced by
anion substitutions (nitrate, formate, etc.). This is apparently because these ions have such a low mobility and penetrate so slowly that
their entrance or exit is little affected by changes of temperature. This
is in good agreement with the small temperature effect upon the normal
P.D., which is itself ascribed to organic anions in the protoplasm.

In *Valonia* there is a somewhat larger temperature effect [11] especially
when calculated upon the basis of the small normal P.D. (The Q_{10}
may be 1.5–2.0 or more in some temperature ranges.) No close parallel
with respiratory rate exists, for the P.D. is lowest in the range 20–
25° C., rising as the cell is warmed to 35° but *also* when it is cooled to
15° C. This curious behavior is closely paralleled by the magnitude
of the P.D. change produced by doubling, quadrupling, or halving the
KCl content of the sea water. At 25° C. the potassium effect has its
usual cusped time curve, first rising, then falling. At 15° C. the rise

is slower but the final value is higher because the cusp is prolonged into a flat plateau, much as in *Halicystis* (mentioned above).   At 35° C. it is considerably higher, because, although there is a cusp and a fall, there soon follows a later rise.

These time curves might be due to a moving KCl boundary or the desensitization to K mentioned earlier, temperature affecting the speed of either process.   Whatever the mechanism, the close parallel between

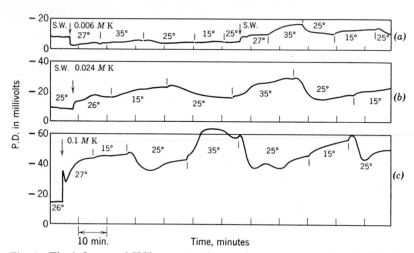

Fig. 4.   The influence of KCl concentration on the temperature effect in *Valonia*. In the presence of 0.006 M KCl, there is little or no change of potential on warming or cooling the cell between 15 and 35° C.   In sea water (KCl = 0.012 M) a larger effect appears (S.W.).   When the KCl concentration is increased to 0.024 M and 0.1 M, progressively larger effects of changing the temperatue occur.

the P.D. and the size of the potassium effect suggests that the potassium of the sea water may be responsible for the normal temperature effect in *Valonia*.   This was borne out by experiments in which cells were exposed to a low potassium sea water.   Here the P.D. was low and practically unaffected by temperature.   On the other hand, increase of KCl in sea water increased the temperature effect (Fig. 4).

   Light.   All the plant cells mentioned here have chloroplasts and display photosynthetic activity with consequent opportunity for oxygen production, CO_2 consumption, and metabolite formation.   In view of the influence of some of these factors (as mentioned in earlier sections), it is not surprising that light has important effects on bioelectric behavior.   Most of these effects are clearly photosynthetic, caused by wave lengths absorbed by chlorophyll (or by carotenoids) and not by infrared, or ultraviolet.   The time, intensity, and temperature factors are consistent with photosynthetic activity, rather than with some direct light effect upon the membrane.

The light effects are also under the control of experimental conditions. In *Halicystis* there is very little effect of illumination upon the normal positive P.D., which is augmented perhaps 5% at high light intensities. However, a variety of agents can "sensitize" the cells so

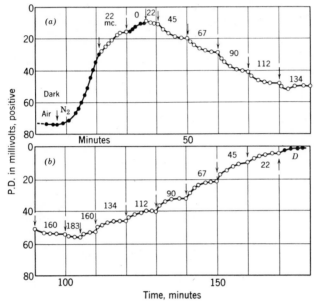

Fig. 5. The effect of light on the potential of impaled *Halicystis*. Nitrogen (N₂) is first bubbled in the dark, then lights of increasing intensity (in meter candles as indicated) are given. The potential is restored by 183 mc. to almost 60 mv.; decreasing intensities then hold it at varying levels, down to zero.

that large changes in P.D. occur on illumination.[12] An obvious treatment is low oxygen tension; normal potentials are quickly restored by light—evidently by the photosynthetic production of oxygen, which in turn restores the surface properties (Fig. 5). The extent of this recovery can be nicely regulated by the light intensity in a stepwise manner that is quite reversible.

A depression of P.D. is produced by excess CO_2 and can be overcome by light; but the extent of this change is more limited, since photosynthesis cannot greatly reduce the high concentration of CO_2 necessary to depress the P.D. to low levels.

If low concentrations of NH_4Cl are added to the sea water (too little to reverse the P.D. in the dark), illumination has a very large effect,

at first decreasing and then reversing the P.D. to negative values
(Fig. 6). This effect is evidently accomplished by reducing external
CO_2, thereby raising the pH which allows more NH_3 to enter the cell

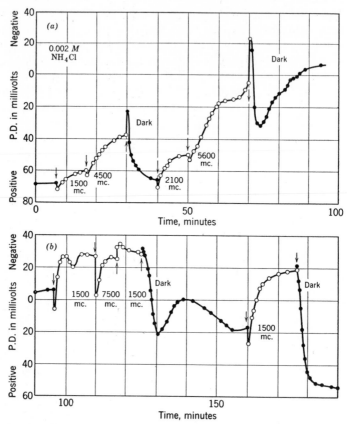

Fig. 6. The effect of light on the potential of *Halicystis* in the presence of
0.002 M NH_4Cl, which in this cell was not sufficient to reverse the potential.
Illumination with 1500 meter candles (mc.) decreases the potential; 4500 mc.
decreases it considerably more; and 5600 mc. drives it close to zero, with reversal
on darkening. Note the reverse cusps on later illuminations and darkenings.
Recovery of positive potential in the dark after 1500 mc.

and produce its effects (as already described). We may note that here
light *lowers* the P.D. instead of *raising* it, as with low O_2 tension.
    One curious anomaly, a reverse cusp in the time curve, often preced-
ing predicted trends during the first moments of illumination, has been
interpreted as an acidity gush preceding the regular alkaline trend
later developing in photosynthesis. This suggestion was confirmed by

the glass electrode method, and studies on photosynthesis indicate that a release of CO_2 precedes its consumption.

In *Valonia* the "normal" light effect is sometimes rather small, scarcely greater than in *Halicystis;* but at other times it may reach 10 or 20 mv., doubling the natural P.D. Marsh [13] ascribed this to oxygen production; but since the P.D. of *Valonia* is not altered by increased oxygen tension (above atmospheric values) it seems more likely to be due to an acidity change. Thus CO_2 depresses (or reverses) the P.D., and its effect is *overcome* by light; ammonia in low concentrations slightly raises the negative P.D., and its effect is *aided* by light. (Some cells that naturally showed a large light effect were found to have considerable ammonia in the vacuole.)

Light effects are likewise correlated with the KCl content of the sea water. When this was decreased by half (in an artificial sea water), the light effect was decreased; in K-free water it was abolished or sometimes reversed in sign. On the other hand, doubling or even quadrupling the KCl content of sea water increased the light effects (rather like Fig. 4). Conversely, in an illuminated cell, the effects of increasing the KCl content of the sea water were usually enhanced. These effects are adequately explained by the photosynthetic increase of external pH, which increases the potassium effects (see above). But internal changes may also contribute, e.g., by the manufacture of organic acids that can combine with the entering potassium.

Curiously enough, the very large effects of light that appear when one end of a *Nitella* cell has been illuminated for some time are also under the control of potassium but in the opposite manner to those in *Valonia*. The effects, amounting to a 50–80 mv. reduction of the normal potential, are greatest in pond water but become much smaller in the presence of 0.01 M KCl. (Several action potentials have the same effect.) Changing the oxygen content of the pond water has practically no influence on the effect; but increasing CO_2 to 1% decreases it, and 2% abolishes or reverses the effect. An increased alkalinity of the cytoplasm may result from light under normal conditions, which cannot occur under higher CO_2 tensions; all other effects of photosynthesis ought to be enhanced.

CURRENT FLOW

The measurements thus far discussed have been electrostatic, as far as the external circuit is concerned, although small local circuits sometimes complicate the measurements, especially in cells with two external contacts. Many other facts have been learned, however, by purposely allowing the cell to discharge its own e.m.f. or by applying larger external potentials in the same or opposite directions so that current definitely flows across the protoplasm. By this means one can determine energy output (about 1 μw.); measure resistance and capacity, induce counter-e.m.f. or polarization, and cause stimulation or breakdown.

Resistance. The living cells all display a fairly high resistance to the flow of direct current. This ranges from about 1000 ohms per square centimeter of cell surface in impaled *Halicystis*[3] through some 10,000 ohms in *Valonia*[14] to 100,000 ohms or more in *Nitella*.[15] The resistance depends on the ions present; thus potassium markedly lowers the resistance of *Nitella*, whereas nitrates, formates, etc., raise the resistance of *Halicystis*. This agrees on the whole with the relative mobilities as shown by the potential effects.

Weak acids tend to raise the resistance of *Valonia*, whereas weak bases (ammonia) tend to lower it. The natural variations of resistance, found especially in *Valonia* (the "regular" and "delayed polarization" states, are probably conditioned in this manner, since they may be experimentally altered toward either high or low resistance by treatment with weak acid or weak base. Both temperature and light possibly influence the resistance via such acidity changes. The resistance tends to rise in the dark, as CO_2 accumulates, and to fall in the light, as photosynthesis reduces it and raises the pH.

Capacity. When cells have a high resistance they also display large electrical *reactance*, giving large "transients" at both make and break of direct current.[16] These transients are in the direction corresponding to the charge and discharge of a capacity. (This effect is probably present at all times, but when shunted by low resistances it is not very apparent.) Large capacity values are found, ranging from 1–3 μf. per square centimeter of cell surface. These values would be expected if the cell surface were a very thin dielectric, acting like a static condenser. However, it often displays the capacity found at blank platinum or other electrodes in electrolyte solutions, which has been called "polarization." This effect can be shown by placing the cells in a Wheatstone bridge and balancing against resistances and a static mica condenser. Occasionally a nearly perfect balance can be made, especially with *Valonia* cells in their high resistance state; this suggests a purely static capacity. But it is often not possible to balance the cell's capacity with any single setting for the whole d-c. transient or over an a-c. frequency range. Instead both the balancing capacity and its series resistance fall off with frequency; this resembles the behavior of a polarizing platinum electrode, although the cell does not show as pronounced a change with frequency as do electrodes. It is suggested that the usual capacity of the *Valonia* cell is mainly static but has a partial polarization component.[17]

This is consistent with the idea of a thin dielectric, which nevertheless permits the passage of some ions. The different relative mobilities of the ions cause both diffusion potentials and the counter-e.m.f.'s of "polarization." The capacity, like the resistance, is subject to some experimental control. Under some conditions *Valonia* cells display a nearly static capacity. This state is favored by dark and hindered by light. It seems again conditioned by acidity. Adding CO_2 or acetic acid to the sea water renders the capacity almost strictly static, whereas ammonia (or illumination) overcomes this effect, producing deviations from a perfect balance and lowering resistance.

Weak acids increase the resistance of *Halicystis* and make it display large capacity effects; so also does low oxygen tension.

Directional Effects: "Rectification." An important condition of both resistance and capacity measurements in plant cells is the direction and density of the current used. Most of the results mentioned above were found with the smallest currents possible for measurement, often with the application of only 25–50 mv. external potential to the cell. These currents give results essentially alike for either direction across the protoplasm and for different values of applied potential.

If, however, larger currents are passed, the protoplasmic properties are *altered*. This effect is sometimes "restorative." Thus *Valonia* cells are often found in a state of low resistance to small currents in either direction.[18] They remain in this state when currents pass *outward* across the protoplasm, up to large current densities (Fig. 7a). But, if the current is reversed to pass *inward* (from sea water to sap), a sudden alteration occurs at a certain threshold of current density. The resistance rises abruptly, and large transients appear at break of current (Fig. 7b). These transients may have a time curve very different from the exponential decay curve of a static condenser. The current has actually built up a large positive P.D., which persists for a time thereafter. It also *conditions* the protoplasm so that succeeding inward current flows build up the resistance and counter-e.m.f. more quickly or at lower current densities. The resistance consequently appears greater at the anode than at the cathode.

A possible mechanism of this resistance and potential rise is that inward currents, consisting largely of the poorly mobile Na ions, sweep the more mobile K ions back into the cell, leaving the protoplasmic surface depleted. Conversely, outward currents might restore K to the protoplasm from the sap. But the same effects occur to a large extent when high potassium concentrations are added to sea water. A more likely mechanism is based on acidity. Inward current over-

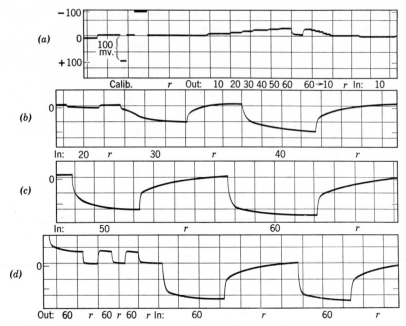

Fig. 7. Effect of current flow on the potential of *Valonia*. The small negative potential (10 mv.) is increased but slightly by currents passed outward across the protoplasm, up to 60 μa. per cm.² of cell surface. Passage of inward currents, however, causes reversal of potential to positive values, reaching 150 mv. positive during the flow of 60 μa. (*c*). In (*d*) an outward current of the same magnitude does at first produce larger polarization, which, however, decreases on repetition. The much larger effect of inward current is again shown at the end. The cell was in a bridge that balanced out resistances, allowing the potential changes to be recorded. Time marks are 1 sec. apart. *r* is the small residual current due to the cell's own potential.

comes the effects of ammonia, and produces much the same effects as weak acids (i.e., high resistance and a positive P.D.). It may actually increase the acidity at some critical locus (probably just inside the outer membrane). This effect could result from "membrane electrolysis"—a mechanism suggested long ago by Bethe and Toropoff and found by them in models.

Acidity changes due to current flow are also suggested in *Halicystis*.[19, 20] Here the P.D., already strongly positive, is not greatly influenced by fairly large inward currents; the resistance remains low, and counter-e.m.f.'s are slight. But with outward currents a threshold occurs at which the P.D. begins to fall, and, if the current is continued or increased, a sigmoid time curve results that carries the P.D. to negative values (Fig. 8). These values are maintained as long as the cur-

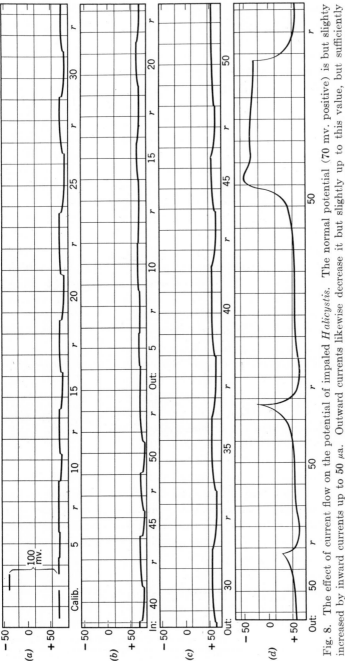

Fig. 8. The effect of current flow on the potential of impaled *Halicystis*. The normal potential (70 mv. positive) is but slightly increased by inward currents up to 50 μa. Outward currents likewise decrease it but slightly up to this value, but sufficiently long current flow (5 to 10 sec.) causes a reversal to negative values, which are maintained as long as the current flows. Recovery to positive potential occurs on reduction of current to residual value *r* (owing to discharge of cell's inherent potential). Measurements in a bridge balance out resistances. Time marks, 1 sec. apart.

rent continues to flow; positive P.D. reappears after it is stopped. The threshold, sigmoid time curve, recovery, and reversibility all resemble the effects of ammonia on this organism (Fig. 3) except that the time is measured in seconds rather than in minutes. This resemblance seems more than formal, for the two agents can assist each other; traces of ammonia greatly lower the threshold of outward current density necessary for reversal. Conversely, when the P.D. has already been reversed by ammonia alone, oppositely directed current (*inward* across the protoplasm) restores positive P.D. In this it resembles the effects of current on the natural P.D. of *Valonia*. If ammonia acts via changes of acidity in the protoplasm, then outward current seems to do the same thing, and inward current counteracts such changes.

This *Halicystis* effect closely resembles "stimulation." A positive P.D. is abolished by an outward (cathodal) current, with a threshold ("rheobase"), approximately all-or-none breakdown, prompt recovery, etc. It resembles squid "action potentials" in that the P.D. actually reverses, instead of approaching zero, probably owing to the alteration of the outer surface only, the vacuolar surface still contributing its inwardly directed potential. It differs from *Nitella* in that the current must continue to flow in order to produce reversal; the process does not normally go on to completion if the current is stopped short of reversal (though it can be made to do so if the cell is sensitized with just sufficient ammonia). There is also no recovery until the exciting current stops flowing, contrary to the situation in *Nitella* and nerve. Finally, the resistance becomes *higher* when the P.D. is reversed, not lower as at the height of most action potentials (see below); the outer surface apparently becomes *less* rather than more permeable to ions.

So far as yet known, the *Halicystis* "stimulation" does not transmit itself spontaneously along the cell from the region of cathodal "stimulation." Therefore, it cannot quite qualify as an "action current," probably because the current available from the "active" spot to neighboring regions is not high enough to stimulate them in turn. Some 25 μa. per square centimeter of surface is necessary to initiate the P.D. change in *Halicystis*. The same is true to even greater degree in *Valonia;* no evidence of a transmitted "action" exists there.

STIMULATION PHENOMENA IN *NITELLA*

Nitella cells exemplify many important aspects of stimulation phenomena: all-or-none character; conduction ordinarily without a decrement; conduction past a block or killed spot via a completed salt bridge; pacemakers, etc., as well as a decrease of resistance during the action current. The complex of phenomena represents a truly propagated impulse; it obeys many of the laws of nervous and other irritable tissues but it occurs more slowly and hence is capable of easier resolution. Whatever may be its present status in other irritable tissues, in *Nitella* the local circuit theory of transmission of the action current appears valid, a completed electrical circuit between an excited and unexcited region being adequate to excite the latter in turn, without direct structural contacts or the diffusion of substances.

Since the flow of current is apparently able to *transmit* stimulation, it is instructive to consider current flow as the initiating agent, under controlled conditions. Just as in *Valonia* and *Halicystis,* directional aspects are important. The flow of positive current inward across the protoplasm (at the anode) only serves to demonstrate the normally large resistance and capacity of the protoplasm—100,000 ohms or more resistance, and about 1 μf. capacity, per square centimeter of cell surface. Cole and Curtis,[21] using refined a-c. measurements of these quantities, essentially confirm these d-c. values. When the cell is balanced to the effective resistance, large charge and discharge curves occur at make and break of the current, owing to the capacity. With sufficiently large inward currents, breakdown eventually occurs, but potentials up to 100 or 200 mv. may be applied without injury (Fig. 9a). (Stimulation may occur at break of large inward currents.)

Outward currents (at cathode), if sufficiently small, also indicate merely the normal resistance and capacity, with charge and discharge curves, as in Fig. 9a. But the threshold for breakdown is very low, the application of 10–25 mv. sometimes sufficing to initiate stimulation. This stimulation appears as an inflection during or after the "charging" time curve (depending on the current density); the P.D. rapidly decreases from its normal 100 mv. or more positive, to zero (or close to zero) (Fig. 9b). Resemblance to the effects of outward current in *Halicystis* is striking, except that in *Nitella* the P.D. usually goes to about zero (or close to zero), not to negative values. But, whereas the reversal of P.D. in *Halicystis* only occurs if the current continues to flow, stimulation in *Nitella,* once properly initiated, goes to completion, even after the exciting current ceases. Conversely, the reversal of P.D. in *Halicystis* continues indefinitely as long as the current flows, whereas in *Nitella* recovery occurs (in 1 or 2 sec. up to 5 or 10 sec.) even though the outward current, which originally caused the stimulation, continues to flow. Two things thus distinguish the *Nitella* action potential: a "trigger action," which initiates the process at a certain threshold of current density; and a spontaneous recovery process, which occurs even if stimulation is continued. (During recovery there is first

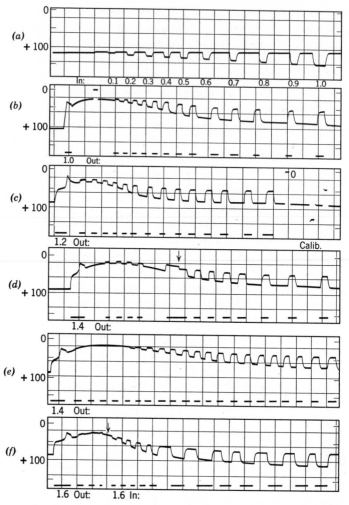

Fig. 9. Effects of current flow on potential of *Nitella*. One end of the cell has been previously chloroformed, leaving about 120 mv. at the normal end. Inward currents of 0.1 to 1 μa./cm.² were then passed (a). The potential was further increased to 150 mv. in regular charge and discharge curves. In (b) the current was reversed and passed outward across the protoplasm; a prompt stimulation occurred, the potential dropping to about 20 mv. This stimulating current was then repeated as the potential recovered; increased polarization (or "resistance") occurred, but no further stimulation. In (c), the current was increased to 1.2 μa., which produced a new stimulation and recovery; 1.4 μa. was used in (d) and (e), 1.6 μa. in (f). At the arrow in (f), the current was reversed and passed inward. Note the quicker recovery induced by these polarizations. Cell in bridge with resistance balanced to the "dead" value, which makes the polarizations appear as deflections from the base line. Time marks are 1 sec. apart; duration of current is indicated by bars.

an absolute refractory period and later a relative refractory period, the later period permitting stimulation at higher applied potentials.) The stimulating current is evidently stronger than the *normal* processes maintaining the surface but less strong than the *restorative* processes set into action by stimulation.

The mechanism of both stimulation and recovery is obscure—a sudden release and later disappearance of a substance is suggested. It is apparently not acetylcholine, which is without effect on the plant cells here reported. Metabolism is evidently involved, for respiration increases some 20 or 30% for many minutes following a single stimulation.[22] Yet anaerobic processes are effective in recovery, as shown by the continued irritability of *Nitella* when kept in purified hydrogen or nitrogen for many hours; indeed, the action current is perhaps propagated even more rapidly than in air and recovers more promptly.

Resistance. Beside the depression of P.D. at the height of the action, the d-c. resistance of the protoplasm also falls, almost, if not quite, to that of a dead cell. The transient deflections due to the high resistance of the protoplasm ("polarizability") almost disappear when the P.D. is lowest and reappear as the P.D. recovers (Fig. 9). Auger and Cotton, and Auger [23] used alternating current to follow the changes more closely, likewise finding a close correspondence between P.D. and impedance changes.

Cole and Curtis [24] further refined these measurements by using the cathode ray oscillograph to indicate the bridge unbalance during the action. With this they could distinguish between capacity and resistance changes and found that, although the resistance dropped greatly, from about 100,000 to 500 ohms/cm.^{2}, at the time of maximum P.D. change, the protoplasmic capacity only decreased about 15%. Evidently the surface is not completely disrupted; much of its condenser quality remains, but its ionic permeability becomes greatly increased.

In *Nitella* (as well as in *Halicystis*) the time curve of "action" is not a simple spike, as in nerve, but has three major parts, a spike, a partial recovery, and a later, less abrupt fall followed by recovery. This shape has been explained by Osterhout as being due to the movement of potassium ions out of the sap into the protoplasm (either by diffusion under the lowered resistance, or to electromigration in the stimulating current). The spike might occur as the ions move across Y (the vacuolar surface); the partial recovery, as they strike X (the outer surface) and the second fall, as they cross X. Recovery may be due to backward movement of these ions, possibly under the influence of the normal accumulatory process, which may be speeded up by increased metabolism (mentioned earlier). When the outer surface has been rendered insensitive to potassium, as by leaching with distilled water, the action curve is single peaked because the moving K boundary causes no change of potential when it reaches the outer surface (X). Restoration of the potassium effect (as by guanidine) restores the double-peaked action curve.

ALTERATIONS OF THE ACTION CURRENT

In addition to the single peaks caused by abolition of the potassium effect just referred to, other treatments affect its shape. Thus guaiacol greatly prolongs the action curve, giving a flat top with a sudden recovery very late in its course.[24] Somewhat the opposite effect is induced by NaCl, which causes much quicker, and often rapidly repeated, action curves; this effect is ascribed to increased conductivity of the aqueous part of the protoplasm (W), which lowers the resistance of the local circuit and permits more frequent stimulation and rapid recovery, leading to repetitive action curves often with single peaks. Guanidine also lowers the threshold and gives rise to trains of stimulation.[24] Such trains of action currents at one spot can serve as pacemakers for propagation down the cell; often the entire cell seems to follow the pace set from one spot, with many, perhaps hundreds of regular actions in a series. At other times, however, partial or complete block develops, only every second or third impulse becoming propagated; or a complete arrhythmia sets in with different regions acting independently. Simple and complex patterns may also be due to progressive loss of the potential at Y.

Auger[23] has been able to produce rapid, rhythmical impulses by applying sodium citrate, tartrate, oxalate, etc., to a spot on the cell. These agents evoke rapid small trains of potential changes, which he differentiates from the normal action potential. They tend to make the spot of application *more positive*, instead of more negative, and, therefore, can hardly initiate the normal action potential by acting as a sink into which neighboring positive sources discharge. Auger has also found rapid local variations of resistance (polarizability) at the points where these agents are applied and argues for an instability of the surface, possibly via decalcification of soaps, etc., permitting rapid breakdown under small local circuits constantly flowing between these points and nearby regions. He has found rhythmic changes of P.D. and resistance to be produced by intense constant currents under such conditions, the frequency depending upon the current density.

ELECTROÖSMOSIS

In conclusion, a few remarks may be appropriate concerning an electrochemical property that has long been of speculative interest to biologists. The movement of water is not always in response to osmotic gradients. Secretion, as in kidney or roots, often is against such gradients—a case of "active" transport. What mechanism could account for this? Almost inevitably the suggestion is made that the cell's electric potential might serve to move water by means of "electroösmosis"—the electrokinetic converse of cataphoresis. Two necessary conditions for effective electroösmosis are a system of pores (a porous membrane) and a fairly large potential or current flow. Another condition for active electroösmosis is a low salt concentration; it is not usually large at salt concentrations higher than 0.001 to 0.01 M. A priori, the biological system does not seem to supply these conditions. The potentials are small, the currents very low, and the salt concentrations usually 0.1 M—sometimes 0.5 M or higher in marine organisms. It is also a question as to whether the cell surface is porous. (Conceivably, the cellulose walls or proteinaceous interstices of cells would be effective.)

Strangely enough—as is too often true in biology—the matter has usually been left in the realm of speculation. Definite and positive results occurred with dead wood, and with rapidly killed serous membranes; hundreds of volts were applied, and many milliamperes of current passed. But living systems under biologically possible potentials and without injury to cells have been seldom studied.

Nitella lends itself admirably to such studies. Its potential and resistance are well known, and its protoplasmic streaming offers an excellent and immediate test of the state of the cell. The cells tolerate very dilute solutions (even distilled water for long periods) so that the conditions (cellulose wall and very low salt solution) are favorable for electroösmosis. Yet, applied potentials, ranging from the normal value (about 100 mv.) up to ten or 15 times normal (1.5 volts) evoke no measurable flow of water across the cells, even for long periods. If the applied potential is increased to 5 or 10 volts, an appreciable movement of water is observed, and at 20–40 volts it becomes large. This is, of course, 200–400 times the normal bioelectric potential. The effect, furthermore, often persists after the current is stopped and then slowly dies away; if the current is reversed, the flow stops entirely. Our interpretation is that the first large current injures one end of the cell (the cathodal end) abolishing its normal osmotic properties, while the anodal end pumps water osmotically across the proto-plasm to the sap (and out the other end). On reversing the current, the cell is injured at both ends, and flow of water stops.[25]

It is concluded that in *Nitella*, true electroösmosis is negligible com-pared to osmotic pumping, in the range of normal bioelectric poten-tials and currents. An artifact is produced at 10–100 times the normal values, which, however, is due to differential damage at the two ends of the cell. Electroösmosis in completely dead cells is also very low and is evoked only at currents completely unbiological in density.

It is evident that the surfaces of plant cells are the seat of many interesting phenomena, which should eventually find electrochemical explanation.

REFERENCES

1. Osterhout, this book, chapter 11.
2. L. R. Blinks, *Proc. Nat. Acad. Sci. U. S.*, *35*, 566 (1949).
3. L. R. Blinks, M. L. Darsie, and R. K. Skow, *J. Gen. Physiol.*, *22*, 255 (1938).
4. L. R. Blinks, *J. Gen. Physiol.*, *17*, 109 (1933).
5. W. J. V. Osterhout, *J. Gen. Physiol.*, *20*, 13 (1936).
6. W. J. V. Osterhout, *J. Gen. Physiol.*, *21*, 707 (1938).
7. W. J. V. Osterhout, *J. Gen. Physiol.*, *22*, 417 (1939).
8. L. R. Blinks and M. J. Pickett, *J. Gen. Physiol.*, *24*, 33 (1940).
9. L. R. Blinks, R. D. Rhodes, and G. A. McCallum, *Proc. Nat. Acad. Sci. U. S.*, *21*, 123 (1935).
10. W. J. V. Osterhout and S. E. Hill, *J. Gen. Physiol.*, *17*, 105 (1933).
11. L. R. Blinks, *J. Gen. Physiol.*, *25*, 905 (1942).
12. L. R. Blinks, *J. Gen. Physiol.*, *23*, 495 (1940).
13. G. Marsh, *Carnegie Inst. Year Books*, *34*, 89 (1935); *35*, 88 (1936); *36*, 99 (1937); *37*, 94 (1938); *38*, 228 (1939).
14. L. R. Blinks, *J. Gen. Physiol.*, *13*, 361 (1930).
15. L. R. Blinks, *J. Gen. Physiol.*, *13*, 495 (1930).
16. L. R. Blinks, *J. Gen. Physiol.*, *24*, 247 (1940).
17. L. R. Blinks, *J. Gen. Physiol.*, *19*, 673 (1936).
18. L. R. Blinks, *J. Gen. Physiol.*, *19*, 633 (1936).
19. L. R. Blinks, *J. Gen. Physiol.*, *19*, 867 (1936).
20. L. R. Blinks, *J. Gen. Physiol.*, *20*, 229 (1936).
21. K. S. Cole and H. J. Curtis, *J. Gen. Physiol.*, *21*, 189 (1937).
22. R. K. Skow and L. R. Blinks, *Collecting Net*, *15*, 205 (1940).
23. D. Auger, *L'Activité protoplasmique des cellules végétales*, 88 pp., Hermann, Paris, 1939.
24. K. S. Cole and H. J. Curtis, *J. Gen. Physiol.*, *22*, 37 (1938).
25. L. R. Blinks and R. L. Airth (in preparation).

II·

Apparent Violations of the All-or-None Law
in Relation to Potassium
in the Protoplasm

W. J. V. Osterhout *

Much may be learned about protoplasmic behavior by producing changes in the protoplasmic potentials that are everywhere present at the surfaces of living cells. In muscle and in nerve and in such plant cells as those of *Nitella* an outwardly directed electric current of suitable strength and duration causes a sudden loss of the normal potential and produces a characteristic action current. In *Nitella* this process involves the temporary loss of practically all the normal potential and the process is said to obey the all-or-none law.

In some exceptional cases the loss of potential is not complete, and an examination of these cases reveals important facts about the distribution of KCl in the protoplasm.

As a rule cells of *Nitella* lose all their potential when stimulated, and they may therefore be said to obey the all-or-none law; but cells [1] are occasionally found in which there is only a partial loss of potential on stimulation.

In *Nitella* the protoplasm forms a layer about 15 microns thick surrounding a large central vacuole filled with sap. Outside the protoplasm is the cellulose wall, which is very permeable to solutes.

At the inner surface of the protoplasm is a non-aqueous layer (Y). At the outer surface is a similar non-aqueous layer (X). The observed potential is the sum of the potential at X, i.e., P_X, and the potential at Y, i.e., P_Y. It seems possible that the inner protoplasmic surface (Y) can lose its potential (P_Y) without disturbing P_X so that the loss of potential is not complete. This involves no violation of the all-or-none law since Y loses all its potential and X loses nothing.

---

* From the Laboratories of The Rockefeller Institute for Medical Research, New York, N. Y.

The sap contains about 0.05 M KCl and 0.05 M NaCl and small amounts of other electrolytes, but the effect of KCl is so important that the other electrolytes may be neglected.[2]

Previous experiments indicate that the electrical properties of X and Y are very similar,[3] so that if KCl is present in the protoplasm its effect on the total potential may be disregarded since it will be equal and opposite on X and on Y as long as X and Y are intact.

The experiments [4] indicate that the potential at X, P_X, as well as at Y, P_Y, is due to diffusion potential of KCl across the non-aqueous layers.

Let us now consider the value of the potential (P). The experiments indicate that this is due chiefly to the diffusion potential of KCl, so that the effect of other electrolytes may be neglected. The potential may therefore be calculated by means of the Nernst equation, which for 25° C. may be written

$$P = 59 \, \frac{U - V}{U + V} \log_{10} \frac{a_s(S)}{a_o(S)}$$

where U is the mobility of K^+ and V the mobility of Cl^- in the non-aqueous layers. a_o is the activity of KCl in the external solution and a_s is its activity in the sap. S is the activity partition coefficient of KCl in the non-aqueous layers.[5]

This equation gives excellent results with *Nitella*.[1] For example, with 0.001 M KCl outside and 0.05 M KCl in the sap, if we use concentrations in place of activities, neglect any change in the concentration of incoming ions due to their combination with carrier molecules (which would be small and difficult to estimate), and if we put $U = 73$ and $V = 1$ we obtain $P = 97$ mv. which is close to the usual observed value.[6] The X layer thus acts almost like a potassium electrode, for which $(U - V)/(U + V)$ has the value of unity. The value of this expression for the X layer becomes very small when cells are leached in distilled water,[7] and the value of P_X becomes approximately zero.

The X layer thus becomes indifferent to K^+ as happens in *Chara* [8] *coronata*, Ziz. It is very interesting to find that *Nitella* can be made to act like *Chara* merely by leaching it in distilled water. The Y layer appears to act alike in both species. The distilled water appears to remove from the X layer of *Nitella* an organic substance, called, for convenience, R, since application of dilute mammalian blood after leaching at once restores the X layer to its normal condition. It would seem that the blood contains R and this substance may cause animal cells to be sensitive to K^+. It seems possible that in *Chara R* is formed in the vacuole and does not come in contact with the X layer,

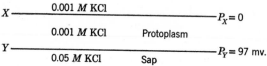

Fig. 1. The values of P_X and P_Y with 0.001 M KCl in the external solution.

which consequently is not sensitive to K^+, but the Y layer appears to behave like the Y layer in *Nitella*.

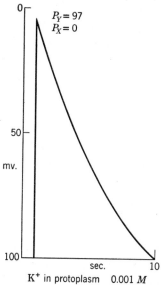

It may seem strange that an organic substance can show large potential differences between KCl and NaCl, but we know that when 1 M KCl in contact with nitrobenzene is replaced by 1 M NaCl there is a change of 67 mv. in a positive direction.[9]

Leaching does not change the total value of P so that we have, after leaching, $P = P_X + P_Y = 0 + 97 = 97$ mv. We may therefore assume that the value of P_X before leaching was zero, since if P_X had a higher value the value of P_Y would have to be less than 97 mv. in order to make the total 97 mv. and the value of P_Y would have to be increased by leaching, which seems very improbable. If the usual value of P_X in unleached cells is zero when the external solution contains 0.001 M KCl, it means that the protoplasm also contains 0.001 M KCl and, therefore, there is no diffusion potential of KCl across the X layer and consequently no potential.

The Y layer, then, has 0.001 M KCl on one side and 0.05 M KCl on the other as in Fig. 1, so that we have (using concentrations in place of activities)

Fig. 2. An action curve in a normal cell with 0.001 M KCl in the protoplasm, 0.05 M KCl in the sap, and 0.001 M KCl in the external solution. The potential at the outer surface, P_X, is zero. The potential at the inner surface, P_Y, is 97 mv. This disappears on stimulation causing an abrupt rise of the curve, which is called the "spike." As soon as the spike is completed the recovery process sets in as shown by the fall of the curve. Diagrammatic.

$$P = 59\, \frac{73 - 1}{73 + 1}\, \log_{10} \frac{0.05\ (S)}{0.001\ (S)} = 97 \text{ mv.}$$

This result is close to the usual observed value.

Let us now consider Fig. 2, which shows stimulation when the external concentration is 0.001 M KCl. We may suppose that the protoplasm contains 0.001 M KCl as stated above. Since we have 0.001 M KCl outside, there is no diffusion potential across the X layer and $P_X = 0$. If $P_Y = 97$ mv., we have, before stimulation occurs, $P = P_X + P_Y = 0 + 97 = 97$ mv. We assume that when stimulation occurs Y loses its potential so that P_Y becomes zero. P_X is already zero.

Before the rise of the curve we have 0.001 M KCl in the protoplasm and 0.05 M KCl in the sap. In the resting state the concentration of KCl in the protoplasm and in the sap remains constant because the non-aqueous layers X and Y are practically impermeable to electrolytes as shown by their very high electrical resistance.[10] When stimulation occurs the Y layer becomes permeable as shown by the decrease in electrical resistance [11] and KCl moves from the sap into the protoplasm. In consequence, P_Y disappears and the curve shows a rise of 97 mv. This part of the curve is called the spike.

As soon as the spike is completed the process of recovery begins as shown by the fall of the curve. During this process the accumulative [12] forces carry K^+ back into the sap.[13] If this process is complete it restores the cell to its previous condition with 0.001 M KCl in the protoplasm.[14] The next stimulation will then give the same result.

Let us suppose that after stimulation the process of recovery is not complete and that 0.003 M KCl remains in the protoplasm instead of the usual 0.001 M KCl. This will not alter the resting potential (P), since the extra KCl in the protoplasm will have equal and opposite effects on X and on Y and these effects will cancel out so that the potential P will depend solely on the concentration of KCl in the external solution and in the sap. Hence, although P_X and P_Y may vary, the total $P = P_X + P_Y$ will remain constant at 97 mv.

If we have 0.003 M KCl in the protoplasm, there is a diffusion potential across the X layer and the calculation (given below) shows that this potential (P_X) is 27 mv. The potential across the Y layer is 70 mv. When stimulation occurs we assume that P_Y disappears but P_X remains unaltered. We therefore have the curve shown at A in Fig. 3; at B, with 0.007 M KCl in the protoplasm as in Fig. 2, we have: $P_X = 48$ mv. and $P_Y = 49$ mv.

We may suppose that when stimulation occurs at A (Fig. 3) P_Y disappears leaving P_X intact and that the same thing happens at B. Hence, the loss of potential is not complete, but this need not be regarded as a violation of the all-or-none law since we may assume that the Y layer loses everything but the X layer loses nothing. Hence, if there is a loss in any layer, the loss is always complete in that layer.

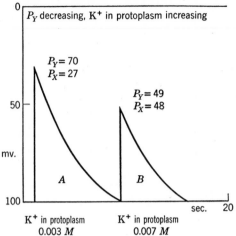

Fig. 3. The effect of successive stimulations in a cell with 0.001 M KCl in the external solution and 0.05 M KCl in the sap. When stimulation occurs at A the protoplasm contains 0.003 M KCl. The potential at the outer protoplasmic surface (P_X) is 27 mv. The potential at the inner protoplasmic surface (P_Y) is 70 mv. This potential disappears, with the result that the curve rises abruptly, but the spike is only 70 mv. because the potential at the outer protoplasmic surface (P_X) does not disappear. When stimulation occurs at B the protoplasm contains 0.007 M KCl. The potential at the outer protoplasmic surface (P_X) is 48 mv. The potential at the inner protoplasmic surface (P_Y) is 49 mv. On stimulation, the curve rises abruptly, but the spike is only 49 mv. because P_X does not disappear. At A and at B the spike is less than 97 mv., but this is not in violation of the all-or-none law because the inner protoplasmic layer Y loses all its potential (P_Y) but the outer protoplasmic layer (X) loses nothing, as shown by the fact that the potential (P_X) at this layer remains intact. Diagrammatic.

If the protoplasm after recovery contains 0.003 M KCl we have:

$$P_Y = 59 \, \frac{73 - 1}{73 + 1} \, \log_{10} \frac{0.05}{0.003} = 70 \text{ mv.}$$

This is the condition when the cell is stimulated at A, Fig. 3, and the protoplasm contains 0.003 M KCl. Since the figure shows that the total potential $P = P_X + P_Y = 97$ mv., it is evident that if $P_Y = 70$ mv. P_X must equal $97 - 70 = 27$ mv.

We suppose that when stimulation occurs at A, Fig. 3, the Y layer becomes permeable and P_Y falls to zero so that the height of the spike is 70 mv., but the X layer does not become permeable and P_X does not change but remains at 27 mv.

When the protoplasm contains 0.007 M KCl we have for the potential across the Y layer

$$P_Y = 59 \frac{73 - 1}{73 + 1} \log_{10} \frac{0.05}{0.007} = 49 \text{ mv.}$$

This is the condition when stimulation occurs at B, Fig. 3. Since the total potential $P = P_X + P_Y = 97$ mv. and $P_Y = 49$ mv., it is evident that $P_X = 97 - 49 = 48$ mv.

When stimulation occurs at B, Y loses all its potential, but X remains unaltered so that the curve rises only 49 mv.; but this does not constitute a violation of the all-or-none law since the Y layer loses all its potential but the X layer loses nothing.

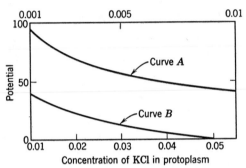

Fig. 4. The relation between the height of the spike (ordinates) and the molar concentration of KCl in the protoplasm (abscissas), when the external solution contains 0.001 M KCl and the sap contains 0.05 M KCl. The scale of abscissas for curve A is at the top; for curve B it is at the bottom. The curve is drawn free-hand to give approximate values.

On this basis we may say that with 0.001 M KCl in the external solution and 0.05 M KCl in the sap the height of the spike depends on the concentration of KCl in the protoplasm and may be ascertained by using the curve shown in Fig. 4.

As already stated, the electrical resistance of the surface layers X and Y is very high and this resistance largely disappears in normal cells during stimulation. We may suppose that this does not happen to the X layer in cells containing relatively high concentrations of KCl in the protoplasm, in which the outer protoplasmic layer does not become permeable during stimulation so that the potential of this layer remains intact, as in Fig. 3. It seems possible that the outer surface layer is stabilized by the higher concentration of KCl in the protoplasm. We need measurements to determine whether the electrical resistance and behavior in polarizing current of the X layer remain unaltered during stimulation in such cases. These determinations may be difficult as such cells are not often met with.

Stimulation in the Y layer is produced by a propagated electrical disturbance that travels along the cell in this layer. If no stimulation occurs in the X layer, we may suppose that no propagated electrical disturbance occurs in this layer.

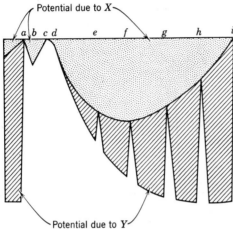

Fig. 5. Hypothetical diagram of the distribution of potential in the protoplasm, which is supposed to consist of an aqueous portion bounded by two very thin non-aqueous layers (X, at the outer surface, and Y, at the inner surface). When stimulation occurs, Y loses its potential and this produces the sudden rise (spike) of the action curve at a. Potassium moves outward and on reaching X sets up some potential (b), which disappears when the potassium reaches the outside of X (at c). The process of recovery now sets in, and potassium moves back into the sap, decreasing the potassium outside of X and increasing it inside of X, thus increasing the potential across X. As potassium continues to move inward its concentration just inside X decreases and the potential across X decreases. Hence the potential due to X first increases and then decreases. When stimulation occurs during recovery, Y loses its potential but X does not. Hence, there is no response at d, and the responses at e, f, g, and h are incomplete but increase as recovery proceeds because the potential at Y increases. At i the response becomes complete.

The idea that the value of P_X may remain unaltered when the value of P_Y disappears is confirmed by experiments in which the cell is stimulated while the process of recovery is still going on.[15]

Figure 5 shows that when stimulation occurs the potential at Y disappears and the action curve rises.[16] In this case the external solution contained 0.005 M NaCl + 0.0025 M CaCl$_2$. When stimulation occurred K$^+$ came out of the cell; and during recovery the accumulative forces moved it back into the outer region of the protoplasm so that the value of P_X increased but as these forces carried K$^+$ from the protoplasm into the sap the concentration of K^+ in the protoplasm fell off and the value of P_X diminished, as shown in the figure. In consequence, the spike, which was small at first, became gradually larger and finally reached full value.[17] During the process of recovery the value of P_X first increased and then decreased; but each time P_Y disappeared as the result of stimulation P_X remained intact.

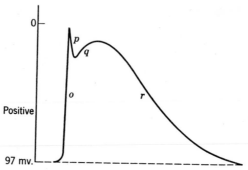

Fig. 6. The broken line shows the potential in the resting state, before the outward movement of potassium begins. The unbroken line shows changes in potential during the action current. The o movement shows a loss of potential as the Y layer becomes permeable and K^+ comes out into the protoplasm; the p movement shows a gain in potential as the K^+, moving outward through the Y layer, comes in contact with the outer surface X; the q movement shows a loss of potential as K^+ diffuses outward through the X layer, which has now become permeable; the r movement shows a gain in potential as K^+ is carried back into the vacuole by the accumulative forces during the process of recovery. The duration of the action current is usually about 15 sec. The rate of transmission is of the order of 2 to 20 cm. per sec.

The outward movement of K^+ during stimulation may produce an action curve [18] of the type shown in Fig. 6. As K^+ moves out of the sap into the protoplasm and comes in contact with the X layer it sets up an outwardly directed potential that causes the action curve to fall at p; but as K^+ diffuses through the X layer (now become permeable) into the external solution free from K^+ the outwardly directed potential falls off and the curve rises at q to zero. This gives a double peak.

The downward movement of the curve at p would not be expected if the outer protoplasmic layer X were not sensitive to the action of K^+. This expectation is realized in leached cells of *Nitella* [19] and in normal cells of *Chara coronata* Ziz.[20] In cells of *Chara* [21] that have been made sensitive to K^+ by treatment with guanidine, we have the downward movement of p because X is sensitive to K^+.

It is very interesting to find that *Nitella* can be made to act like *Chara* and vice versa. Both reactions are reversible.

A single peak may occur in *Nitella* [22] even when the X layer is sensitive to K^+ as is seen in Fig. 4. This situation is favored by the presence of KCl in the external solution and by a relatively rapid breakdown of the X layer.

We may ask why stimulation in *Nitella* is sudden and complete and obeys the all-or-none law. This would be expected if stimulation were due to a rupture of the non-aqueous layers. We have no positive evidence that such a rupture occurs, but we may consider the following facts. A stimulation is readily produced by a mechanical disturbance of the surface layers,[23] which might cause a rupture. In electrical stimulation 100 mv. or more is suddenly applied across a non-aqueous layer less than half a micron in thickness, and it may be asked if this can cause a rupture. In chemical stimulation when the resting potential at any point is suddenly reduced to zero by applying a solution of KCl, so that this point becomes an electrical sink and a neighboring region acts as an electrical source and discharges into it, the electrical pressure at the point of discharge amounts to about 100 mv. Therefore, the situation is similar to that in which 100 mv. is applied from an external source, which is usually enough to stimulate. The response is very sudden, and the electrical resistance falls to a very low value as would be expected in rupture; but there is not much change in electrical capacity and this would also be expected if rupture occurred.

In the giant axon of the squid there are other phenomena that cannot be explained as a result of a rupture but which might be the result of other changes taking place after a rupture has occurred.

In discussing potentials in *Nitella* it has been assumed that the chain

Sap / X layer / Protoplasm / Y layer / Sap [24]

will give little or no potential, which is in agreement with experimental results.

This indicates that X and Y have similar electrical properties. Let us suppose that we eliminate the protoplasm and cause X and Y to fuse together into one layer that we shall call XY. We should then find that the chain Sap / XY layer / Sap would give no potential. This would also apply to the chain Sap / X layer / Sap and to the chain Sap / Y layer / Sap. We may therefore regard the X layer and the Y layer as symmetrical.

There is evidence to show that asymmetrical layers are found in living protoplasm.

Let us now consider the situation in certain marine plant cells that resemble *Nitella* in having a large central vacuole surrounded by a thin layer of protoplasm. We find [25] that in *Valonia macrophysa* Kütz the chain Sap / Protoplasm / Sap gives an inwardly directed potential of 20–80 mv. This indicates that X and Y are unlike in their behavior and that one or both surfaces might have electrical asymmetry, since we obtain a potential with identical solutions on both sides of the protoplasm.

Francis [26] found that when crushed frog muscle was applied to the outside of living muscle there was an inwardly directed potential of 10–20 mv. In view of these facts, the observations of Shedlovsky [27] are very important. He finds that a single asymmetrical membrane may give potentials up to 300 mv. This membrane consists of thin glass, to one side of which is fused a layer of lauric acid. The membrane separates two identical solutions of buffered $BaCl_2$. On one side of the membrane the solid lauric acid reacts with the barium in the solution to form insoluble barium laurate, and as a result a potential difference between the two solutions is created that may amount to 300 mv.

Since the protoplasm may act like a hydrogen electrode and thus behave like the glass membrane in the model, it may be asked whether in some cases a potential may be produced as in the model described by Shedlovsky.

SUMMARY

The protoplasm of *Nitella* forms a thin layer surrounding a large central vacuole filled with sap. At the inner surface of the protoplasm there is a non-aqueous layer called Y, and at the outer surface there is a similar layer called X. At each of these layers there is a potential due to the diffusion of KCl in contact with the layer. We thus have $P = P_X + P_Y$; where P is the total potential, P_X is the potential at X, and P_Y the potential at Y. We assume that when stimulation occurs P_Y disappears and P_X remains unaltered. The loss of part of the potential, therefore, involves no violation of the all-or-none law since the Y layer loses all of its potential and the X layer loses nothing.

If the concentration of KCl in the external solution and in the sap is known, the concentration in the protoplasm can be calculated at each stimulation by measuring the height of the spike.

REFERENCES AND NOTES

1. The experiments were performed on *Nitella flexilis*, Ag., using the technique employed in former papers [*cf*. S. E. Hill and W. J. V. Osterhout, *J. Gen. Physiol.*, *21*, 541 (1938)]. Temperature was 20–25° C. The cells were freed from neighboring cells and kept for 30 days or more at $15 \pm 1°$ C. in solution A [*cf*. W. J. V. Osterhout and S. E. Hill, *J. Gen. Physiol.*, *17*, 87 (1933)]. It may be added that the cells are quite variable and in order to avoid confusion the presentation has adhered in general to the more typical behavior.

2. W. J. V. Osterhout, *J. Gen. Physiol.*, *13*, 715 (1930).

3. W. J. V. Osterhout and E. S. Harris, *J. Gen. Physiol.*, *11*, 391 (1928); L. R. Blinks, *Proc. Nat. Acad. Sci. U. S.*, *35*, 566 (1949).

4. S. E. Hill and W. J. V. Osterhout, *J. Gen. Physiol.*, *21*, 541 (1938).

5. We assume for convenience that the value of S is the same at each surface of these layers, but this is not necessarily true. See M. Irwin, *Proc. Soc. Exp. Biol. and Med.*, *25*, 127 (1927); H. Davson and J. F. Danielli, *The Permeability of Natural Membranes*, Cambridge Univ. Press, 1943. The value of S is independent of the concentration of KCl.

6. W. J. V. Osterhout, *J. Gen. Physiol.*, *13*, 715 (1930); *Proc. Nat. Acad. Sci. U. S.*, *35*, 548 (1949).

7. W. J. V. Osterhout and S. E. Hill, *J. Gen. Physiol.*, *17*, 105 (1933); *23*, 743 (1940). W. J. V. Osterhout, *J. Gen. Physiol.*, *18*, 987 (1935); *19*, 423 (1936). S. E. Hill and W. J. V. Osterhout, *J. Gen. Physiol.*, *22*, 107 (1938). W. J. V. Osterhout and S. E. Hill, *Proc. Nat. Acad. Sci. U. S.*, *24*, 427 (1938).

8. W. J. V. Osterhout, *J. Gen. Physiol.*, *18*, 215 (1934); *27*, 91 (1943). W. J. V. Osterhout and S. E. Hill, *J. Gen. Physiol.*, *23*, 743 (1940).

9. W. J. V. Osterhout, *J. Gen. Physiol.*, *27*, 91 (1943).

10. L. R. Blinks, *J. Gen. Physiol.*, *13*, 495 (1930); H. G. Curtis and K. S. Cole, *J. Gen. Physiol.*, *21*, 189 (1937).

11. L. R. Blinks, *J. Gen. Physiol.*, *20*, 229 (1936); K. S. Cole and H. G. Curtis, *J. Gen. Physiol.*, *22*, 37 (1938).

12. W. J. V. Osterhout, *J. Gen. Physiol.*, *35*, 579 (1952).

13. The volume of the sap is so large that the concentration of KCl in the sap may be regarded as practically constant since it will be very little affected by the small amounts of KCl moving into the protoplasm.

14. W. J. V. Osterhout and S. E. Hill, *J. Gen. Physiol.*, *23*, 743 (1940). In some cases the potential at the end of the recovery period is temporarily somewhat higher than it was just before stimulation occurred. This is known as positive after-potential. Regarding positive after-potential in nerve cells see H. S. Gasser, *Amer. J. Physiol.*, *117*, 113 (1936). See also H. S. Gasser, in: *Electrical Signs of Nervous Activity*, Univ. Pennsylvania Press, Phila., 1937.

15. W. J. V. Osterhout, *J. Gen. Physiol.*, *27*, 61 (1943). During recovery the concentration of K^+ in the protoplasm is not the same at both surfaces so that the value of $P_X + P_Y$ is not constant.

16. W. J. V. Osterhout, *J. Gen. Physiol.*, *27*, 61 (1943).

17. Under certain conditions P_X may first decrease and then increase. W. J. V. Osterhout, *J. Gen. Physiol.*, *30*, 47 (1946).

18. W. J. V. Osterhout, *Physiol. Rev.*, *16*, 216 (1936).

19. W. J. V. Osterhout and S. E. Hill, *J. Gen. Physiol.*, *23*, 743 (1940).

20. W. J. V. Osterhout, *J. Gen. Physiol.*, *18*, 215 (1934).
21. W. J. V. Osterhout and S. E. Hill, *J. Gen. Physiol.*, *24*, 9 (1940).
22. See: K. S. Cole and H. J. Curtis, *J. Gen. Physiol.*, *22*, 37 (1938).
23. W. J. V. Osterhout and S. E. Hill, *J. Gen. Physiol.*, *14*, 611 (1931).
24. W. J. V. Osterhout and E. S. Harris, *J. Gen. Physiol.*, *11*, 391 (1928); L. R. Blinks, *Proc. Nat. Acad. Sci. U. S.*, *35*, 566 (1949).
25. E. B. Damon, *J. Gen. Physiol.*, *15*, 525 (1932).
26. W. L. Francis, *Proc. Roy. Soc.* (London), *122 B*, 140 (1937).
27. T. Shedlovsky, *Cold Spring Harbor Symposia Quant. Biol.*, *17*, 97 (1952); *Natl. Bur. Standards (U. S.) Circ.* 524 (1953).

12.

Diffusion in Liquids and
the Stokes-Einstein Relation

L. G. LONGSWORTH *

Diffusion is an irreversible transport phenomenon that plays an important role in many vital processes. Although diffusion in, and through, membranes is probably the most important aspect of this phenomenon in biological systems, a thorough understanding of the process in a single phase is a necessary prerequisite to the more complex problem. Although not very descriptive, it is formally correct to say that diffusion in liquids is the movement of dissolved particles in a thermodynamic potential field just as electrophoresis is the movement of ions in an electric field. In either case the velocity of the particle in unit field is its mobility; and, at infinite dilution, at least, this mobility is independent of the nature of the field. Diffusion measurements thus permit the evaluation of the mobilities of uncharged molecules as well as ions.

The author's work on diffusion began several years ago in an effort to provide precise data on proteins for combination with the sedimentation constant, as obtained in the ultracentrifuge, and the partial specific volume to give a molecular weight. The goal was a precision of 0.1% in the diffusion coefficient. Several false starts were made, both in the selection of a method for following the concentration changes that occur in diffusion and in cell design. A satisfactory cell for small volumes has not yet been found. Moreover, it was soon learned that few, if any, proteins are sufficiently pure and well characterized to serve as test materials in the development of an adequate procedure for diffusion measurements. Consequently, most of the results to be considered in this report refer to relatively small molecules.

* From the Laboratories of the Rockefeller Institute for Medical Research, New York, N. Y.

225

The purpose of this report is to describe briefly the diffusion process in dilute solutions, followed by an outline of the experimental method used by the author. The results obtained with the aid of this method will then be combined with recent work of others in a correlation of the diffusion coefficient with other properties of the molecule and the solvent. In this correlation the Stokes-Einstein relation will serve as a guide.

THE DIFFUSION PROCESS

At about the same time that Einstein developed the special relativity theory he also showed [1] that diffusion in liquids is a result of the Brownian movement of the particles. In ideal diffusion there is no preferred direction for this movement, the particle being as likely to move into a region where its concentration is high as into one where it is low. In a diffusing boundary between a solution below and the solvent above there are, however, more solute particles per unit volume immediately below a given horizontal plane than above. Thus the random Brownian movement carries a larger number of particles upward through this plane than simultaneously across it against the gradient in the other direction.

Since the chemical potential μ of a solute depends upon its concentration, it is permissible to say that the gradient $d\mu/dx$ of this potential represents a force that imparts a velocity v to the diffusing substance.

$$v = -u \, d\mu/dx$$

Here the proportionality factor u is the velocity in unit field, i.e., the mobility, and the minus sign indicates that the movement is down the gradient. If the particles are charged, Nernst [2] showed that the mobility has the same value at infinite dilution as in an electric field. It also has the same value in a gravitational field, although the ultracentrifuge workers use the reciprocal of the mobility and call it a friction coefficient.

The flow of solute is the product of the concentration and the velocity,

$$\phi = cv = -cu \, d\mu/dx$$

Since the relation between chemical potential and concentration is

$$\mu = \mu_0 + RT \ln fc$$

so that

$$\frac{d\mu}{dx} = \frac{RT}{c} \left(1 + \frac{d \ln f}{d \ln c}\right) \frac{dc}{dx}$$

and

$$\phi = -RTu \left(1 + \frac{d \ln f}{d \ln c} \right) \frac{dc}{dx}$$

Some fifty years before Einstein's work, Fick [3] found experimentally that the flow was proportional to the difference in concentration,

$$\phi = -D \frac{dc}{dx}$$

and defined the proportionality factor D as the diffusion coefficient. Comparison of these relations gives

$$D = RTu \left(1 + \frac{d \ln f}{d \ln c} \right)$$

In real solutions this coefficient may thus vary with the concentration either as a result of the concentration dependence of the mobility u or the activity coefficient f or both.

In the year following Fick's discovery of the "law" bearing his name, Stokes [4] solved the hydrodynamic problem of the force on a spherical particle of radius r past which a fluid continuum is streaming with a velocity v. The relation is

$$\text{Force} = 6\pi\eta r v$$

where η is the viscosity of the liquid. Some fifty years elapsed, however, before Sutherland [5] and Einstein [1] applied this result to diffusion, obtaining

$$D = kT/6\pi\eta r \tag{1}$$

This has come to be known as the Stokes-Einstein relation. In 1936 it was extended by Francis Perrin [6] to include ellipsoidal particles. The treatment of the fluid as a continuum implies that for the relation to be valid the diffusing particles must be large in comparison with the molecules of the solvent. Moreover, since the theory allows for no interaction between the diffusing particles, the D to be used in equation 1 is the limiting value at zero concentration. Although the concentration dependence of the diffusion coefficient is an interesting and important subject, this report is restricted largely to results obtained in dilute solutions. Values will be extrapolated to zero concentration only if failure to do so would invalidate the conclusions.

DIFFUSION MEASUREMENTS WITH RAYLEIGH FRINGES

The method employed [7] has been that of free diffusion from an initially sharp boundary between solution and solvent, the spreading of the boundary with time being followed optically with the aid of Rayleigh interference fringes. As a diffusion cell the Tiselius electrophoresis cell, modified by addition of the windows as shown at W in Fig. 1, has been used. The boundary is first formed at a by sliding the bottom section into the position shown, after which liquid is withdrawn slowly through the capillary siphon b. This causes the boundary to rise in the channel; but as it does, it becomes blurred. However, when it reaches the tip of the capillary, both solution and solvent begin to enter and the boundary again becomes sharp at this level. Siphoning is continued for a time after all solvent has been rinsed out of the bottom half of the channel, and the boundary is in a steady state as shown by photographs taken during this interval. At zero time the sharpening flow is stopped, the capillary is removed, and additional photographs are then taken at increasing intervals as diffusion proceeds.

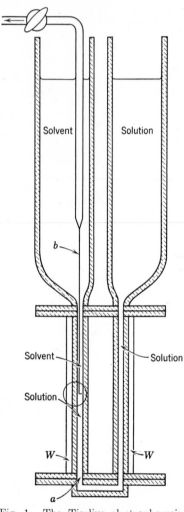

Fig. 1. The Tiselius electrophoresis cell as modified for diffusion measurements.

In Fig. 2 the photograph (a) is one taken during sharpening of the boundary whereas (b) and (c) were recorded after diffusion for the intervals indicated. The set of vertical fringes on the right in each pattern represents an invariant set that aids in the alignment of the photograph in the comparator. Since the vertical coordinates of these patterns represent heights in the channel, fringes conjugate to a homogeneous column of fluid are vertical, whereas those conjugate to the boundary, where the refractive index changes with the height, are bent into overlapping segments of the curve of this index versus height. From the levels H at which these diagonal fringes intersect a vertical, together with their total number J and the time, a diffusion coefficient is computed. The time to be used is the recorded value t plus a small constant increment Δt that corrects for the fact that the boundary is not infinitely sharp at the instant the siphoning flow is stopped. For example, in a of Fig. 2 the separation of the first and forty-ninth fringe is 0.32 mm. This is the separation that these two

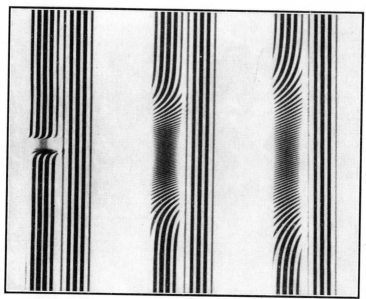

Fig. 2. Rayleigh interference-fringe photographs of the boundary between H_2O and 0.75% levulose during sharpening (a) and after diffusion for 900 sec. (b) and 1800 sec. (c).

fringes would have after the diffusion of an infinitely sharp boundary for 10 sec. Thus 10 sec. is the increment Δt that must be added to all recorded times to allow for the finite thickness of this particular boundary at zero time.

The precision of the measurements increases somewhat with the number of diagonal fringes, i.e., with the difference of refractive index Δn between the solution and solvent. The relation is

$$J = a\, \Delta n/\lambda$$

where a is the cell thickness and λ the wavelength of the mono-chromatic light that is used. The integral part of J is obtained by counting the diagonal fringes in a diffusion photograph, whereas the fractional part is obtained as follows. In Fig. 2a it will be noted that the vertical fringes conjugate to the solution below the boundary are not in line with those above that are conjugate to the solvent. The ratio of this lateral displacement of the vertical fringes to their separation is the fractional part of J. If D is to be accurate to 0.1% and $J \simeq 50$ the fractional part of J must be known to within 0.02 of a fringe. In Fig. 2, $J = 50.52$.

Most of my work refers to fifty-fringe patterns. In the Tiselius cell this corresponds to a 0.6% solution of an amino acid or a 0.75% solution of a sugar. In this case the position of every other diagonal fringe is determined with the aid of a comparator and, as shown for a typical pattern in column 3 of Table 1, the separation of the second and twenty-sixth, the fourth and twenty-eighth, etc. . . . , fringes computed. Since J is known, the separations that these fringes would have in the time-independent coordinates of the Gauss error integral may be computed [7] and are entered in column 4 of Table 1. This integral is the solution of the equation for free diffusion

TABLE 1.   TREATMENT OF FRINGE DATA, PATTERN OF 0.75% LEVULOSE
AFTER DIFFUSION FOR 13,003 SEC. AT 1°

1 j_k	2 j_l	3 $\Delta H = H_l - H_k$ cm.	4 $\Delta h/(4Dt)^{1/2}$ $J = 50.52$	5 $(4Dt)^{1/2}\Delta H/\Delta h$
2	26	0.5296	1.2673	0.4179
4	28	0.4566	1.0939	0.4174
6	30	0.4182	1.0031	0.4169
8	32	0.3962	0.9490	0.4175
10	34	0.3828	0.9172	0.4174
12	36	0.3770	0.9017	0.4181
14	38	0.3755	0.9000	0.4172
16	40	0.3797	0.9118	0.4164
18	42	0.3913	0.9390	0.4167
20	44	0.4117	0.9864	0.4174
22	46	0.4441	1.0654	0.4168
24	48	0.5037	1.2081	0.4169
				Av. 0.4172$_2$

$4(\Delta H/\Delta h)^2 = 4.140$; $Dt = 0.042047$; D(uncorr.) $= 3.234 \times 10^{-6}$; $\Delta H/\Delta h =$ camera magnification.

when the coefficient is a constant. Consequently if the ratios, column 5, of the entries in columns 3 and 4 are constant the boundary is "Gaussian" and a diffusion coefficient may be computed from this constant ratio.

NON-GAUSSIAN BOUNDARIES

If the boundary is not strictly Gaussian, the diffusion coefficient obtained as just outlined is a mean value. It is of interest, then, to see if the levulose boundary of Fig. 2 is accurately Gaussian. A non-Gaussian boundary results if the diffusion coefficient is concentration dependent and also if impurities are present. In the case of levulose there is no reason to suspect impurities and the ratios of column 5, Table 1, are about as constant as is ever observed. All diffusion coefficients are, however, more or less concentration dependent, and from

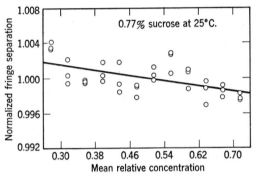

Fig. 3.   Effect on the fringe separation of a variation of the diffusion coefficient with the concentration in an aqueous sucrose–H_2O boundary.

results on other sugars there is reason to think that D decreases about 1% over the concentration interval across the boundary. In Table 1 it will be noted that 5 of the 6 ratios from the solvent half of the boundary exceed the average value whereas the converse is true for the solution half. By averaging the results for several exposures, in order to minimize the effect of random errors, it may be shown that this drift is real and affords a measure of the change in D with the concentration.

In the deviation plot, Fig. 3, sucrose has been taken as the example instead of levulose, since the concentration dependence of D as obtained from the skewness of the boundary may then be compared with the results of Gosting and Morris.[8] Here the ratio of the observed fringe separation to the Gauss value has been "normalized," by division by the average in order to eliminate time as a variable, and the result for several exposures has been plotted as ordinates against the concentration in the boundary, i.e., $(j_k + j_l)/2J$, cf. Table 1, as abscissa. The scatter of the points for a given pair of fringes corresponds to an uncertainty of 2–4 microns in their location. If the boundary were Gaussian, the scatter would be uniform about a horizontal line at unity. However, least-squares treatment of the data gives the line drawn in the figure, and its slope corresponds to a decrease of 0.9% in the diffusion coefficient on passage through the boundary from solution to solvent. The value obtained independently from a plot of the mean diffusion coefficients for several concentration intervals [8] is 1.1%.

A similar plot for an HDO-H_2O boundary at 25° is shown in Fig. 4 and indicates a decrease of 5.4% in the diffusion coefficient. Average values of D have also been obtained by the author for several concentrations of deuterium oxide, and the results, at both 1 and 25° C., are given in Fig. 5. The slope of the line at 25° C. corresponds to a change of 4.6% in D across the boundary represented by Fig. 4.

Although fairly high concentrations of D_2O must be used to obtain a reasonable number of fringes, the data of Fig. 5 indicate that the extrapolation to $N_{D_2O} = 0$ is unambiguous. Insofar as HDO is kinetically indistinguishable from H_2O, the extrapolated values represent the self diffusion of liquid water at the two temperatures. Although these values, 22.61 and 11.28 $\times$ 10^{-6}, respectively, are somewhat less than the tracer results [9] the difference is probably near the limit of error of that technique. The agreement as to the effect of temperature is quite satisfactory.

When the Rayleigh fringe photographs were first analyzed, the theory for skew boundaries was not available,[10, 11] with the result that deviations of the type shown in Figs. 3 and 4 were ignored and only an average value for the diffusion coefficient obtained. It has been a source of satisfaction to go back over the data and find that the deviations afforded additional important information. Before the introduction of the interference methods, the skewness of the sucrose boundary, for example, and probably even that of the HDO boundary, would have been lost completely in the experimental uncertainty.

The other type of departure from the Gaussian distribution is that introduced by impurities. Here, each solute is assumed to diffuse ideally and give a Gauss curve, but the camera sees only the sum of these. Now, the sum of two or more Gauss curves is not a Gauss curve; but, unless the impurity is present to a considerable extent or has a diffusion coefficient appreciably different from that of the main component, the sum is virtually indistinguishable from a Gauss curve.[12] Thus a diffusion measurement is of limited value for the detection of impurities, although if the amount and diffusion coefficient of the impurity are known adequate correction can be made.[13]

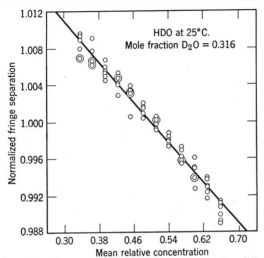

Fig. 4. Effect on the fringe separation of a variation of the diffusion coefficient
with the concentration in an HDO–H₂O boundary.

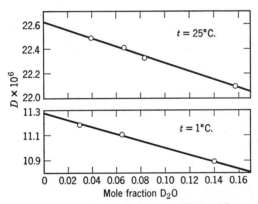

Fig. 5. Variation of the diffusion coefficient of HDO with concentration at 1
and 25° C.

Figure 6 affords an idea of how the symmetrical, but non-Gaussian, boundary differs from one that is skew. Glucose diffuses about $1\frac{1}{2}$ times as fast as raffinose, and in the experiment represented by Fig. 6 each was present in the solution at such a concentration as to contribute twenty-five fringes to the pattern. If the Gauss curve for each solute is computed and the sum is plotted on any reasonable scale, the sum does not deviate from a Gauss curve by more than the width of a pencil line except near the edges of the boundary that are experi-

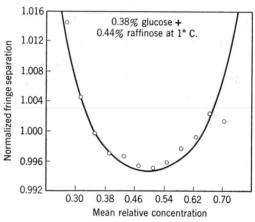

Fig. 6.   Effect on the fringe separation of the diffusion of two solutes.

mentally accessible only with difficulty. This illustrates the inadequacy of the usual graphical methods. However, numerical interpolation for this sum may be made with any accuracy desired. In Fig. 6, the curve represents the computed departure of the normalized fringe separation from unity, whereas the circles are the observed values. Here the agreement between theory and experiment is satisfactory, the residual differences being due, possibly, to the fact that the theory does not allow for the skewness introduced by the slight concentration dependence of the diffusion coefficients.

An understanding of the behavior of mixtures is essential to the interpretation of the diffusion of proteins since these are present in buffer solutions and gradients of buffer salts may thus be superimposed on those due to the macromolecule. This is also true of diffusion in mixed solvents.[14] Moreover, the superimposed gradients may be either additive or subtractive, i.e., the flow of the second component may be either with, or against, that of the first. As is shown in the illustrative plots of Figs. 7 and 8, additive gradients, although leading to non-Gaussian boundaries, do not produce unusual effects whereas subtractive ones can. In both figures the light lines are Gauss curves of the *gradient* of refractive index as a function of the height

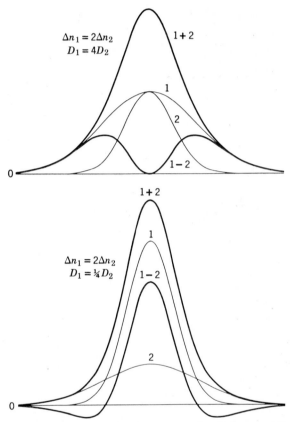

Figs. 7, 8. In these figures the light lines are graphs of the computed refractive index gradient for two ideally diffusing solutes 1 and 2, whereas the heavy lines are the sum and difference, respectively, of the ordinates for the light lines. In Fig. 7, $\Delta n_1 = 2\Delta n_2$, and $D_1 = 4D_2$; whereas in Fig. 8, $\Delta n_1 = 2\Delta n_2$, and $D_1 = \frac{1}{4}D_2$.

in the boundary whereas the heavy lines are the sum and difference, respectively, of the Gauss curves. In both figures the concentration of the major component has been taken as twice that of the minor one, i.e., $\Delta n_1 = 2\Delta n_2$. In Fig. 7 the major component diffuses four times as fast as the minor one, whereas the converse holds in Fig. 8.

The bimodal character of the subtractive curve of Fig. 7 has been noted previously [15] and observed experimentally.[16] In the subtractive curve of Fig. 8 the negative gradients at each edge of the boundary would frequently lead to gravitational instability and localized convection.[17] Exceptions may occur, however. The Rayleigh fringes shown in Fig. 9 were recorded during the diffusion of digitonin in 63% aqueous ethanol; and the reversal in the bending of the fringes at the edges of the boundary is discernible, although most pronounced on the solution side. The boundary in this experiment was between the aqueous ethanol and an aliquot of this mixed solvent to which the digitonin had been added. Since the addition of the digitonin "dilutes" both the alcohol and the water, inverted gradients of both are present in the boundary. Regardless of whether the flows are referred to water or ethanol as the "stationary" component, both diffuse much more rapidly than digitonin and a situation comparable to the subtractive curve of Fig. 8 occurs. Results of this type are of considerable interest because they indicate some of the problems that must be solved before a precise interpretation of the diffusion of proteins will be possible.

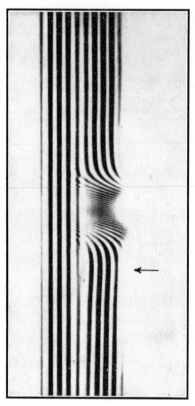

Fig. 9. Pattern of the Rayleigh fringes for the diffusion of 0.4% digitonin in 63% aqueous ethanol.

THE STOKES-EINSTEIN RELATION

The dimensions of submicroscopic particles in solution are not known with sufficient accuracy to permit a direct test of the numerical factor 6π in the Stokes-Einstein relation or in Perrin's extension thereof. For rigid macromolecules in a solvent of low molecular weight, e.g., aqueous solutions of proteins, it is customary to assume [18] that 6π is the correct factor and that r may be computed from the molal volume V of the solute at infinite dilution, i.e., $V = \frac{4}{3}\pi N r^3$ where $N = 6.026 \times 10^{23}$. For most proteins, a diffusion coefficient computed in this manner exceeds the observed value, and the difference is then ascribed to asymmetry, or hydration, or such a combination of the two as to satisfy simultaneously not only Perrin's equation but also Simha's relation for viscous flow. This procedure restricts, however, the molal volume of the hydrated particle to a value equal to, or greater than, the thermodynamic volume, and it is not always possible to satisfy both the Perrin and Simha relations with this restriction.

In an alternative procedure Scheraga and Mandelkern [19] retain the 6π but abandon the use of the volume V obtained from solution densities. They suggest that an ellipsoidal shape be assumed and that the axial ratio F_h and volume V_h of this ellipsoid be evaluated from the observed diffusion coefficient and weight intrinsic viscosity, say, with the aid of the Perrin and Simha relations. V_h is an effective hydrodynamic volume and may be either greater or less than the thermodynamic value V.

DIFFUSION AND THE MOLECULAR VOLUME

It was noted above that the volume obtained from solution densities cannot afford a quantitative measure of the effective radius if the particle is not spherical or if interaction with the solvent occurs. For the smaller molecules, however, the molal volume V is about the only available index of size, and much can be learned from a comparison of the diffusion coefficient with the cube root of this volume.[11] This comparison is shown in Fig. 10 for a series of solutes in water at 25° C., the only solvent with sufficient data available. Here the $DV^{1/3}$ product is plotted as ordinate against the diffusion coefficient as abscissa, this plot being used empirically because a roughly linear relationship results. If all the solutes were unhydrated spheres obeying Stokes' relation the points would fall on the horizontal line at

$$DV^{1/3} = \frac{kT}{6\pi\eta}\left(\frac{4\pi N}{3}\right)^{1/3} = 33 \times 10^{-6}$$

Since both asymmetry and hydration reduce the mobility, whereas many of the values for $DV^{1/3}$ in the figure exceed 33×10^{-6}, it is clear that as the size of the diffusing particle approaches that of the solvent molecule the numerical factor in the denominator of Stokes' relation becomes appreciably less than 6π. For the most rapidly diffusing solute, HDO, a value of 3π would still allow for some asymmetry and solvent interaction. It is not until a solute-solvent volume ratio of about 5 to 1 is reached, e.g., in the monosaccharides,[20] that 6π becomes appropriate. Even for these materials the apparent validity of Stokes' relation doubtless results from a compensation of asymmetry and hydration on the one hand and a numerical factor somewhat less than 6π on the other.

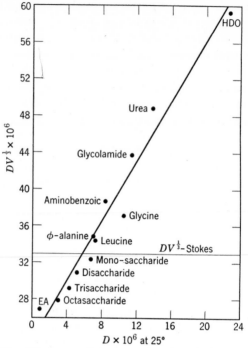

Fig. 10.   The diffusion coefficient as a function of the molal volume.

Results recently obtained in water indicate some of the factors influencing the volume and diffusion coefficient and are given in Tables 2 to 5. Even for the glycines, the hexose polymers, and the amino acid homologs of Table 2, in which the increment in volume between

TABLE 2.   DIFFUSION OF HOMOLOGS

$\bar{c} = 0.3$–0.4 wt. %

	$D_{25} \times 10^6$ cm.^{2}/sec.	V ml.	$DV^{1/3} \times 10^6$
Glycine	10.554	43.5	37.12
Diglycine	7.909	77.2	33.68
Triglycine	6.652	113.5	32.21
Glucose	6.728	111.9	32.42
Sucrose	5.209	209.9	30.96
Raffinose	4.339	306.6	29.26
Glycine	10.554	43.5	37.12
Alanine	9.097	60.6	35.73
α-Amino butyric acid	8.288	76.5	35.18
α-Amino valeric acid	7.682	92.7	34.77
α-Amino caproic acid	7.249	108.4	34.56

successive members of a series is fairly constant, the $DV^{1/3}$ product tends to decrease with increasing particle size.

A study of the diffusion of isomers has, however, been helpful. In Table 3 the results for three pairs of the α-amino derivatives of the

TABLE 3. DIFFUSION OF STRAIGHT—AND BRANCHED—CHAIN AMINO ACIDS

$$\bar{c} = 0.3 \text{ wt. } \%$$

	$D_{25} \times 10^6$	V	$DV^{1/3}$
α-Amino butyric acid	8.288	76.5	35.18
α-Amino isobutyric acid	8.130	78.1	34.75
α-Amino valeric acid	7.682	92.7	34.77
α-Amino isovaleric acid	7.725	91.3	34.79
α-Amino caproic acid	7.249	108.4	34.56
α-Amino isocaproic acid	7.255	107.5	34.50

normal and iso acids are presented. With all three pairs the change in volume on branching is accompanied, in accord with Stokes' relation, by a change of opposite sign in the diffusion coefficient. With the five- and six-carbon acids, branching leads to a more compact diffusing entity, whereas the converse is true for the butyric acids. In the case of the four-carbon compounds a similar behavior has been noted in the diffusion of the isomeric butyl alcohols. Here the coefficient decreases in the order: normal, iso, secondary, and tertiary. A shift of methyl groups to the carbon to which the hydroxyl group is attached appears to enhance the effective volume of the diffusing unit.

As would be expected, polarity also plays an important role in determining the effective volume. Thus Dunlop and Gosting [21] have found that glycolamide, the uncharged isomer of glycine, diffuses more rapidly than the dipolar ion.[22] Another example is afforded by the amino benzoic acids, Table 4. Here, the ortho and para acids have essentially the same volume and diffusion coefficient, whereas the values for the meta compound are quite different. Note, however, that a decrease in volume has been accompanied by a decrease in the diffusion coefficient.

Owing to the lack of resonance in the benzene ring of the meta compound this acid exists in aqueous solution largely as the dipolar ion whereas the ortho and para acids are present in the uncharged state.[23] The observed results are the ones to be expected then if the assumption is made that the charge decreases the apparent volume by condensing, through electrostriction, the water in its neighborhood and that some, at least, of this condensed solvent becomes part of the

TABLE 4. SOME EFFECTS OF POLARITY ON DIFFUSION

$\bar{c} \simeq 0.3$ wt. %

	$D_{25} \times 10^6$	V	$DV^{1/3}$
Glycine	10.554	43.5	37.12
Glycolamide	11.385	56.2	43.60
o-Amino benzoic acid	8.40	96.7	38.56
m-Amino benzoic acid	7.741	90.3	34.73
p-Amino benzoic acid	8.425	97.3	38.75
α-Amino propionic acid (alanine)	9.097	60.6	35.73
β-Hydroxy-α-amino propionic acid (serine)	8.802	60.8	34.61
α-Amino butyric acid	8.288	76.5	35.18
β-Hydroxy-α-amino butyric acid (threonine)	7.984	76.9	33.95

diffusing entity. Consequently the hydrodynamic volume is larger for the meta acid than for the ortho and para compounds.

This picture of the possible role of polarity is also consistent with the results for the hydroxyl derivatives in Table 4. The volumes of both serine and threonine are about the same as those of the unsubstituted amino acids, from which it would appear that the increment in volume due to the hydroxyl oxygen is balanced by a decrement due to electrostriction by this polar group. The increased electrostriction results, however, in an increase in the hydrodynamic volume, i.e., greater hydration, and the diffusion coefficient is depressed accordingly.

The results for the materials of Table 5 are more difficult to interpret. These materials are isomers of the same charge type but

TABLE 5. DIFFUSION OF ISOMERS OF THE SAME CHARGE TYPE BUT DIFFERENT CHARGE SEPARATION

$\bar{c} = 0.3$ wt. %

1	2	3	4
Solute	Charge Separation	$D_{25} \times 10^6$	V
α-Aminopropionic acid (alanine)	1	9.097	60.6
β-Aminopropionic acid (β-alanine)	2	9.327	58.9
N-Methylglycine (sarcosine)	1	9.674	62.7
α-Aminobutyric acid	1	8.288	76.5
β-Aminobutyric acid	2	8.367	76.4
γ-Aminobutyric acid	3	8.259	73.3
Asparagine	1	8.300	78.0
Glycylglycine	4	7.909	77.2
Glutamine	1	7.623	....
Glycylalanine	4	7.221	93.9

different charge separation, the number of atoms in the chain between the COO^- and the NH_3^+ groups being given in column 2 of the table. In the alanines the lower volume of the β compound is supposed to be due to increased electrostriction resulting from the greater charge separation.[24] If this were the explanation, however, the diffusion coefficient should also be reduced, but the opposite occurs. The amino butyric acids present a similar problem; although with a sufficient charge separation, e.g., the γ acid and also the isomers of asparagine and glutamine, the diffusion coefficient is depressed.

The author has found it helpful to think of the diffusing particle as having an intrinsic volume V_i and an intrinsic shape factor F_i. With free rotation at single bonds F_i would be a time-average value, but V_i should be the same for any group of isomers. In the absence of interaction with the solvent these parameters would describe the hydrodynamic behavior of the particle and the three volumes, V_i, V_h, and V would be essentially identical. If, however, the particle is polar and is dissolved in a polar, and openly packed, solvent such as water the interaction would lead to $V_h > V_i > V$. In this case the difference $V_i - V$ would be a measure of the electrostriction, $V_h - V_i$ would be a measure of the hydration, and the hydrodynamic shape F_h might then differ from the intrinsic one.

In isomers of marked difference in polarity, such as those in Table 4, the volume effect appears to outweigh any change in shape. With the smaller differences in polarity illustrated in Table 5 it may be necessary to consider possible alterations in this parameter. However, if ΔD for sarcosine and alanine were ascribed entirely to a difference in shape and the N methyl compound were taken as spherical, Perrin's relation would require the improbably large axial ratio of 2.2 for the α-aminopropionic acid. A more attractive possibility is that the proportion of dipolar ions in which alanine is present in aqueous solution exceeds that for sarcosine.

DIFFUSION OF THE SAME SOLUTE IN DIFFERENT SOLVENTS

The Stokes-Einstein relation may also be used to interpret the diffusion of a given solute in different solvents. R. H. Stokes and his associates [25] have recently obtained data on the diffusion of iodine in some organic solvents, and their results are given in Table 6. Here, the first three entries refer to solvents in which the iodine is thought to be present as the simple diatomic molecule; and the $D \cdot \eta$ product varies by only 7%, whereas the viscosity varies by 300%. In the remaining five solvents there is spectroscopic evidence for the presence of iodine-

TABLE 6. DIFFUSION COEFFICIENTS OF IODINE AT ZERO CONCENTRATION IN
SOME ORGANIC SOLVENTS AT 25° C.

Solvent	$D \times 10^6$ cm.^{2} sec.$^{-1}$	$\eta \times 10^3$ poise	$D\eta \times 10^7$	V_{I_2} ml./mole
Hexane	40.5	3.19	1.29	
Heptane	34.2	3.96	1.35	63.8
Carbon tetra- chloride	15.0	9.18	1.38	65.8
Dioxane	10.7	12.16	1.30	
Benzene	21.3	6.05	1.20	
Toluene	21.3	5.59	1.19	61.9
m-Xylene	18.9	5.89	1.11	
Mesitylene	14.9	6.81	1.01	

solvent complexes and the depression of the $D \cdot \eta$ product may reflect the enhanced size of the diffusing entity.

Reliable density data for iodine solutions in three of the solvents of Table 6 are available [26] and yield the volumes given in the last column. A parallelism will be noted between the $D \cdot \eta$ product and the volume, as in solutions of isomers in water where the solute-solvent interaction differed. If, however, a volume of 64 ml. per mole is used to compute a radius for I_2 the resulting value of $D\eta$, 0.74×10^{-7}, is only about one-half of that observed in normal solvents. In these systems the ratio of the volume of the solute to that of the solvent V/V_0 is somewhat less than unity and, as in aqueous solutions of small molecules, the numerical factor in the Stokes-Einstein relation is less than 6π but greater than 3π.

Lyons and Sandquist [27] have recently studied the diffusion of diphenyl in benzene at 25° where V is 149 ml. and D is 15.58×10^{-6}. For this solute in benzene $V/V_0 = 1.7$ and $DV^{1/3} = 82.6 \times 10^{-6}$. For iodine in the same solvent $V/V_0 = 0.7$ and $DV^{1/3} = 85.2 \times 10^{-6}$. As in water, a rather large solute-solvent volume ratio would have to be reached before $DV^{1/3}$ approached the Stokes value of 48.9×10^{-6} for benzene, and 6π became the appropriate factor.

THE DIFFUSION COEFFICIENT AS A FUNCTION OF THE TEMPERATURE

If the dimensions of the particle are independent of the temperature, the Stokes relation predicts that in a given solvent the ratio of the diffusion coefficient at T_1 and T_2 should be independent of the solute and equal to $T_1\eta_2/T_2\eta_1$. Some representative results of modern precision in water as solvent are given in Table 7. Here the solutes are listed in the order of increasing molecular weight and include the extreme values for the ratio that have been observed thus far. Over the 24° temperature interval of this table, the ratio, column 3, varies less than

LONGSWORTH 243

TABLE 7. EFFECT OF TEMPERATURE ON DIFFUSION IN DILUTE AQUEOUS
SOLUTIONS

$\bar{c} = 0.3$ wt. %

1 Solute	2 $D_{25} \times 10^6$	3 D_{25}/D_1	4 E_D
HDO ($c = 0$)	22.61	2.004	ca. 13° 4700
Methyl alcohol ($\bar{c} = 1.3\%$)	15.3 *	2.08	4970
Urea	13.78	2.002	4700
Glycine	10.554	2.049	4850
Alanine	9.097	2.107	5040
Leucine	7.255	2.166	5230
Glucose	6.728	2.145	5160
Raffinose	4.339	2.159	5210
Cyclo hepta amylose	3.224	2.161	5220
Bovine plasma albumin	0.658	2.145	5160

$$\frac{T_{25}\eta_1}{T_1\eta_{25}} = 2.105$$

* D strongly concentration dependent on refractive index scale.

10%, although the diffusion coefficients, column 2, vary over twenty-fold.

Most of the twofold increase in D on raising the temperature from 1 to 25° C. is due to the decreased viscosity of the solvent, less than 10% being due to the increase in the kinetic energy kT of the diffusing particles. Although the Stokes-Einstein relation predicts a proportionality between T and the $D\eta$ product it does not indicate the temperature dependence of either factor. The reaction-rate theory [28] is more useful in this regard, as may be illustrated with the aid of the data of Cohen and Bruin [29] for the diffusion of dilute solutions of tetrabromethane in tetrachlorethane. These are the most complete data available on the effect of temperature and are given in Table 8, to-

TABLE 8. DIFFUSION OF TETRABROMETHANE IN TETRACHLORETHANE AT
DIFFERENT TEMPERATURES

$\bar{c} = 0.5$ wt. %

1 t	2 $D \times 10^6$ cm.²/sec.	3 100η	4 E_D calories	5 100α
0.44	3.50_7	2.628		
7.70	4.19_0	2.248	3740	2.67
15.00	4.96_5	1.951	3730	2.53
25.00	6.11_1	1.637	3540	2.30
35.61	7.40_7	1.386	3310	2.00
51.10	9.53_7	1.116	3250	1.85

gether with the viscosity, column 3, of the solvent at each temperature. Subsequent columns of the table contain derived quantities that are useful in considering the temperature dependence of the diffusion coefficient. Thus the activation energy, E_D, column 4, defined by the relation

$$E_D = \frac{2.303RT_1T_2}{T_1 - T_2} \log \frac{D_1}{D_2} \tag{2}$$

varies by 14%, whereas the conventional temperature coefficient

$$\alpha = \frac{1}{D_2} \frac{D_1 - D_2}{t_1 - t_2}$$

changes by some 36%, column 5. Since E_D is more nearly independent of T than α, it provides a better index of the temperature dependence of the diffusion coefficient for the comparison of data obtained over different temperature intervals.

Referring again to Table 7, a tendency for the diffusion coefficient ratio to increase with increasing particle size may be noted. This was first observed by Oholm,[30] and the illustrative table that he prepared has been quoted elsewhere.[31]   It is reproduced in Table 9 after

TABLE 9.   TEMPERATURE COEFFICIENTS OF DIFFUSION ACCORDING TO OHOLM

$D_{20} \times 10^6$	28	23–21	18–16	14–13	9–8	5–3	2–1
D_{20}/D_{10}	1.18	1.20	1.22	1.25	1.29	1.35	1.40
E_D	2730	3010	3280	3680	4200	4950	5550

conversion of his coefficients to cm.²/sec.   In order to compare his data with those of Table 7, activation energies have been computed with the aid of equation 2 and are given in the bottom row of Table 9. Although Tables 7 and 9 cover much the same range of particle size, the new results show a variation in E_D of only some 10%, whereas in the case of the older data the variation is about 100%. Since Oholm did not specify the solutes on which his table is based, it is difficult to find the source of the discrepancy.   Apparently HCl was the most rapidly diffusing solute that he studied.   This accounts for his low value for E_D, since the low temperature coefficient for the electric mobility of the hydrogen ion is one of the arguments for its "non-Stokesian" conductance.[32]

The identity of the diffusion and electric mobilities of ions at infinite dilution has already been noted.   The relation for univalent ions is

$$D = RT\lambda/F^2$$

where λ is the limiting ionic conductance, F the Faraday equivalent, and D the ion diffusion coefficient as measured, for example, with the aid of tracers.[33-36] Thus, from the extensive conductance and transference data on electrolytes inferences may be drawn as to the diffusion behavior of ions. Some typical data are given in Table 10.

TABLE 10. TEMPERATURE COEFFICIENTS OF IONIC DIFFUSION

$$c = 0$$

1	2	3
Ion	$D_{25} \times 10^6$	E_D
		18° C.
H	93.11	3230
OH	52.7	3610
Cl	20.32	4220
K	19.57	4230
NO$_3$	19.01	4030
Na	13.34	4690
Acetate	10.89	4590
Li	10.30	5040

The ion diffusion coefficients in column 2 were computed [37] from the conductances at 25° C. and are thus comparable with the values for non-electrolytes in Table 7. The activation energies, column 3, were computed from the values of $a = (1/\lambda)(d\lambda/dT)$ at 18° C. as given in the I.C.T.[38] The relation is $E_D = RT(1 + aT)$. Since E_D decreases somewhat with increasing T and the mean temperature in Table 7 is 13° C., the values of E_D in Tables 7 and 10 are not strictly comparable. However, if the hydrogen and hydroxyl ions are excluded from consideration, because of their abnormal transport in water, it is clear that the activation energies for ionic diffusion are similar to those for non-electrolytes and also tend to increase slightly, though irregularly, with increasing size.

Since the Stokes value for the diffusion coefficient ratio over the 24° C. interval of Table 7 is 2.105, it is clear that deviations of both signs occur. When an observed value exceeds that predicted by Stokes' relation, the tendency has been to ascribe the excess to decreasing hydration with increasing temperature. The occurrence of negative deviations would, at first glance, cast doubt on the validity of this interpretation. It should be noted, however, that negative deviations occur only for those materials for which the numerical factor in Stokes relation appears to be less than 6π. In fact, the data of Tables 7 and 10 suggest the generalization that *if the diffusing particle is large enough for the solvent to be considered a continuum its temperature coefficient will not be less than the Stokes value.*

Acknowledgment. The author is grateful to Dr. D. A. MacInnes of these Laboratories and to Dr. J. L. Oncley of the Harvard Medical School for the care with which they reviewed this article.

REFERENCES AND NOTES

1. A. Einstein, *Ann. Physik.*, *19*, 289, 371 (1906).
2. W. Nernst, *Z. physik. Chem.*, *2*, 613 (1888).
3. A. Fick, *Ann. Physik.*, *94*, 59 (1855).
4. G. Stokes, *Trans. Cambridge Phil. Soc.*, *9*, 5 (1856).
5. W. Sutherland, *Phil. Mag.*, *9*, 781 (1905).
6. F. Perrin, *J. phys. radium*, *7*, 1 (1936).
7. L. G. Longsworth, *J. Am. Chem. Soc.*, *74*, 4155 (1952).
8. L. J. Gosting and M. S. Morris, *J. Am. Chem. Soc.*, *71*, 1998 (1949).
9. J. H. Wang, C. V. Robinson, and I. S. Edelman, *J. Am. Chem. Soc.*, *75*, 466 (1953).
10. R. H. Stokes, *Trans. Faraday Soc.*, *48*, 887 (1952).
11. L. G. Longsworth, *J. Am. Chem. Soc.*, *75*, 5705 (1953).
12. E. M. Bevilacqua, E. B. Bevilacqua, M. M. Bender, and J. W. Williams, *Ann. N. Y. Acad. Sci.*, *46*, 309 (1945).
13. D. F. Akeley and L. J. Gosting, *J. Am. Chem. Soc.*, *75*, 5685 (1953).
14. D. M. Clarke and Malcolm Dole, *J. Am. Chem. Soc.*, *76*, 3745 (1954).
15. P. B. Taylor, *J. Phys. Chem.*, *31*, 1478 (1927).
16. L. G. Longsworth, *Natl. Bur. Standards (U. S.) Circ.* 524, 59 (1953).
17. For solutions in which the density increases with increasing concentration of solute, gravitational instability can be expected at the *edges* of all boundaries in which the flow of 2, the minor component, is against that of 1 and $D_1 < D_2$. With a counterflow and $D_1 > D_2$ instability can be expected at the *center* of the boundary for values of $\Delta n_1 / \Delta n_2 < \sqrt{D_1/D_2}$ if the density parallels the refractive index. It is not possible at present to say whether or not the instability will produce localized convection.
18. J. L. Oncley, *Ann. N. Y. Acad. Sci.*, *41*, 121 (1941).
19. H. A. Scheraga and L. Mandelkern, *J. Am. Chem. Soc.*, *75*, 179 (1953).
20. L. Onsager, *Ann. N. Y. Acad. Sci.*, *46*, 241 (1945).
21. P. J. Dunlop and L. J. Gosting, *J. Am. Chem. Soc.*, *75*, 5073 (1953).
22. M. S. Lyons and J. V. Thomas, *J. Am. Chem. Soc.*, *72*, 4506 (1950).
23. E. J. Cohn and J. I. Edsall, *Proteins, Amino Acids, and Peptides as Ions and Dipolar Ions,* Reinhold Publishing Co., p. 124, New York, 1943.
24. Reference 23, p. 159.
25. R. H. Stokes, P. J. Dunlop, and J. R. Hall, *Trans. Faraday Soc.*, *49*, 886 (1953).
26. *International Critical Tables,* Vol. 3, p. 132, McGraw-Hill Book Co., New York, 1926.
27. P. A. Lyons and C. L. Sandquist, *J. Am. Chem. Soc.*, *75*, 3896 (1953).
28. S. Glasstone, K. J. Laidler, and H. Eyring, *The Theory of Rate Processes,* p. 521, McGraw-Hill Book Co., New York, 1941.
29. E. Cohen and H. R. Bruin, *Z. physik. Chem.*, *103*, 404 (1923).

30. L. W. Oholm, *Nobelinstitut 2*, 1 (1913).
31. H. S. Taylor, *J. Chem. Phys., 6*, 331 (1938).
32. J. D. Bernal and R. H. Fowler, *J. Chem. Phys., 1*, 515 (1933).
33. A. W. Adamson, *J. Chem. Phys., 15*, 762 (1947).
34. J. H. Wang and J. W. Kennedy, *J. Am. Chem. Soc., 72*, 2080 (1950).
35. J. H. Wang, *J. Am. Chem. Soc., 73*, 510 (1951).
36. R. Mills and J. W. Kennedy, *J. Am. Chem. Soc., 75*, 5696 (1953).
37. D. A. MacInnes, *The Principles of Electrochemistry*, p. 342, Reinhold Publishing Co., New York, 1939.
38. Reference 26, Vol. 6, p. 230.

13·

Hydrogen Ion Titration Curves
of Proteins [1]

CHARLES TANFORD *

INTRODUCTION

We do not as yet have an understanding of the structure of proteins or of their biological activity. Protein molecules are known to consist of one or more polypeptide chains, and it has been proposed that these may often be in a coiled configuration; but this does not help us to understand why so many protein molecules, even those thought to consist of a single polypeptide chain, have a compact over-all shape, close to spherical. The specific and potent biological activity of many of these proteins, such as insulin, lysozyme, pepsin, the specific blood antibodies, etc., has not been given even tentative explanation.

It is reasonable to suppose that a solution to one or both of these problems may be found in the chemistry of the reactive groups residing on the side chains of protein molecules. Chemical, electrostatic, or hydrogen bonds between such reactive groups may play a large role in the maintenance of a compact structure. The spatial arrangement and possible cooperation between reactive groups of a given protein may explain its biological properties.

For these reasons the quantitative study of any chemical reaction of these reactive groups is of the greatest interest. One of the most useful of such reactions is the reaction with hydrogen ions. It has the advantage of being simple to study and also of providing information simultaneously about a large number of reactive groups. Carboxyl, amino, imidazole, phenolic, sulfhydryl, and arginyl groups all react with hydrogen ion in the measurable pH range.

The study of the reaction of proteins with hydrogen ion usually has as its objective the preparation of a titration curve such as that of bovine serum albumin, shown in Fig. 1. The purpose of this paper is

* From the Department of Chemistry, State University of Iowa, Iowa City, Ia.

248

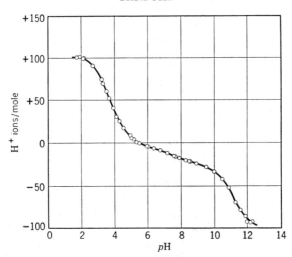

Fig. 1. Hydrogen ion titration curve for purified bovine serum albumin; ionic strength, 0.15 at 25° C.

to describe in some detail the experimental method employed and the electrochemical assumptions made in the construction of such a curve and to suggest a general method for its interpretation.

EXPERIMENTAL PROCEDURE

Each experimental point on a titration curve represents a separate experiment. A solution is prepared by weight to contain appropriate amounts of protein, acid and/or base, and neutral salt. The total ionic strength for all points is kept the same to facilitate subsequent calculation. The only measurement required is the measurement of pH.

Cells with liquid junction are used for pH determination. Either a hydrogen or a glass electrode may be used in the half-cell sensitive to hydrogen ion. If a hydrogen electrode is used, it is usually necessary to employ Clark's rocking cell[2] in order to avoid foaming of the protein solution. Even then, surface denaturation may occur during shaking. At least half an hour is required to reach equilibrium in such a cell; therefore, inaccurate results may be obtained with proteins that undergo slow acid or base denaturation. For these reasons, as well as for their greater convenience, glass electrodes are preferred to hydrogen electrodes. However, at very acid pH values (below pH 2.5), it is often desirable to take advantage of the greater precision attainable with a hydrogen electrode.

For measurements with a glass electrode, the apparatus shown in Fig. 2 has been found very useful. The two principal compartments are constructed so as to be just wide enough for a shielded Beckman glass electrode.[3] One compartment can be used for a pH standard [4] while the other contains the solution whose pH is being measured. Nitrogen is passed over the solutions to avoid contamination by carbon dioxide. Connection to a sealed-off saturated calomel reference half-

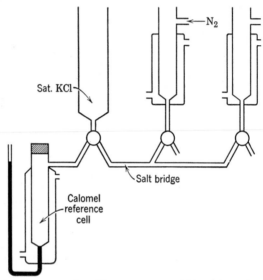

Fig. 2. Apparatus for pH measurement with a glass electrode.

cell is made through a saturated KCl salt bridge. All temperature-sensitive parts are maintained at constant temperature by water circulating through the jackets shown in the figure. Liquid junctions are made in the stopcocks under the two solution compartments. The connection between the compartments and the stopcocks is 3 or 4 cm. in length, and, preferably, made of capillary tubing, so that contamination of the solutions by KCl is eliminated and new liquid junctions can be made frequently with a minimum loss of material.

The electrodes come to equilibrium within 5–10 min., and pH measurements can be made with a precision of about 0.01 pH unit with a Beckman Model G pH meter.

For both glass and hydrogen electrodes the pH scale is defined as

$$pH = \frac{E - E'}{2.303(RT/F)} \tag{1}$$

where E is the observed e.m.f., F the faraday, and E' a constant determined from an e.m.f. reading with a solution of known pH. The value of E' is a constant for hydrogen electrodes; but for glass electrodes it differs from electrode to electrode; and for a given electrode it varies slightly from day to day. If the Beckman pH meter is used, the operations inherent in equation 1 are performed by the instrument and pH is read directly.

The pH of a given solution may be determined at several temperatures merely by changing the temperature of the water flowing through the jackets.

For some proteins conditions may be met where irreversible changes occur even within the 5–10 min. required for the pH measurements here described. For such proteins a flow method has been devised by Steinhardt and Zaiser [5] that makes possible a reading of pH within 3 sec. of mixing a solution.

ELECTROCHEMICAL ASSUMPTIONS

In the construction of a titration curve such as that of Fig. 1, pH values are used not only directly, as the abscissa, but also indirectly, in the evaluation of the ordinate. In order to obtain the number of hydrogen ions bound or removed per molecule of protein at any pH, it is necessary to subtract from the amount of acid or base added that which remains free in solution, which will be an appreciable fraction of the total for pH values below pH 4 and above pH 10. It is therefore necessary to convert pH values to hydrogen ion molalities.

For example, in the most acid solution of Fig. 1, the amount of HCl added was 0.0551 molal and the pH was 1.765, with the result that the molality of free H^+ was surely of the order of 0.02. Only the difference between these quantities, i.e., about 0.035 molal, represents hydrogen ions bound to the protein. Clearly, the molality of free H^+ must be known accurately, if an accurate value for the ordinate of Fig. 1 is to be obtained.

To achieve this objective, we must examine more closely the meaning of the electromotive force of the type of cell, with liquid junction, here under consideration. This electromotive force is the sum of a number of terms, one for each phase boundary. Some of these terms are identical for the measurements with pH standard and unknown solution and therefore cancel out in the definition of pH given by equation 1. The potentials at the hydrogen or glass electrode and the junction potential between the KCl bridge and the solution whose

pH is being measured, however, do not cancel and the pH as defined by equation 1 is actually equal to

$$pH = - \log m_{H^+} - \log \gamma_{H^+} + \delta E_J/(2.303RT/F) + G \qquad (2)$$

where m_{H^+} and γ_{H^+} represent the molality and activity coefficient of hydrogen ion in the solution under study, δE_J represents the difference between the liquid junction potential between the salt bridge and the unknown solution and that between the salt bridge and the pH standard, and G represents, where a glass electrode is used, the glass electrode error, i.e., any deviation that the glass electrode may show from theoretical response to hydrogen ion activity. The quantity G is measurable by actual comparison between glass and hydrogen electrodes and is probably quite small in the absence of Na^+ ion.

If equation 2 is now rewritten

$$pH = - \log m_{H^+} - \log \gamma_{H^+}' \qquad (3)$$

the problem becomes the evaluation of $\log \gamma_{H^+}'$, which, from equation 2, is the sum of three quantities that are impossible to determine by any thermodynamic method,

$$- \log \gamma_{H^+}' = - \log \gamma_{H^+} + \delta E_J/(2.303RT/F) + G \qquad (4)$$

To obtain a value for $\log \gamma_{H^+}'$, we make the customary assumption [6] that the value of $\log \gamma_{H^+}'$ in a protein solution is the same as it is in a solution not containing protein that has the same ionic strength (using, as far as possible, the same electrolytes) and the same pH. The ionic strength of a protein solution is computed from the sum of the concentrations of added electrolytes, the fact that some of the ions are bound to protein molecules being ignored.

These assumptions are inherently reasonable. The liquid junction potential is more likely to be disturbed by fast-moving H^+ or OH^- ions than by any other component, leading to the comparison with protein-free solution at the same pH; and a protein molecule with a net charge of Z can certainly not make the same contribution to the ionic strength as a Z-valent ion because of the wide separation of the charges.

Where glass electrodes are used, the value of G could, of course, be quite different for otherwise equivalent solutions containing different concentrations of Na^+ ions (the well-known sodium error in alkaline solutions); but this difficulty is avoided by never using sodium compounds in any phase of this work. With the corresponding potassium compounds, the glass electrode error appears to be quite small.

In order to favor the validity of the assumptions made, a relatively high ionic strength (~ 0.1) is always maintained so that the contribution of protein-bound ions is relatively small. In addition, only 1–1 electrolytes are used, since log γ_{H^+} is most nearly dependent on ionic strength alone if only univalent ions are present.

For alkaline solutions we define

$$pOH = pK_W - pH \qquad (5)$$

where K_W is the dissociation constant of water [7,8] and then place

$$pOH = - \log m_{OH^-} - \log \gamma_{OH^-}' \qquad (6)$$

making the same assumptions about log γ_{OH^-}' as were made about log γ_{H^+}'. Equations 5 and 6 are used in alkaline solutions, where the number of H^+ ions removed (equivalent to the number of OH^- ions bound) is calculated as the difference between the molality of OH^- added and that found free.

Some typical values of log γ_{H^+}' and log γ_{OH^-}' are shown in Tables 1 and 2. There appears to be a small difference between different glass electrodes (which may, however, be a reflection of inaccuracies in the slide wire scales of the different pH meters used). In any event, Table 1 clearly shows that the glass electrode error G is smaller than 0.01 pH unit at pH 2. Reasonable calculated values of $- \log \gamma_{H^+}$ in KCl-HCl mixtures of ionic strength 0.15 lie somewhere near 0.10. This suggests that the value of δE_J for such solutions is about 1.5 mv., with 0.05 M potassium acid phthalate used as reference solution. A similar calculation at pH 12 leads to a value of about 3 mv. for δE_J. In both cases

TABLE 1. TYPICAL VALUES OF $- \log \gamma_{H^+}'$ IN HCl-KCl MIXTURES
AT 25° C.

$- \log \gamma_{H^+}'$

	H₂ Electrode		Glass Electrodes		
			No. 1	No. 2	No. 3
pH	$\mu = 0.075$	$\mu = 0.150$ *	$\mu = 0.075$	$\mu = 0.150$	$\mu = 0.150$
1.75	....	....	0.060	....	0.078
2.0	0.071	0.079	0.067	0.074	0.077
2.25	0.073	0.078	0.076	0.078	....
2.5	0.077	0.083	....	0.079	0.074

* A few years ago the author obtained values near 0.05 in similar solutions containing NaCl instead of KCl. Since $\gamma_\pm$ for HCl in NaCl does not differ appreciably from values in KCl, there is no obvious explanation for this difference.[7]

TABLE 2. TYPICAL VALUES OF $-$ LOG $\gamma_{OH}-'$ IN KOH-KCl MIXTURES AT 25° C.

		$-$ log $\gamma_{OH}-'$	
		Glass Electrode No. 1	Glass Electrode No. 2
pH	pOH	$\mu = 0.075$	$\mu = 0.150$
12.25	1.75	0.153	0.174
12.0	2.0	0.148	0.170
11.75	2.25	0.154	....
11.25	2.75	....	0.171

the potential for the junction, solution/KCl (saturated), is more *negative* with the test solution than with 0.05 M potassium acid phthalate.

It is difficult to make an *a priori* estimate of the correctness of the assumption that the values of log γ' given in Tables 1 and 2 are also valid for protein solutions of the same pH and ionic strength. Our experience has indicated, however, that the error introduced cannot be greater than 0.01 in log γ'. Whenever titration curves are plotted using log γ' values differing by 0.01 from those obtained by the use of our assumptions, less reasonable results are obtained; for example, the ends of the curves become dependent on protein concentration and do not extrapolate to horizontal straight lines.

REVERSIBILITY

Because of the complex structure of protein molecules, the dissociation or binding of hydrogen ions may be accompanied by far-reaching and frequently irreversible structural changes. As a result, hydrogen ion titration curves do not necessarily represent reversible equilibrium. Before any attempt is made to interpret such curves, tests for reversibility must therefore be made. A series of solutions is prepared, containing, say, sufficient acid to bring each solution to pH 2. Different amounts of base are then added to each solution, so that final pH values of, say, pH 3, pH 4, pH 5, etc., are reached. Calculations of the number of hydrogen ions bound or dissociated are made for the final pH values. If the resulting values fall precisely on the titration curve obtained without previous exposure to pH 2, then the acid portion of the titration curve presumably represents true thermodynamic equilibrium. Similar tests can be performed for other regions of the titration curve.

When such tests are carried out, it is found that the titration curves of some proteins are almost entirely reversible, whereas others are largely irreversible. However, even the best proteins contain regions of irreversibility, and even the worst ones may contain reversible regions. A different procedure must be used to interpret reversible and irreversible portions of a titration curve. Thermodynamic methods are directly applicable to the reversible portions but not to the irreversible portions.

TITRATION CURVES REPRESENTING TRUE EQUILIBRIUM

The total number of groups titrated is usually large. For serum albumin, for example, it is about 227 (Fig. 1). One way to treat the equilibrium with hydrogen ion, therefore, would be to consider the protein at its acid end point as a polybasic acid PH_n, where n is the total number of hydrogen ions capable of dissociation. The n equilibrium constants for the dissociations $PH_n \rightleftharpoons PH_{n-1} + H^+$; $PH_{n-1} \rightleftharpoons PH_{n-2} + H^+$; etc., could then be determined. This method of treating the equilibrium, however, has the disadvantage of leading to a large number of equilibrium constants, from which, it turns out, it is not possible to obtain the kind of information we should like to have about the groups being titrated.

An alternative approach is therefore used, which takes cognizance of the fact that many of the groups being titrated are most probably intrinsically identical, or very nearly so. Accordingly, the titration curve is divided into a number of overlapping regions, each of which is taken *tentatively* to correspond to the titration of intrinsically identical groups. The titration of a number of intrinsically identical groups must lead to a regular curve not unlike that for the titration of a monobasic acid, though it will be flatter because of electrostatic interaction.[9] The over-all titration curve is then a superposition of a number of such regular curves.[10]

This division into titration regions is achieved with the aid of all available information. A starting point might be the amino acid composition of the protein under study. The α-carboxyl groups, at the ends of peptide chains, might well be all intrinsically identical and thus form a titration region, which might be expected to overlap in part with a second region, corresponding to the titration of side-chain carboxyl groups derived from the aspartyl and glutamyl residues of the protein. A third region might consist of the imidazole groups derived from histidyl residues; another, of α-amino groups from the ends of peptide chains; another, of ϵ-amino groups derived from lysyl residues; another, of phenolic groups derived from tyrosyl residues; another, of guanidine groups derived from arginyl residues. Further information is supplied from examination of the titration curve itself. Can it be thought of as the superposition of regularly shaped curves each containing the number of groups required by the amino acid composition? The apparent heat of ionization, obtained from titration curves at different temperatures, is another great aid on this point.[11,12] Independent methods may be available for the titration of some of the groups, especially the phenolic groups, for which a spectroscopic method is available.[13,14]

A more detailed account is beyond the scope of this paper. In any event, the subdivision into titration regions, no matter how firm its foundations, is only a tentative one, as the subsequent discussion will show. For the present it suffices to say that the acid region of the serum albumin curve of Fig. 1, presumably consisting of carboxyl groups, is such a titration region, and, by means of the techniques just outlined, one would tentatively assign one hundred five groups to it.[15]

As an illustration of the mathematical analysis, we shall make use of this region of one hundred five groups, as well as a similar region of fifty-eight carboxyl groups that can be chosen from the titration curve of β-lactoglobulin.[16]

All the groups of a given titration region are tentatively assumed to be intrinsically identical, as has been stated. They are also treated as independent ionizing units. Because of this, they do not necessarily represent isolated groups. The carboxyl groups being used as an illustration may, for example, actually be acting in concert with ϵ-amino groups, so that the ionizing process (defined as independent of all specific interaction) may actually be

$$-CH_2-COOH \qquad -CH_2-C{\overset{\displaystyle O}{\underset{\displaystyle O^-}{<}}}$$

$$\rightleftharpoons$$

$$-CH_2-NH_3^+ \qquad -CH_2-NH_3^+$$

The standard free energy of dissociation of a hydrogen ion from any one of the groups under consideration may now be written as

$$\Delta F^\circ = \Delta F^\circ_{int} + \Delta F^\circ_{elec} \qquad (7)$$

where ΔF°_{int} is the intrinsic standard free energy of ionization, which includes all specific interaction with other groups; whereas ΔF°_{elec}

arises as a result of the non-specific electrostatic interaction with the many charged groups on a protein molecule, representing the work done in removing a hydrogen ion, after dissociation, from the immediate vicinity of the protein molecule to infinity. The value of $\Delta F°_{int}$ is, by definition, the same for all the groups in a given region. The electrostatic term is a complex function of the charges on the protein molecule and their positions. Since these positions are not known, it is necessary to make some simple assumption concerning them. In view of the fact that so many of the ionizable groups are intrinsically identical, the charges on any one molecule are likely to be distributed in a quite different way from those on another. As a result, a reasonable assumption is that the average electrostatic free energy of all the molecules is not a function of the separate charges of the protein molecule but only of the total charge Z, to which it is directly proportional. We place the proportionality factor equal to $2RTW$, and, since $\Delta F°_{elec}$ is positive when Z is negative, we obtain

$$\Delta F° = \Delta F°_{int} - 2RTWZ \qquad (8)$$

The value of W will depend on the temperature, the ionic strength, and the size and shape of the protein molecule. For given values of Z, and of temperature and ionic strength, $\Delta F°_{elec}$ will be smaller the further the charge is spread out; i.e., W will be smaller for a large molecule (or for a very asymmetric one) than for a small one (or for a symmetric one).

Introducing the customary relations between degree of association and dissociation constant, and between the latter and $\Delta F°$, equation 8 becomes [17]

$$pH - \log \frac{x}{1-x} = pK'_{int} - 0.868WZ \qquad (9)$$

where x is degree of dissociation, and pK'_{int}, the negative log of the intrinsic dissociation constant for the corresponding group. Since measurements cannot be made at very low ionic strength for reasons given previously, pK'_{int} must refer to the ionic strength actually used and does not represent the value at zero ionic strength. (That is, the standard state of the dissociating group here refers to that group located on a protein molecule with zero net charge, at the particular ionic strength being used.)

At any pH, the value of Z can be determined by adding to the charge due to hydrogen ions bound or dissociated at that pH the charge due to other bound ions, i.e., K^+ and Cl^- if KCl is used as indifferent electrolyte. The number of such bound ions can be computed from equilibrium dialysis studies [18] or from electromotive force measurements with suitable electrodes, such as silver-silver chloride electrodes [18] or perm-selective membrane electrodes.[19]

The value of $x/(1 - x)$ can be determined directly from the titration curve. Since all the groups being considered have been assumed to be identical, $x/(1 - x)$ must be equal to $r/(n - r)$, where n is the total number of such identical groups per protein molecule and r the number of these, at any pH, from which a hydrogen ion has been dissociated. The value of r is read off the titration curve. In a pH range in which two different kinds of groups are being titrated there may be some difficulty in determining how many of a particular type of group have been titrated. In practice, this turns out to be a relatively minor difficulty, easily circumvented by two or three successive approximations, except in the alkaline region where phenolic and amino groups overlap throughout. Here the value of r for phenolic groups can be obtained by independent spectrophotometric experiments.[13, 14]

It is thus seen that only pK'_{int} and W remain to be determined, and it is the evaluation of these terms that leads to information concerning protein structure, as will be shown below. It should be noted here that equation 9 is not new but has been generally used in the past.[20] There is, however, one important difference. In the past W has always been considered a constant independent of Z. Furthermore, it has usually been considered a calculable constant. In the present treatment, on the other hand, W is considered an experimental parameter, and it will be a constant only over such regions of charge and pH over which the size and shape of the protein molecule remain unaltered.

To evaluate pK'_{int} and W, the left-hand side of equation 9 is plotted against Z. The intercept at $Z = 0$ will yield the value of pK'_{int}. If the protein molecule has a constant size and shape throughout the titration region, the plot will be a straight line of slope $-0.868\ W$; if the size and shape change, the value of W at any pH is determined by substituting into equation 9 the value of pK'_{int}.

Figures 3 and 4 show plots of this kind for the carboxyl groups of β-lactoglobulin and bovine serum albumin, the former at several ionic strengths. The charge Z at any pH has been estimated by using the chloride-binding data of Carr [21] for β-lactoglobulin and of Scatchard, Scheinberg, and Armstrong [18] for human serum albumin, which should also be applicable to bovine albumin.[19] It can be seen that for β-lactoglobulin straight lines are obtained, indicating a constant value of W, differing, of course, at each ionic strength. For serum albumin, however, a straight line is not obtained. One possible reason for this is that our original supposition, that the one hundred five acid groups of this protein are identical, is false, and that equation 9 is therefore

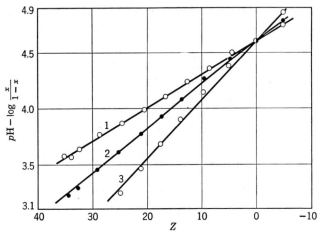

Fig. 3. Titration of the carboxyl groups of β-lactoglobulin (data of Cannan et al.[10]). Values of Z were estimated with the aid of chloride-binding studies by Carr.[13] Curve 1: $\mu = 0.270$; curve 2: $\mu = 0.069$; curve 3: $\mu = 0.019$.

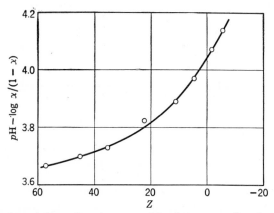

Fig. 4. Titration of the carboxyl groups of bovine serum albumin. Values of Z were obtained from Fig. 1, together with estimates of chloride binding made from the studies by Scatchard et al.[11] These estimates have a relatively high probable error since Scatchard's data were obtained almost entirely with isoionic serum albumin.

not applicable to them. However, if calculations are made of the type of plot to be expected in Fig. 4 if non-identical groups are treated by equation 9 (with W constant), one obtains a curve that is concave downwards or an S-shaped curve with a prominent concave downward portion; or, if there is an even distribution of pK'_{int} values over a range of up to 0.5, a straight line is obtained that has a slope corresponding to a value of W larger than the assumed value.

It must therefore be concluded that the curvature of Fig. 4 is primarily due to a change in W with pH. If a single value of pK'_{int} is

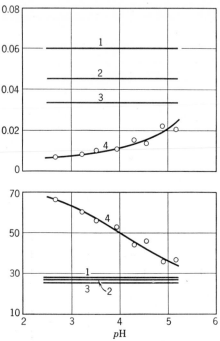

Fig. 5. Values of W (eq. 9, top figure) and of the radius of an equivalent electrostatic sphere (in Angstrom units, bottom figure) as functions of pH. Curves 1, 2, 3: β-lactoglobulin at ionic strengths 0.019, 0.069, and 0.270, respectively. Curve 4: bovine serum albumin, ionic strength 0.15.

assumed, the values of W shown in Fig. 5 are obtained. A rapid decrease in W with decreasing pH is seen to occur. Throughout the range, the value of W is smaller than the calculated value used in the past for serum albumin.[12, 18] If a variation in pK'_{int} were superimposed on the variation in W, the true values of W would be even smaller. It must be concluded that an expansion of the serum albumin molecule occurs as the pH is decreased on the acid side. That such expansion takes place has already been suggested by Scatchard.[10]

The curvature of Fig. 4 could also be caused by dissociation rather than unfolding, since, if a constant molecular weight is assumed, dissociation would appear formally in equation 9 as an increased charge separation. That such dissociation occurs has been suggested by Weber.[22] The reversibility of the titration curve and, especially, its independence of protein concentration would appear to favor the unfolding process. A more detailed study of these points is in progress.

No theory is at present available to enable one to estimate the size and shape of a protein molecule from the value of W, unless the molecule is spherical.[23] Figure 5 accordingly shows the radius of a sphere electrostatically equivalent to the serum albumin molecule as a function of pH. It is seen that the "theoretical" value of 30 A.[24] is approached in the neutral region. On the acid side, however, a radius as high as 70 A. is attained. It is of interest that the values of W for β-lactoglobulin at different ionic strengths all lead to essentially the same radius for the equivalent electrostatic sphere, i.e., it appears that the size of the β-lactoglobulin molecule in the acid pH range is independent not only of pH but also of ionic strength.

Finally, Table 3 shows the values of pK'_{int} obtained from Figs. 3 and 4. If the independent dissociating units of the acid titration region

TABLE 3. INTRINSIC IONIZATION CONSTANTS OF CARBOXYL GROUPS

	pK'_{int} *	Reference
ROOC—$(CH_2)_2$—COOH	4.52	†
ROOC—$(CH_2)_4$—COOH	4.60	†
CH_3—CO—$(CH_2)_2$—COOH	4.59	†
β-Lactoglobulin	4.60	Fig. 3
Bovine serum albumin	4.03	Fig. 4

* These constants will depend somewhat on ionic strength. None of the data here presented are likely to be sufficiently precise to show this variation.

† Reference 6, pp. 121, 135.

of a protein are *isolated* carboxyl groups derived from aspartyl or glutamyl residues, then the value of pK'_{int} should be roughly the same as the acid pK of an aliphatic acid with a polar group in the β or γ position. The pK's of three such acids are listed in Table 3. They all fall between 4.5 and 4.6. The fact that pK'_{int} for the carboxyl groups of β-lactoglobulin also falls into this range, therefore, indicates strongly that these groups do indeed act as isolated units. This is far from true in the case of bovine serum albumin, however. The very low value of pK'_{int} obtained for this protein indicates a specific interaction of its carboxyl groups with some other groups in such a way that the ionized form is favored by about 1000 calories in free energy. One is tempted to suggest that this interaction represents some form of cross-link that helps to maintain the albumin molecule in a compact configuration. The binding of hydrogen ions by the carboxyl groups would then rupture these cross-links and cause an expansion of the molecule, as is actually observed.

The analysis here illustrated for the carboxyl groups of a protein can now be extended to other regions containing identical groups, and conclusions about the nature of these groups and the shape and size of the protein molecule in the appropriate pH region can be reached. An important test of consistency must be met when this is done: since W represents a non-specific effect of the protein molecule as a whole, it must show no discontinuity as we proceed from one region to another and, in particular, at any pH in a region of overlap, the value of W must be the same for each type of group being titrated.

If this test of consistency is not met, one must proceed by a method of trial and error. The number of groups assumed to belong to a given region may be changed by one or two (e.g., there might be one hundred six groups in the acid region of serum albumin, rather than one hundred five), or it may be necessary to assume a range of intrinsic pK values in a given region, rather than one single value. The final test must always be this: All reversible portions of a hydrogen ion titration curve must be reproduced exactly by a calculated curve computed from the assigned values of W, the number present of each type of group, and the corresponding values of pK'_{int}.

IRREVERSIBLE CURVES

A typical example of an irreversible titration curve is that recently reported for hemoglobin by Steinhardt and Zaiser.[25] If neutral hemoglobin is titrated towards the acid side, a relatively flat curve is obtained, suggesting the presence of relatively few carboxyl groups. Near pH 3, however, a time-dependent transition occurs, corresponding to the liberation of thirty-six new groups per hemoglobin molecule. This process is irreversible and back-titration from the acid side yields an entirely different curve. An attempt to characterize precisely these thirty-six groups and their liberation has not been made, although the groups have been tentatively identified as carboxyl and/or imidazole groups.

Actually, no systematic analysis of such irreversible hydrogen ion titration curves has ever been made. One possible approach would be to test the reversibility of the back-titration curve. It is possible that after the release of the thirty-six previously inaccessible groups of hemoglobin a stable configuration is reached that may be capable of reversible equilibrium with hydrogen ion over a wide range of pH.

If this is so, an equilibrium analysis may be made for this irreversibly altered form of hemoglobin. A similar analysis for the native form can probably be made at least for a limited pH range, and it is possible to extend the range by intelligent extrapolation of the titration curve for the native form. A comparison between the two forms can then be made, and the thirty-six groups may be unequivocally identified.

A similar procedure may probably be employed in other instances of irreversibility. In some cases of irreversibility the situation may be simpler. It has already been shown in the case of serum albumin that portions of a titration curve may be accompanied by changes in configuration, although equilibrium is maintained throughout. The equilibrium may, however, be a metastable one so that reversal of the direction of titration may lead to a different curve. In this case both curves would, of course, be amenable to an equilibrium analysis.

THE COMBINATION OF PROTEINS WITH METALLIC AND OTHER IONS

A considerable amount of work has been done in recent years on the combination of ions other than hydrogen ion with proteins. Some of these ions may well have specific affinity for one kind of group only. It can be argued that the state of reactive groups in protein molecules can be better investigated by obtaining thermodynamic constants for a series of such specific reactions rather than by study of hydrogen ion equilibria. This is probably true. However, any ion wishing to combine with one of the reactive groups must compete with either hydrogen or hydroxyl ion, since the presence of these ions in aqueous solutions cannot be avoided. Except at extreme pH values far removed from the hydrogen-ion titration region of a reactive group, significant thermodynamic data for the combination of any other ion with such a group cannot be obtained unless the thermodynamic constants for the equilibrium of the reactive group with hydrogen ion are first obtained. Furthermore, electrostatic interaction plays a role in the combination of all ions with proteins, and the charge on the protein molecule at any pH must therefore be known, which again is not possible without a previous study of the reaction with hydrogen ion.

It is clear, therefore, that hydrogen ion titration curves not only have great value in themselves but are also a necessary prerequisite to the study of the combination of any other ion with protein molecules.

Finally, it should be pointed out that it is theoretically possible to study the interaction of ions other than hydrogen ion with proteins by the effect of these ions on hydrogen ion titration curves. This method has been applied to the combination of metals with weak bases, including amino acids, but not as yet to proteins.[26]

REFERENCES AND NOTES

1. This investigation was supported by a research grant from the National Institutes of Health, Public Health Service.

2. D. A. MacInnes, *The Principles of Electrochemistry*, p. 261, Reinhold Publishing Corp., New York, 1939.

3. The general-purpose type has been used. Even at high pH, this electrode gives results more reproducible than those obtained with a type E electrode, provided that sodium ions are excluded.

4. Obtained from the National Bureau of Standards, Washington 25, D. C.

5. J. Steinhardt and E. M. Zaiser, *J. Biol. Chem., 190,* 197 (1951).

6. E. J. Cohn and J. T. Edsall, *Proteins, Amino-Acids and Peptides,* Chapter 20, Reinhold Publishing Co., New York, 1943.

7. H. S. Harned and B. B. Owen, *The Physical Chemistry of Electrolytic Solutions,* 2nd Ed., Appendix A, Reinhold Publishing Corp., New York, 1950.

8. It is not implied here that pOH and pH are equal to $-\log a_{OH^-}$ and $-\log a_{H^+}$, respectively, or that the activity of water is equal to unity. Equation 5 is merely intended to convert pH into an arbitrary quantity more closely equal to $-\log m_{OH^-}$.

9. G. Scatchard, *Ann. N. Y. Acad. Sci., 51,* 660 (1949).

10. G. Scatchard, *American Scientist, 40,* 61 (1952).

11. J. Wyman, *J. Biol. Chem., 127,* 1 (1939).

12. C. Tanford, *J. Am. Chem. Soc., 72,* 441 (1950).

13. J. L. Crammer and A. Neuberger, *Biochem. J., 37,* 302 (1943).

14. C. Tanford and G. L. Roberts, Jr., *J. Am. Chem. Soc., 74,* 2509 (1952).

15. On the basis of amino acid analysis, one of these one hundred and five groups is likely to be an α-carboxyl group with characteristics different from the remainder, which are derived from glutamyl or aspartyl side chains. The presence of one different group among one hundred and four identical ones is however experimentally not detectable.

16. R. K. Cannan, A. H. Palmer, and A. C. Kibrick, *J. Biol. Chem., 142,* 803 (1942).

17. It is here assumed that the measured pH is identical with $-\log a_{H^+}$. This is, of course, not true. The uncertainty so introduced is, however, smaller than the final uncertainty in computed values of pK'_{int}.

18. G. Scatchard, I. H. Scheinberg, and S. H. Armstrong, Jr., *J. Am. Chem. Soc., 72,* 535 (1950).

19. C. W. Carr, *Arch. Biochem. and Biophys., 40,* 286 (1952).

20. See, for example, R. K. Cannan and co-workers, *Ann. N. Y. Acad. Sci., 41,* 243 (1941); also references 9, 12, and 16.

21. C. W. Carr, personal communication.

22. G. Weber, *Discussions Faraday Soc.,* No. 13, 33 (1953).

23. K. Linderstrøm-Lang, *Compt. rend. trav. lab. Carlsberg, 15,* No. 7 (1924); see also references 9 and 12.

24. G. Scatchard, A. C. Batchelder, and A. Brown, *J. Am. Chem. Soc., 68,* 2320 (1946).

25. J. Steinhardt and E. M. Zaiser, *J. Biol. Chem., 190,* 197 (1951); *J. Am. Chem. Soc., 75,* 1599 (1953); *Federation Proc., 12,* 295 (1953).

26. Since this paper was written, this method has been applied to the combination of zinc with insulin. See C. Tanford and J. Epstein, *J. Am. Chem. Soc., 76,* 3331 (1954).

14·

Determination of Ionic Activity
in Protein Solutions with
Collodion Membrane Electrodes *

CHARLES W. CARR †

INTRODUCTION

The study of the interaction of various ions with proteins in solution has been of considerable interest for many years. It is now well known that the activity of many ionic substances is markedly influenced by the presence of proteins, the most familiar case being that of the binding of acids and bases. Through the use of various experimental techniques it has also been shown that the activity of many organic ions, heavy metal cations, and alkaline earth cations is decreased considerably in protein solutions, owing to combination with the proteins. More recently it has been found that many of the common inorganic anions, including chloride, are bound to a certain extent to proteins.[1] There are some indications that the alkali metal cations may also interact with some proteins, but this problem has not been completely elucidated.[2]

It is our intention here to show how membrane electrodes can be applied to the study of the interaction of small ions with various proteins. With such electrodes it is possible to measure the activity of many ions in a manner similar to the measurement of hydrogen ion activity with the glass electrode. In experiments of this nature, any decrease in activity of a given species of ion in a protein solution below that which it shows in a solution of the same ionic concentration

* This investigation was supported in part by a research grant awarded by the National Institutes of Health, U. S. Public Health Service; and in part by a grant from the Medical Research Fund of the Graduate School of the University of Minnesota.

† From the Department of Physiological Chemistry, University of Minnesota, Minneapolis, Minn.

without protein is taken to be an indication of some type of interaction between the ion and the protein.

Specific electrodes for the determination of the activities of certain small ions have occasionally been used in the past. Many attempts have been made to use calcium amalgam and sodium amalgam electrodes for the determination of calcium and sodium ion activities in protein solutions. However, extreme care is necessary in the preparation and use of such electrodes, and in addition it appears that an error is introduced by the presence of protein. For these reasons amalgam electrodes are limited in their usefulness for such studies. Hitchcock [3] and Northrop and Kunitz [4] have used the silver-silver chloride electrode to measure the chloride ion activity in gelatin solutions. Scatchard, Scheinberg, and Armstrong [5] have very successfully used this electrode to measure the binding of chloride ions in solutions of serum albumin. These workers have also measured the binding of thiocyanate ion in serum albumin solutions with the silver-silver thiocyanate electrode.[6] These are the only two ions, however, whose activity in protein solutions has been accurately measured by such electrodes.

Membrane electrodes for the determination of ion activities other than hydrogen have just recently been developed. Sollner and co-workers [7] have prepared collodion membranes that may be used for the determination of most of the common anions and cations. Marshall and his collaborators [8] have used clay membranes successfully for the activity determinations of sodium, potassium, ammonium, magnesium, and calcium ions. Wyllie and Patnode [9] have prepared artificial membranes by bonding a cation-exchange resin in an inert plastic. Their membranes have been found to give good results for the determination of sodium ion activities in solutions as concentrated as 4 molal sodium chloride. Juda and co-workers [10] have prepared membranes similar to those of Wyllie and Patnode,[9] and Scatchard [11] discusses the use of such membranes in another chapter of this volume.

EXPERIMENTAL PROCEDURE

COLLODION MEMBRANES AS ELECTRODES

The procedure that is used in the present work was first described by Sollner [12] and later worked out in detail by Gregor and Sollner.[13] The activity of the ion being studied is determined by making potential measurements across specially prepared membranes. If the activity of an anion is desired, an anion-selective membrane is used, and a cation-selective membrane is used for the measurement of cation activities. An anion-selective membrane is positively charged and allows the passage of anions but restricts the passage of cations. The reverse is true for a cation-selective membrane. We have used the positively charged protamine-collodion membrane [14] for the measurement of anion activities and the negatively charged sulfonated polystyrene collodion membrane [15] for the measurement of cation activities. These membranes allow the rapid exchange of ions of one charge across them but are almost completely impermeable to ions of the opposite charge. Thus when only one kind of anion is present on both sides of the protamine-collodion membrane, it behaves as a reversible electrode for that particular anion. Since all small anions give rise to potentials across the membrane, only one anion (the one being measured) can be present in the solution at the time of measurement. This is the one major difference between such specific electrodes as the silver-silver chloride electrode and the membrane electrode. In other respects the behavior of the two types of electrodes may be considered in much the same light. Errors inherent in the measurement of single-ion activities by the use of a specific electrode will also arise in the use of the membrane electrode.

The exact procedure for making the activity determinations involves the carrying out of a potentiometric titration. The membranes are bag shaped, being cast on the outside of rotating test tubes. The membranes that have been used for most of our measurements hold about 30 ml.; however, it has been shown that accurate measurements can be made with membranes that hold as little as 3 ml. of solution.[16]

A known volume of water is added to a beaker of such size that the beaker is one-half to two-thirds filled. Next, the membrane is filled with the solution to be investigated. About two-thirds of its length is immersed in the beaker containing the water, and the membrane is then clamped in position. For a clamp a wooden test tube holder held to a ring stand with a right-angle clamp is convenient. Thus, at the beginning of the titration we have the solution of unknown activity on one side of the membrane and a known volume of water on the other side.

The titrating solution is a known concentration of an electrolyte that has the same ion as the one being determined. Its concentration should be at least ten times that of the solution being titrated to avoid the addition of excessively large volumes that would be needed to reach the end point. A known volume of this solution is added to the known volume of water, and, after thorough mixing, the e.m.f. of the following system is measured:

$$\text{Hg} \,|\, \text{Hg}_2\text{Cl}_2(s) \,\, \text{KCl(sat.)} \,\Big|\, \begin{matrix} \text{outside} \\ \text{solution} \\ c_1 \end{matrix} \,\Big|\, \text{membrane} \,\Big|\, \begin{matrix} \text{inside} \\ \text{solution} \\ c_2 \end{matrix} \,\Big|\, \text{KCl(sat.)} \,\, \text{Hg}_2\text{Cl}_2(s) \,|\, \text{Hg}$$

The saturated calomel electrodes are connected with the two solutions by means of specially constructed agar bridges saturated with potassium chloride. These bridges are made with 3-mm. glass tubing, and the tips, which make contact with the solutions, are about 1 mm. in diameter. The small contact area is necessary to minimize the diffusion of potassium chloride into either solution. To minimize this diffusion still further, the bridges are removed from the two solutions after each measurement of the potential and placed in saturated potassium chloride solution.

In making the potential measurements, two readings are always taken. After the first reading, the agar-potassium chloride bridges are changed around so that the solutions with which they are in contact become reversed. A second reading is then taken, which usually varies from the first by a few tenths of a millivolt. The average of the two readings is taken to be the observed potential. This procedure is repeated after each addition of titrating solution and is continued until the potential reverses in sign. Usually three points are sufficient to complete a titration.

The potential measurements are plotted on the linear axis of semilogarithmic graph paper, and the concentration of the outside solution is plotted on the logarithmic axis. A straight line with nearly the theoretical slope is always obtained. The intersection of this line with the line of zero potential gives the concentration (and thus the activity) of the ion being measured in the outside solution that equals the activity of that ion in the protein (inside) solution. This concentration at which the zero potential is obtained is referred to as the end point of the titration. For known solutions in the range of concentration of 0.005 to 0.2 M, the correct end point can be reproduced with an accuracy of about ± 1–2%.

Before making a general study of the binding of ions to proteins, it was necessary to determine the pH range in which the membranes can be used without introducing serious error. Sodium chloride solutions (0.100 N) were prepared, and the pH of these solutions was varied by addition of small amounts of hydrochloric acid or sodium hydroxide. Although the pH values of these unbuffered solutions were not known very accurately, they were known with sufficient accuracy to determine in which range of pH the membranes would be useful. The solutions were titrated immediately after preparation with the use of a neutral solution of 1 N sodium chloride as the titrant. It was found with our titration procedure that the correct end point was obtained only in the pH range of 4.5–11.0 when the negative membranes were used.[17] Similarly, with the positive membranes accurate results were obtained only in the pH range of 2.0–9.5.

THE PREPARATION AND MEASUREMENT OF THE PROTEIN SOLUTIONS

In preparing the protein solutions for measurement, it is first necessary to remove any electrolyte which might be present. This is usually done by exhaustively dialyzing and finally electrodialyzing the protein to be studied. Protein solutions containing a single salt are then prepared from this electrolyte-free protein and standard solutions of the salt containing the ion that is to be measured. For anion measurements the sodium salt has always been used, and for cation measurements the chloride salt has been used. The pH is adjusted to the desired value by the addition of the appropriate solution of standard acid or alkali as required. For example, in the chloride ion measurements, hydrochloric acid is used to adjust the pH below the isoelectric point; in the thiocyanate ion measurements, thiocyanic acid is used; and for all the various anions, sodium hydroxide is added to adjust the pH above the isoelectric point. On the other hand, for sodium ion measurements, sodium hydroxide is used to adjust the pH above the isoelectric point; for the calcium ion measurements, calcium hydroxide is used; and for all the various cations, hydrochloric acid is used to adjust the pH below the isoelectric point. For those proteins that are insoluble at the isoelectric point, the proteins are first dissolved in solutions of either standard acid or alkali, and the pH is adjusted by the addition of the appropriate solution.

When the protein solution has been prepared containing a known amount of the ion being studied and adjusted to the desired pH, it is titrated according to the procedure outlined in the previous section. The concentration at the end point of the ion being studied in the outside solution is then compared with the known concentration of that ion in the protein solution. If that is less than the concentration in the protein solution, it is assumed that the difference is caused by the binding of that particular ion to the protein molecule. The amount of this ion bound to the protein is then calculated directly from this difference in concentration between the two solutions. The accompanying figures are given as a sample calculation. In those instances

Solution titrated: serum albumin (2%) + CaCl₂, pH = 7.4

Concentration of Ca added: 0.00619 M
Concentration of Ca measured: 0.00485 M
Concentration of Ca bound   0.00134 M

$0.00134/20 \times 70,000 = 4.7$ moles Ca/mole albumin

where the molecular weight of the protein is not known or it is desirable to compare various proteins, it has been found convenient to express the binding in terms of moles ion bound/10^5 gm. protein.

Since we are taking the difference in concentration between two solutions to be a measure of ion binding, the probable error in this quantity may be quite large. This error in the measurement of the amount of binding decreases as the difference in concentration between the two solutions increases. For example, let us consider a protein solution in which the calcium concentration is known to be 0.1000 ± 0.0001. If this is titrated and the end point is found to be 0.096 ± 0.001, the probable error in the calculated amount of bound calcium is 27%. If, for the same calcium concentration, the end point is 0.090 ± 0.001, then the error is 11%; and if the end point is 0.080 ± 0.001, the error is only 5%.

EXPERIMENTAL RESULTS

THE BINDING OF ANIONS

Our first experiments on the binding of anions to proteins were concerned with chloride and bovine serum albumin.[18] Scatchard and his co-workers had shown by several techniques that chloride is bound in significant amounts by serum albumin, and it was therefore of considerable interest to compare our method with these other better-established methods. In Figure 1 is shown such a comparison of results obtained with the protamine collodion membrane and those of Scatchard, Scheinberg, and Armstrong[5] obtained with the silver-silver chloride electrode and the technique of equilibrium dialysis. The average number of chloride ions bound per albumin molecule ($\bar{v}$) is plotted on one axis, and the logarithm of the free chloride ion concentration is plotted on the other axis.

In most of the published investigations on the binding of anions by serum albumin, the bovine serum albumin has been used. Some experiments, including those of Scatchard and his group, have been carried out with human serum albumin. Also, Klotz and Urquhart[19] have compared the binding of some anions to bovine and human serum

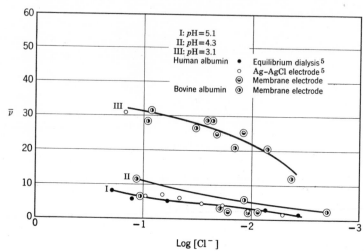

Fig. 1. The binding of chloride ion in solutions of serum albumin. [*Arch. Biochem. and Biophys., 40*, 290 (1952).]

albumin. Most indications have been that there is no appreciable difference between the two types of albumin in their binding of a given kind of anion. However, just recently Klotz, Burkhard, and Urquhart [20] have shown that above a pH of 7 the binding of certain dye anions to human albumin differs considerably from that for bovine albumin. To make the comparison of our results with those of Scatchard, Scheinberg, and Armstrong more significant, we have compared the two types of albumin for their binding of chloride.

Two experiments were carried out with human serum albumin fractionated with ammonium sulfate, one at pH 5.1 and the other at pH 3.1; the values obtained for $\bar{\nu}$ are plotted in Fig. 1. Similarly, two measurements were made with the albumin fractionated with ethanol by the procedure developed by Cohn, Edsall,[21] and co-workers. It can be seen from the graph that these values are the same, within the experimental error, as those obtained for bovine serum albumin.

The binding of chloride to several other proteins has also been determined.[22] A summary of our results obtained with six different proteins is shown in Fig. 2. In this instance, the pH is plotted as abscissa, and the extent of binding is plotted as the ordinate. In order to compare the various proteins, the binding is calculated as moles chloride bound/10^5 grams protein. The concentration of free chloride ion in all cases was in the range of 12–19 mmoles/liter. For example,

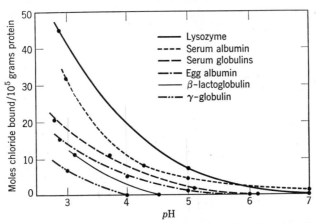

Fig. 2. The binding of chloride to various proteins when the chloride concentration is 12–19 mmoles/*l*. [*Arch. Biochem. and Biophys.*, *46*, 419 (1953).]

in the curve for lysozyme the chloride concentration at *p*H 5.1 was 19.1 mmoles/liter and at *p*H 2.9 was 17.2 mmoles/liter. Although the binding is known to increase with increasing concentration,[5,22] it was felt that over this range the differences were insignificant when compared with the effect of *p*H.

According to our results, the binding of chloride to proteins in the *p*H range 3–6 decreases in the order lysozyme > serum albumin > serum globulins > egg albumin > β-lactoglobulin > γ-globulin. In addition, several other proteins tested at single *p*H values showed no detectable binding of chloride. These include casein and gelatin at *p*H 5.0, fibrinogen at *p*H 3.9, hemoglobin at *p*H 6.8, and pepsin at *p*H 3.7.

Measurements of the thiocyanate ion activity in solutions of bovine serum albumin also have been found to be in agreement with the results of Scatchard, Scheinberg, and Armstrong.[6] A summary of these results is shown in Fig. 3. The curves are much the same as those for chloride except that, at a given *p*H and anion concentration, $\bar{\nu}$ for thiocyanate is considerably greater than for chloride.

Experiments have also been carried out to show that the protamine collodion membrane electrode can be used to determine the activity of many different small anions. For some of these anions there is no other type of reversible electrode that can be used for these measurements. The activity of chloride, bromide, iodide, thiocyanate, nitrate, perchlorate, and sulfate ions in solutions of bovine serum albumin are compared in Table 1. It can be seen that the amounts of these ions

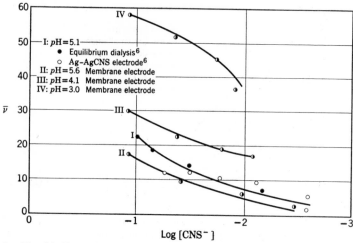

Fig. 3.   The binding of thiocyanate ion in solutions of bovine serum albumin.
[*Arch. Biochem. and Biophys., 40*, 291 (1952).]

TABLE 1.   THE BINDING OF VARIOUS ANIONS BY BOVINE SERUM ALBUMIN *

Protein Concentration mmoles/liter	pH	Anion	Concentration of Anion Added molal	Concentration of Anion Measured molal	$\bar{\nu}$
0.310	5.0	Cl^-	0.1000	0.0975	8
0.310	5.1	Br^-	0.1000	0.0955	15
0.310	5.2	NO_3^-	0.1000	0.0940	19
0.310	5.3	CNS^-	0.1000	0.0925	24
0.275	5.1	I^-	0.0250	0.0217	12
0.290	5.1	CNS^-	0.0200	0.0165	12
0.310	5.2	ClO_4^-	0.0450	0.0420	10
0.232	5.1	$SO_4^=$	0.0118	0.0103	6.5

* *Arch. Biochem. and Biophys., 40*, 293 (1952).

bound to serum albumin increase in the order $Cl < Br < NO_3 < I = CNS$. This is in general agreement with other workers using other techniques.[23]

THE BINDING OF CATIONS

Most of the data we have obtained so far on the binding of cations with proteins has been concerned with the alkaline earth cations, the principal one of interest being calcium.[24]   Again, the first measurements were made with bovine serum albumin. Determinations were carried out involving the rate of establishment of the protein-calcium equilibrium, the effect of calcium ion concentration, and the effect of pH.

In comparison with other methods that have been used for measuring calcium binding to proteins, the membrane electrode is especially well adapted to measurements of the rate of establishment of the equilibrium. The procedure consists merely in measuring potentials of systems immediately after mixing. Stable, reproducible potentials are obtained within 1–2 sec. after solutions are brought in contact with the membrane. Therefore, any change in potential after this time must be due to a change in calcium ion activity in one or both of the two solutions on the two sides of the membrane.

In one experiment equal volumes of 4% serum albumin and 0.004 M calcium hydroxide were mixed inside an appropriate membrane. In the outside solution was placed 0.001 M calcium chloride. The membrane potential was measured as soon as possible after mixing (4–5 sec.) and every 5 min. after that for 30 min. The potential at 5 sec. was 11.3 mv., and it remained unchanged throughout the 30 min. A second experiment, in which the protein concentration was increased and the calcium concentration and pH were decreased, showed the same results. It was concluded that the association and dissociation of the calcium-albumin complex is not a slow reaction. When there is a change in concentration of one of the components, the new equilibrium is established in less than 5 sec.

A number of determinations of the binding of calcium by bovine serum albumin had been made at the physiological pH (7.40 ± 0.05). The proteins used for these experiments were three different preparations of Armour's bovine serum albumin. The protein concentration was in the range of 1.0–3.3%, and the total calcium concentration was varied over the range of 1–50 mmoles/liter. The results of these experiments are shown graphically in Fig. 4. The number of moles of calcium bound/10^5 gm. protein is plotted as ordinate, and the measured calcium-ion concentration is plotted as the abscissa. The curve shown in Fig. 4 brings out the striking feature that a definite maximum is reached in the amount of calcium that can be bound by serum albumin. When the calcium ion concentration increases above 15 mmoles/liter, no further increase in the binding of calcium occurs. The maximum amount of calcium bound to bovine serum albumin appears to be 11 ± 1 moles/10^5 gm. protein, which corresponds to about 7–8 calcium ions per albumin molecule.

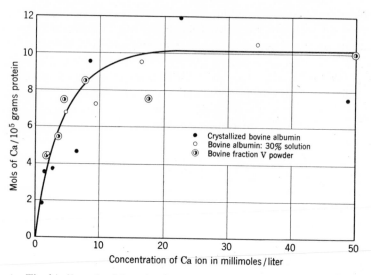

Fig. 4.   The binding of calcium ion in solutions of bovine serum albumin at pH 7.4.   [*Arch. Biochem. and Biophys.*, *43*, 151 (1953).]

To determine the dissociation constant for the calcium-albumin interaction, we have made the calculations in the same way as many other investigators.[25]   The average value for pK$_{\text{CaProt}}$ that we obtain is 2.43 $\pm$ 0.04, it being the same for the three different Armour preparations.   This value for pK$_{\text{CaProt}}$ is a little greater than those obtained by other methods.   The frog heart method [26] gave 2.0, and the use of CaCO$_3$ solubility gave 2.2 for this constant.[27]

Although the idea is well accepted that calcium is bound to the plasma proteins at the physiological pH, the effects of pH changes on this interaction have not been definitely established.   To look into this further we have used the membrane electrode to measure the calcium ion activity in serum albumin solutions of varying pH.   The results of such experiments are presented in Table 2.   These results show that there is a large increase in the binding of calcium ion as the pH increases above the isoelectric point.   For example, over the range 6.7–7.6 there is a 75% increase in the amount of calcium bound per gram of serum albumin.   Also, the binding reaches zero at a pH somewhat above the isoelectric point.   Thus the effect of pH on the binding of calcium to serum albumin seems to parallel the behavior of anion binding to serum albumin.   In the anion interaction, the binding increases as the pH decreases or as the number of net positive charges on the albumin molecule increases.   For calcium, the binding increases as the

TABLE 2. THE BINDING OF CALCIUM BY BOVINE SERUM ALBUMIN AT VARIOUS pH's *

Concentration of albumin = 2.0%
Concentration of added Ca = 2.81 mm./l.

pH	Concentration of Ca Measured mm./l.	Bound Calcium mm./l.	Moles Ca Bound per 10^5 Gram Protein
8.30	1.75	1.06	5.3
7.59	2.05	0.76	3.8
7.36	2.18	0.63	3.2
7.04	2.27	0.54	2.7
6.74	2.38	0.43	2.2
6.42	2.45	0.36	1.8
5.95	2.58	0.23	1.2
5.20	2.84	−0.03	−0.2

* Arch. Biochem. and Biophys., 43, 154 (1953).

pH increases or as the number of net negative charges on the albumin molecule increases.

On the basis of our knowledge concerning the binding of chloride to serum albumin at pH's as high as 7.4, it seemed possible that calcium might not be taken up exclusively by the albumin. Perhaps the binding of the positive calcium ions to the negatively charged protein would even enhance the binding of chloride. Since we had readily available a rapid method for the determination of anion binding, we have made measurements of the chloride-ion activity in a few of the solutions in which the calcium-ion activity has also been measured. The results of these measurements are shown in Table 3. In all but one instance the chloride ion activity remained the same as in a calcium chloride

TABLE 3. CALCIUM-ION AND CHLORIDE-ION MEASUREMENTS IN THE SAME ALBUMIN SOLUTION *

Concentration of Albumin %	pH	Concentration of Added Ca mmoles/liter	Concentration of Measured Ca mmoles/liter	Concentration of Added Cl mmoles/liter	Concentration of Measured Cl mmoles/liter
1.0	7.1	6.8	6.2	11.4	11.1
1.0	8.0	8.2	7.0	11.2	11.2
2.1	7.4	10.8	9.0	14.6	14.7
3.0	7.4	56.0	52.8	100.0	98.0

* Arch. Biochem. and Biophys., 43, 155 (1953).

solution containing no protein. In the one instance where the chloride level is 100 mmoles/liter, there may be a significant decrease in the chloride ion concentration. However, this is no greater than the binding of chloride in solutions of sodium chloride and serum albumin at the same concentration and pH. Therefore, it can be concluded that the binding of calcium to proteins has no detectable effect on the binding of the accompanying chloride ion.

Although considerable attention has been paid to the interaction of calcium with the serum proteins, very little study has been made of

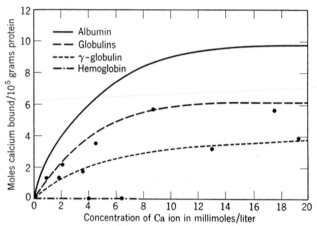

Fig. 5. The binding of calcium to various bovine blood proteins. pH = 7.4.
[*Arch. Biochem. and Biophys.*, *46*, **426** (1953).]

the other proteins. To obtain further insight into the factors affecting calcium binding, we have therefore made a number of measurements with proteins of widely varying composition.

A comparison of the binding of calcium to the various bovine blood proteins at pH 7.4 is shown in Fig. 5. The calcium-binding capacity of the globulin sample we measured is definitely lower than for serum albumin; and hemoglobin solutions show no detectable binding of calcium.

From Figure 6 the binding of serum albumin can be compared with three other well-characterized proteins, all of which have nearly the same isoelectric point. It is easily seen that there are large differences between these proteins. At pH 7.4 β-lactoglobulin and casein are capable of combining with at least twice as much calcium as serum albumin, and serum albumin in turn is capable of combining with at least twice as much calcium as egg albumin.

Experiments with three of the readily available crystalline enzymes
show quite strikingly how the calcium interaction with proteins can

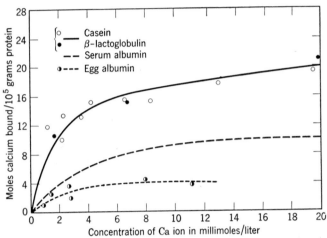

Fig. 6.   The binding of calcium to four proteins with similar isoelectric points.
$pH = 7.4$.   [*Arch. Biochem. and Biophys.*, *46*, **428** (1953).]

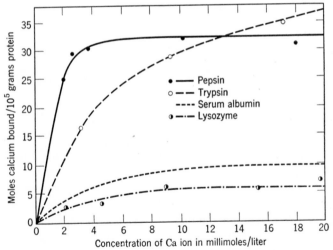

Fig. 7.   The binding of calcium to three different purified enzymes. $pH = 7.4$.
[*Arch. Biochem. and Biophys.*, *46*, **429** (1953).]

vary.   The values for the calcium-binding capacity at pH 7.4 for
lysozyme, trypsin, and pepsin are compared in Fig. 7.   The curve for
serum albumin is again added for reference.

Magnesium ion, which is important physiologically, has not been studied very extensively for its interaction with proteins. For that reason we have carried out several experiments with magnesium and a number of different proteins.

Experiments with solutions of serum albumin and magnesium chloride show that the binding of magnesium ion by this protein is essentially the same as for calcium. The effect of magnesium ion concentration on the extent of the binding at pH 7.4 is shown in Fig. 8. The

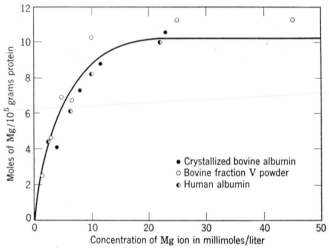

Fig. 8. The binding of magnesium ion in serum albumin solutions at pH 7.4.

solid line is the curve shown previously for serum albumin and calcium, whereas the various symbols are experimental points for magnesium. Measurements of the effect of pH on the binding of magnesium with serum albumin yield results very similar to those obtained for calcium, which were given in Table 2.

Further experiments with magnesium and other proteins result in curves just like those shown for calcium. In Table 4 are listed the values for the maximum binding observed with magnesium and six different proteins at pH 7.4 and a similar set of values for calcium with these same proteins at the same pH. It will be seen that there are no significant differences between the values for calcium and those for magnesium.

It might also be added here that a set of measurements with barium and serum albumin and strontium with the same protein again yielded the same curve as obtained for calcium. Thus with our method of

TABLE 4. A COMPARISON OF THE MAXIMUM BINDING OF CALCIUM AND
MAGNESIUM TO VARIOUS PROTEINS AT pH 7.4

Protein	Moles Ca Bound/10^5 Gram	Moles Mg Bound/10^5 Gram
Serum albumin	10.5	11.3
Serum globulins	5.6	6.2
Hemoglobin	0.0	0.0
Egg albumin	5.0	6.4
Lysozyme	7.0	7.6
Pepsin	31.0	34.0

measuring ion-binding, it is found that each of the four alkaline earths, magnesium, calcium, barium, and strontium, interact to the same extent with serum albumin.

It has been frequently assumed and in some cases actually determined that there is no significant binding of sodium or potassium by proteins. For most of the proteins we have studied, we have also found this to be true. For example, in solutions of the blood proteins serum albumin and hemoglobin at pH 7.4 we have found no significant lowering of the activity of either sodium or potassium over that which they show in pure solutions of sodium or potassium chloride. However, from several measurements with these ions in solutions of casein, it appears that they are bound to a considerable extent. For example, in a 1% solution of casein at pH 7.4 and a sodium ion concentration of 0.01 N, the activity of the sodium ion is decreased by an amount that would correspond to 17.5 moles of sodium/10^5 grams protein. In addition, the effect of pH seems to be very much the same as that observed for the calcium-casein interaction.

Since casein is a phosphoprotein, we thought it would be of especial interest to test another phosphoprotein, vitellin. This protein was prepared in a relatively pure form and tested for its ability to bind sodium. It was found to combine with sodium to about the same extent as casein. It thus appears that the phosphate groups in these proteins may be responsible for their interaction with the alkali metal ions.

CONCLUSIONS

On the basis of the results we have obtained, it has been concluded that the use of membrane electrodes can give useful results for the study of protein-small ion interactions. By measuring the interaction of different ions with proteins, we can get a better picture of protein structure and protein function. It should also be possible to study

enzyme activation by small ions to determine whether or not specific
binding of the ion by the enzyme is responsible for the activation.
Finally, the method is widely adaptable since it can be applied to the
measurement of the interactions of many species of cations and anions
with all types of colloidal electrolytes.

REFERENCES

1. G. Scatchard, I. H. Scheinberg, and S. H. Armstrong, Jr., *J. Am. Chem. Soc.*,
   72, 535, 540 (1950); I. M. Klotz and J. M. Urquhart, *J. Phys. & Colloid Chem.*,
   53, 100 (1949); G. Scatchard and E. S. Black, *J. Phys. & Colloid Chem.*, *53*,
   88 (1949).
2. W. O. Fenn, *Physiol. Rev.*, *16*, 450 (1936); J. P. Peters, *Physiol. Rev.*, *24*, 491
   (1944); H. B. Steinbach, in: *Modern Trends in Physiology and Biochemistry*,
   p. 173, Academic Press, New York, 1952.
3. D. I. Hitchcock, *J. Gen. Physiol.*, *12*, 495 (1928).
4. J. H. Northrop and M. Kunitz, *J. Gen. Physiol.*, *7*, 25 (1924–1925).
5. G. Scatchard, I. H. Scheinberg, and S. H. Armstrong, Jr., *J. Am. Chem. Soc.*,
   72, 535 (1950).
6. G. Scatchard, I. H. Scheinberg, and S. H. Armstrong, Jr., *J. Am. Chem. Soc.*,
   72, 540 (1950).
7. I. M. Abrams and K. Sollner, *J. Gen. Physiol.*, *26*, 369 (1943); C. W. Carr and
   K. Sollner, *J. Gen. Physiol.*, *28*, 119 (1944); H. P. Gregor and K. Sollner,
   J. Phys. Chem., *50*, 53, 88 (1946).
8. C. E. Marshall and A. D. Ayers, *J. Am. Chem. Soc.*, *70*, 1297 (1948); C. E.
   Marshall and W. E. Bergman, *J. Am. Chem. Soc.*, *63*, 1911 (1941); C. E. Marshall and W. E. Bergman, *J. Phys. Chem.*, *46*, 325 (1942); C. E. Marshall and
   L. O. Eime, *J. Am. Chem. Soc.*, *70*, 1302 (1948); C. E. Marshall and C. A.
   Krinbill, *J. Am. Chem. Soc.*, *64*, 1814 (1942).
9. M. J. R. Wyllie and H. W. Patnode, *J. Phys. & Colloid Chem.*, *54*, 204 (1950).
10. W. Juda and W. A. McRae, *J. Am. Chem. Soc.*, *72*, 1044 (1950); W. Juda,
    N. W. Rosenberg, J. A. Marinsky, and A. A. Kaspar, *J. Am. Chem. Soc.*, *74*,
    3736 (1952).
11. G. Scatchard, Chapter 3, this volume.
12. K. Sollner, *J. Am. Chem. Soc.*, *65*, 2260 (1943).
13. H. P. Gregor and K. Sollner, *J. Am. Chem. Soc.*, *58*, 409 (1954).
14. I. Abrams and K. Sollner, *J. Gen. Physiol.*, *26*, 369 (1943); H. P. Gregor and
    K. Sollner, *J. Phys. Chem.*, *50*, 88 (1946).
15. K. Sollner and R. A. Neihof, *Arch. Biochem. and Biophys.*, *33*, 166 (1951).
16. H. P. Gregor, Ph.D. Thesis, University of Minnesota, 1945.
17. C. W. Carr and L. Topol, *J. Phys. & Colloid Chem.*, *54*, 176 (1950).
18. C. W. Carr, *Arch. Biochem. and Biophys.*, *40*, 286 (1952).
19. I. M. Klotz and J. M. Urquhart, *J. Phys. & Colloid Chem.*, *53*, 100 (1949).
20. I. M. Klotz, R. K. Burkhard, and J. M. Urquhart, *J. Am. Chem. Soc.*, *74*, 202
    (1952).
21. J. T. Edsall, *Advances in Protein Chem.*, *3*, 383 (1947).
22. C. W. Carr, *Arch. Biochem. and Biophys.*, *46*, 417 (1953).

23. J. Steinhardt, C. H. Fugitt, and M. Harris, *J. Research Natl. Bur. Standards*, *26*, 293 (1941); G. Scatchard and E. S. Black, *J. Phys. & Colloid Chem.*, *53*, 88 (1949); I. M. Klotz and J. M. Urquhart, *J. Phys. & Colloid. Chem.*, *53*, 100 (1949).
24. C. W. Carr, *Arch. Biochem. and Biophys.*, *43*, 147 (1953); C. W. Carr, *Arch. Biochem. and Biophys.*, *46*, 424 (1953).
25. A. B. Hastings and F. C. McLean, *J. Biol. Chem.*, *108*, 285 (1935); E. G. Weir and A. B. Hastings, *J. Biol. Chem.*, *114*, 397 (1936); A. Chanutin, S. Ludewig, and A. V. Masket, *J. Biol. Chem.*, *143*, 737 (1942); D. M. Greenberg, *Amino Acids and Proteins*, Charles C Thomas, Springfield, Ill., 1951.
26. A. B. Hastings and F. C. McLean, *J. Biol. Chem.*, *108*, 285 (1935).
27. E. G. Weir and A. B. Hastings, *J. Biol. Chem.*, *114*, 397 (1936).

15.

Activity Coefficients of Some Sodium
and Potassium Phosphates
in Aqueous Solutions [1]

FRED M. SNELL [*,2]

In the consideration of the various mechanisms whereby ionic concentration gradients are established and maintained in a selective manner in biological systems, the carrier hypothesis has received considerable attention. For the simplest cases of uni-univalent ion pair association or complex formation, with obvious reference to sodium and potassium, this hypothesis may be formulated as follows:

$$\text{Me}'^{+} + \text{X}'^{-} = \text{MeX}' \xrightarrow[\text{cellular membrane}]{\text{diffusion across}} \text{MeX}'' = \text{Me}''^{+} + \text{X}''^{-}$$

Me^{+} represents the cation to be transported and X^{-} the carrier anion. The single and double prime refer to the two phases separated by the membrane. If the cell membrane is an effective barrier to the diffusion of free ions relative to the diffusion of the complex, MeX and the reactions of ionic association and dissociation are not rate limiting, accumulation of Me''^{+} would occur provided the chemical potential of MeX'' remained less than the chemical potential of MeX'. Coupling of these reactions with metabolic processes could be achieved by postulating a source of X'^{-} and a sink for X''^{-}. The selectivity of this transport process for the various cationic species would be a function of the relative dissociation constants and diffusion coefficients of the complexes and possibly also of their relative partition coefficients, if the membrane barrier is considered as a distinct phase.

The order of magnitude of required differences in dissociation constants may be estimated in systems containing Na^{+}, K^{+}, and X^{-} ions where the following relationship is valid:

* From the Department of Biology, Massachusetts Institute of Technology; the Children's Medical Center, Boston, Mass.

$$pK_{Na} - pK_K = \log \frac{K_K}{K_{Na}}$$

$$= \log \frac{m_{K^+}}{m_{Na^+}} + \log \frac{\epsilon_{NaX}}{1 - \epsilon_{NaX}} + \log \frac{\gamma_{NaX}\gamma_{K^+}}{\gamma_{KX}\gamma_{Na^+}} \quad (1)$$

m is the concentration, ϵ_{NaX} is defined as $\dfrac{m_{NaX}}{m_{NaX} + m_{KX}}$, and γ is the activity coefficient. If the mobilities of the two undissociated complexes, NaX and KX, are equal, ϵ_{NaX} is related to the relative efficiency of the process in its ion selection. For purposes here the last term of equation 1 may be neglected. Considering a sodium transporting process producing a net efflux from the cell, $pK_{Na} - pK_K$ is about 1.8 at values of m_{Na^+} and m_{K^+} equal to 0.01 and 0.15 respectively, and ϵ_{NaX} equal to 0.8. This indicates that for such a single-stage process the "carrier" ion must have a dissociation constant for Na^+ of the order of one hundred times less than that for K^+.

Although such a carrier mechanism is still only hypothetical and there is no direct evidence to support it, it nevertheless remains attractive. It is highly unlikely that biological ionic concentration gradients of Na and K are entirely a result of intracellular association of K. The total ionic concentrations intracellularly and extracellularly are nearly the same, most cell membranes are ineffective barriers to the diffusion of water, and thus the intracellular and extracellular regions must be reasonably isoösmotic. The fact that the ion concentration gradients are dependent upon cellular metabolism is undoubted. Recently there has been considerable evidence purporting to support a more direct relationship of phosphate metabolism to the ionic gradients, as well as a parallelism in glucose utilization to K uptake.[3-11]

These observations coupled with the view that glucose is probably phosphorylated at the cell surface, at least in many organisms and tissues,[12-15] have led to speculation invoking the formation of K complexes of the phosphorylated derivatives of glucose, either transient in existence to serve as carriers or as stable compounds leading directly to the apparent gradients.[3,4,7,8,16] Indeed, non-aqueous extracts of *Escherichia coli* have been shown to contain the K salts of the hexose phosphates. This again has been taken as evidence to support the association of K transport with hexose uptake.[17]

In addition to the above mentioned evidence, there are data indicating that K^+ is necessary for, or at least enhances the activity of, certain transphosphorylating enzymes.[18-22]

In view of the above evidence and inferences, an attempt has been made to measure the extent of ionic interactions, that is, the activity coefficients, of sodium and potassium ions in aqueous solutions of some of their phosphate salts. A brief report of the results has appeared elsewhere.[23]

METHODS AND MATERIALS

The potentiometric method of determining the cation activity coefficients consisted in measuring the e.m.f. developed across a collodion cation exchange membrane placed between a standard chloride solution of known activity and the phosphate solution of known concentration. The following electrochemical cell with liquid junction was utilized:

$$\text{Ag,AgCl, Me}^+ \text{ Cl}^- \mid \text{Me}^+ \text{ P}^{-z} \mid \text{sat. KCl, Hg}_2\text{Cl}_2\text{,Hg}$$
$$\quad (1) \quad M \quad (2) \quad J$$

Me^+ denotes the cation, Na^+ or K^+; P^{-z} denotes the phosphate anion; M is the collodion membrane; and J is the liquid junction.

The potential of this cell may be expressed as

$$E = E^\circ{}_{\text{Ag,AgCl}} + \frac{RT}{F} \ln a_{\text{Cl}_1} - E_{\substack{\text{sat. KCl} \\ \text{calomel}}}$$
$$+ E_M + E_J - \frac{RT}{F} \int_{(1)}^{(2)} \sum_i n_i d \ln a_i \quad (2)$$

$E^\circ{}_{\text{Ag,AgCl}}$ is the standard Ag,AgCl electrode potential at the absolute temperature T; R is the gas constant; F is the faraday; a is the thermodynamic activity; $E_{\substack{\text{sat. KCl} \\ \text{calomel}}}$ is the potential of the $\text{Hg,Hg}_2\text{Cl}_2$, saturated KCl electrode at the temperature T; E_M is the asymmetry potential of the collodion membrane; E_J is the liquid junction potential; and n_i refers to the number of moles of constituent i transferred across the membrane M per faraday. Assuming E_M and E_J independent of the composition of solution 2, the first five terms on the right-hand side of equation 2 are constant for a given concentration of $\text{MeCl}_{(1)}$ and collectively may be designated E_0'. E_0' is then the measured potential when solution 2 is identical with solution 1 since in this case the last term of equation 2 vanishes. If the transfer of water is neglected and unit transference of the cation species across the membrane is assumed, integration may be performed, giving:

$$- \log \gamma_{\text{Me}_2} = \frac{(E - E_0')F}{2.303RT} + \log \frac{m_{\text{Me}_2}}{a_{\text{Me}_1}} \quad (3)$$

m_{Me_2} is known from the experimental procedure. a_{Me_1} is computed using the mean activity coefficients of MeCl obtained by graphic interpolation of data given by MacInnes.[24] This requires the assumption that $\gamma_+ = \gamma_- = \gamma_\pm$, an approximation that is probably without significant error in the concentration range employed. Thus γ_{Me_2}, the activity coefficient of Me^+ in solution 2, is determined with measurement of $E - E_0'$.

Collodion membranes were prepared according to the method of Gregor and Sollner.[25] Three-layered membranes were poured on 12-mm. glass mandrels. The final drying was effected at a relative humidity of 43%. The membranes were secured on short lengths of 12-mm. glass tubing and stored in distilled water. Twelve hours before use, the membranes were transferred either to 0.1 M NaCl or KCl. Since equation 3 depends upon the assumption of unit transference of the cation species across the membrane, the prepared membranes were checked periodically with standard solutions to verify the validity of this assumption. Deviations of the measured potentials from the theoretical were generally not greater than 0.2 mv. and never greater than 0.5 mv. with an approximate 10:1 concentration ratio. The hydrogen ion interfered significantly only at concentrations greater than 10^{-6}.

The silver-silver chloride electrodes were prepared by depositing silver chloride electrolytically on pure silver wire. The glass electrode was a Beckman Type "42." The saturated KCl calomel electrode was either a commercial Beckman type or one so constructed as to allow temperature control.

Measurements of e.m.f. were made with a Leeds and Northrup No. 7552 Potentiometer utilizing a Leeds and Northrup No. 2430 DC Galvanometer. A Leeds and Northrup No. 7673 Thermionic Amplifier was introduced for pH measurements.

All solutions were prepared gravimetrically, utilizing glass distilled water. Reagents were all Mallinckrodt Analytical grade except for the tetraethylammonium hydroxide and the organic phosphates. From stock 10% solution (Eastman Kodak Co.) 0.1 M tetraethylammonium hydroxide was prepared. The alkali metal concentrations of the hydroxides were determined by conversion to the sulfates according to the method of Peters and van Slyke.[26] Glycerophosphate (GP) was obtained as the sodium salt from Eimer and Amend, New York. Glucose-1-phosphate (G1P) as the dipotassium salt, glucose-6-phosphate (G6P), fructose-1-6-diphosphate (FDP), and adenosinetriphosphate (ATP) (chromatographically homogeneous) as the barium insoluble salts were obtained from Schwarz Laboratories, New York. The various phosphates were converted to the sodium and potassium forms by first converting to the acid with an Amberlite IR-120(H) column at

4° C. and subsequently neutralized (within 3 hr.) with equivalent quantities of the Na and K hydroxides.

Inorganic polyphosphate was prepared by the method used by Lamm and Malmgren.[27] The sodium salt so obtained was converted to the

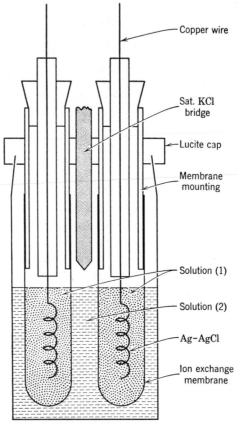

Fig. 1.   A diagrammatic sketch of the electrochemical cell.

acid in the manner used with the other phosphates. Back-neutralization with the Na and K hydroxides yielded the desired salts.

The technique employed in making the e.m.f. measurements was as follows: A pair of membranes on their glass mountings were partially filled with the standard solutions, and the Ag,AgCl electrodes were inserted. The membranes were then immersed in a standard alkali chloride solution in a thermoregulated bath at $25 \pm 0.05°$ C. The physical arrangement is illustrated diagrammatically in Fig. 1. After allowing about 2 hours for the electrodes and solutions to attain equilibrium, the liquid junction was formed and several e.m.f. readings were made with each of the two Ag,AgCl-membrane electrodes. This comprised the E of equation 3. The membranes with their solutions and Ag,AgCl electrodes were then removed as a unit from the standard solution and placed in their respective alkali metal phosphate solutions. After allowing about 30 min. for equilibrium, the liquid junction was formed and the potential readings were made as before. These measurements provided values of E of equation 3. The differences $E - E_0'$ were averaged and $- \log \gamma_{Me_2}$, abbreviated as $\log \gamma$, was computed from equation 3.

RESULTS

The acid-base titration curves for glucose-1-phosphoric acid, glucose-6-phosphoric acid, fructose-1-6-diphosphoric acid, glycerophosphoric acid, adenosinetriphosphoric acid, and inorganic pyrophosphoric acid are shown in Fig. 2. The ordinates have been normalized to allow more convenient comparison. Graphic measurements on the original plot of the titration curve of fructose-1-6-diphosphoric acid disclosed that about 3.8% of the acid equivalents was a strong acid impurity. This appears as a negative quantity of base in the titration curve of Fig. 2. An estimation of the acid dissociation constants may be made from the data obtained to prepare these curves.

In the case of G1P, G6P, and GP, the first acid dissociation constant is estimated, and activity coefficient corrections with the Debye-Hückel limiting law are made.

$$- \log \gamma_i = z_i^2 0.509 \sqrt{I/2} \tag{4}$$

$I/2$ is the weight formal ionic strength, and z_i is the valence of the ith species. In solutions of the pure acid, contributions from the second acid dissociation are neglected, and $I/2 = a_{H^+}/\gamma_{H^+}$, a_{H^+} being the H^+ activity. γ_{H^+} is determined by successive approximations.

In FDP, ATP, and inorganic pyrophosphate (PP), which have two strong acid groups, the assumption that these two groups are equal simplifies the computations materially. The equations are then:

$$x + y + z = \text{Total concentration of acid} \tag{5a}$$

$$y + 2z = a_H/\gamma_1 \tag{5b}$$

$$y/x = K/a_H \cdot \gamma_1 \tag{5c}$$

$$z/y = K/a_H \cdot \gamma_2 \tag{5d}$$

$$- \log \gamma_1 = 0.509(y + 3z)^{1/2} \tag{5e}$$

$$\log \gamma_2 = 4 \log \gamma_1 \tag{5f}$$

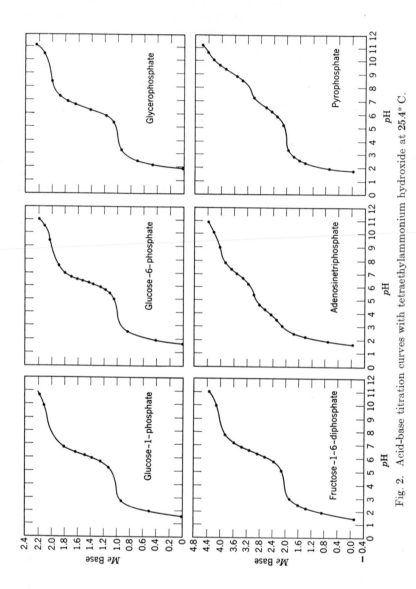

Fig. 2. Acid-base titration curves with tetraethylammonium hydroxide at 25.4° C.

where $x = m_{H_4P}$, $y = m_{H_3P^-}$, $z = m_{H_2P^-}$, K is the dissociation constant, and γ_1 and γ_2 are the single-ion activity coefficients of the univalent and divalent ions respectively. Solution is obtained by successive approximation.

The second acid dissociation constants of G1P, G6P, and GP and the third and fourth dissociation constants of FDP, ATP, and PP are estimated by graphically differentiating the titration curve and locating the resulting maxima. For FDP it is apparent that differences between pK_3 and pK_4 are not resolvable by this procedure.

The pK values of these compounds so determined are given in Table 1. Also tabulated for comparison are values obtained by various other investigators.

TABLE 1. THE ACID DISSOCIATION pK VALUES OF THE VARIOUS PHOSPHORIC ACIDS

	pK_1	pK_2	pK_3	pK_4	Reference
Glucose-1-phosphoric acid	1.1	6.2			
	1.10	6.13			*
Glucose-6-phosphoric acid	1.2	6.2			
	0.94	6.11			†
Glycerophosphoric acid	1.3	6.6			
	1.40	6.44			‡
Fructose-1-6-diphosphoric acid	1.2		6.6		
	1.52		6.31		‡
Adenosinetriphosphoric acid	0.8	4.2	7.0		
		strong		6.6	§
Inorganic pyrophosphoric acid	1.6	6.5	9.1		
	0.9	2.0	6.6	8.5	‖

* C. F. Cori, S. P. Colowick, and G. T. Cori, *J. Biol. Chem.*, *121*, 465 (1937).
† O. Meyerhof and K. Lohmann, *Biochem. Z.*, *185*, 113 (1927).
‡ W. Kiessling, *Biochem. Z.*, *273*, 103 (1934).
§ K. Lohmann, *Biochem. Z.*, *282*, 120 (1935).
‖ G. A. Abbott and W. C. Bray, *J. Am. Chem. Soc.*, *31*, 729 (1909).

In Tables 2–7 are presented the data pertinent to the estimation of the activity coefficients of sodium and potassium ions in aqueous solu-

TABLE 2

The Activity Coefficients of Sodium Glucose-1-phosphate

a_{Na_1}	E (mv.)	a_{Na_2}	m_{Na_2}	m_{G1P}	pH_2	$-\log \gamma$	$\sqrt{I/2}$
0.0256	−12.8	0.0421	0.0591	0.0286	7.78	0.147	0.294
0.0256	3.7	0.0222	0.0290	0.0140	7.80	0.117	0.206
0.0094	1.1	0.0090	0.0107	0.0052	7.67	0.078	0.125
0.0017	−3.9	0.0020	0.0022	0.0010	7.58	0.040	0.056

The Activity Coefficients of Potassium Glucose-1-phosphate

a_{K_1}	E (mv.)	a_{K_2}	m_{K_2}	m_{G1P}	pH_2	$-\log \gamma$	$\sqrt{I/2}$
0.0255	−12.0	0.0406	0.0563	0.0274	7.45	0.142	0.288
0.0255	3.0	0.0227	0.0298	0.0145	7.49	0.119	0.210
0.0091	4.4	0.0077	0.0092	0.0045	7.45	0.077	0.116
0.0018	−0.9	0.0018	0.0020	0.0010	7.47	0.039	0.055

TABLE 3

The Activity Coefficients of Sodium Glucose-6-phosphate

a_{Na_1}	E (mv.)	a_{Na_2}	m_{Na_2}	m_{G6P}	pH	$-\log \gamma$	$\sqrt{I/2}$
0.0297	−7.1	0.0391	0.0547	0.0274	7.53	0.146	0.290
0.0297	9.3	0.0207	0.0274	0.0137	7.56	0.122	0.203
0.0082	1.4	0.0078	0.0092	0.0046	7.55	0.072	0.117
0.0016	−2.0	0.0017	0.0018	0.0009	7.56	0.040	0.053

The Activity Coefficients of Potassium Glucose-6-phosphate

a_{K_1}	E (mv.)	a_{K_2}	m_{K_2}	m_{G6P}	pH	$-\log \gamma$	$\sqrt{I/2}$
0.0300	−5.7	0.0374	0.0528	0.0262	7.54	0.149	0.281
0.0300	10.8	0.0197	0.0263	0.0131	7.55	0.124	0.198
0.0080	2.0	0.0074	0.0088	0.0044	7.52	0.074	0.115
0.0016	−1.5	0.0017	0.0018	0.0009	7.57	0.042	0.052

TABLE 4

The Activity Coefficients of Sodium Glycerophosphate

a_{Na_1}	E (mv.)	a_{Na_2}	m_{Na_2}	m_{GP}	pH	$-\log \gamma$	$\sqrt{I/2}$
0.0295	2.0	0.0272	0.0364	0.0181	7.91	0.126	0.233
0.0135	−0.4	0.0137	0.0173	0.0086	7.64	0.100	0.161
0.0096	0.8	0.0093	0.0112	0.0056	7.77	0.080	0.129
0.0041	−0.2	0.0041	0.0047	0.0024	7.70	0.061	0.084
0.0017	1.1	0.0016	0.0018	0.0009	7.40	0.049	0.052

The Activity Coefficients of Potassium Glycerophosphate

a_{K_1}	E (mv.)	a_{K_2}	m_{K_2}	m_{GP}	pH	$-\log \gamma$	$\sqrt{I/2}$
0.0294	2.5	0.0267	0.0354	0.0176	7.76	0.123	0.230
0.0096	3.1	0.0085	0.0101	0.0050	7.72	0.072	0.123
0.0047	4.2	0.0039	0.0045	0.0022	7.62	0.061	0.082
0.0017	1.3	0.0016	0.0018	0.0009	7.37	0.044	0.051

TABLE 5

The Activity Coefficients of Sodium Fructose-1-6-diphosphate

a_{Na_1}	E (mv.)	a_{Na_2}	m_{Na_2}	m_{FDP}	pH	$-\log \gamma$	$\sqrt{I/2}$
0.0335	−4.2	0.0395	0.0596	0.0144	7.52	0.179	0.381
0.0216	0.4	0.0212	0.0296	0.0072	7.62	0.144	0.268
0.0089	2.3	0.0081	0.0103	0.0025	7.74	0.103	0.159
0.0011	−4.7	0.0013	0.0015	0.0004	7.56	0.058	0.060

The Activity Coefficients of Potassium Fructose-1-6-diphosphate

a_{K_1}	E (mv.)	a_{K_2}	m_{K_2}	m_{FDP}	pH	$-\log \gamma$	$\sqrt{I/2}$
0.0330	−3.3	0.0375	0.0568	0.0138	7.57	0.180	0.373
0.0217	1.8	0.0202	0.0283	0.0069	7.51	0.146	0.263
0.0092	4.1	0.0078	0.0099	0.0024	7.64	0.101	0.156
0.0012	−3.8	0.0014	0.0016	0.0004	7.60	0.061	0.063

TABLE 6

The Activity Coefficients of Sodium Adenosinetriphosphate

a_{Na_1}	E (mv.)	a_{Na_2}	m_{Na_2}	m_{ATP}	pH	$-\log \gamma$	$\sqrt{I/2}$
0.0295	0.1	0.0294	0.0466	0.0114	8.14	0.200	0.339
0.0135	−1.9	0.0146	0.0214	0.0052	8.12	0.166	0.229
0.0096	−1.6	0.0102	0.0139	0.0034	8.14	0.133	0.185
0.0041	−4.1	0.0048	0.0060	0.0015	8.14	0.101	0.122
0.0017	−3.8	0.0019	0.0023	0.0006	7.70	0.074	0.075

The Activity Coefficients of Potassium Adenosinetriphosphate

a_{K_1}	E (mv.)	a_{K_2}	m_{K_2}	m_{ATP}	pH	$-\log \gamma$	$\sqrt{I/2}$
0.0294	0.3	0.0290	0.0449	0.0110	7.94	0.189	0.333
0.0096	2.0	0.0089	0.0118	0.0029	8.00	0.132	0.170
0.0046	−0.3	0.0046	0.0058	0.0014	7.95	0.095	0.119
0.0017	−3.5	0.0019	0.0022	0.0006	7.65	0.064	0.074

TABLE 7

The Activity Coefficients of Sodium Inorganic Pyrophosphate

a_{Na_1}	E (mv.)	a_{Na_2}	m_{Na_2}	m_{PP}	pH	$-\log \gamma$	$\sqrt{I/2}$
0.0295	2.7	0.0266	0.0387	0.0119	7.70	0.164	0.270
0.0135	1.2	0.0129	0.0176	0.0054	7.78	0.135	0.182
0.0096	0.0	0.0096	0.0122	0.0037	7.78	0.103	0.151
0.0041	−0.7	0.0042	0.0050	0.0015	7.80	0.076	0.097
0.0017	−0.4	0.0017	0.0019	0.0006	7.46	0.053	0.060

The Activity Coefficients of Potassium Inorganic Pyrophosphate

a_{K_1}	E (mv.)	a_{K_2}	m_{K_2}	m_{PP}	pH	$-\log \gamma$	$\sqrt{I/2}$
0.0294	3.0	0.0262	0.0375	0.0116	7.64	0.156	0.266
0.0096	2.4	0.0088	0.0110	0.0034	7.71	0.101	0.144
0.0046	3.1	0.0041	0.0048	0.0015	7.70	0.073	0.095
0.0017	0.3	0.0017	0.0019	0.0006	7.35	0.049	0.059

tions of the salts of G1P, G6P, GP, FDP, ATP, and PP. The notation in each table conforms to that of equation 3. Hydrolysis of the salts has been neglected in the computation of $I/2$. The tabulated values of $\sqrt{I/2}$ would be about 3% too high if 10% of the salt were hydrolyzed. For the salts of PP the measurements were made on the salts $K_3HP_2O_7$ and $Na_3HP_2O_7$.

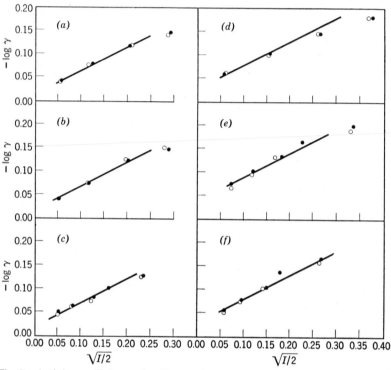

Fig. 3. Activity coefficients of sodium and potassium ions at 25.4° C. ● Na, ○ K: (a) G1P, (b) G6P, (c) GP, (d) FDP, (e) ATP, and (f) PP. Solid line is the Debye-Hückel limiting slope.

Plots of $-\log \gamma$ versus $\sqrt{I/2}$ are seen in Fig. 3a–f. Most obvious in this figure is that in all the salts the differences in the activity coefficients of Na^+ and K^+ in each type of salt are small. These differences fall within the scatter of the experimental points in the entire concentration range considered. It may also be seen that the experimental activity coefficients give a slope in these plots that conforms reasonably well to that given by the Debye-Hückel limiting law. In each case this limiting slope of 0.509 is indicated in the figure by the solid line. However, it is evident that the experimental points do not extrapolate to the origin. This failure may perhaps be attributed in part to variance in the liquid junction potential from the chloride solutions to the phosphate solutions. Since the calculation of this difference in junction potential depends upon knowledge of the transference numbers in saturated KCl as well as upon the relative conductances of the chloride and phosphate solutions, it is not possible to estimate it accurately. However, it may be of the order of 2 mv., and the sign would appear to be in the right direction. Other factors, such as possible

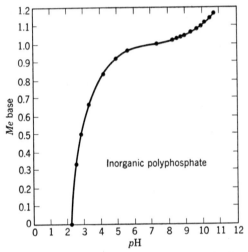

Fig. 4. Acid-base titration curve of inorganic polyphosphoric acid with tetraethylammonium hydroxide at 25.4° C.

variations in the membrane asymmetry potentials, add further to the uncertainties and preclude extrapolation to the origin.

The acid-base titration curve of the inorganic polyphosphoric acid preparation is illustrated in Fig. 4. If one makes the assumption that all the strong acid groups are independent and have equal dissociation constants, the equilibrium constant may be expressed as:

$$K = \frac{a_{H^+} \cdot n_{PyP^-} \cdot \gamma_{PyP^-}}{n_{HPyP}} \tag{6}$$

This becomes

$$K = \frac{a_{H^+}^2}{N_{PyP} - a_{H^+}/\gamma_{H^+}} \tag{7}$$

in a solution of the pure acid assuming that $\gamma_{PyP^-} = \gamma_{H^+}$. n_{PyP^-} and n_{HPyP} are the weight equivalent concentrations of dissociated and undissociated PO_3 units respectively. N_{PyP} is the total weight equivalent concentration of the polyphosphate. Estimating γ_H from the Debye limiting law one obtains a $pK = 2.25$. The pK of the weak-acid end groups are not satisfactorily estimated because of the lack of a clear inflection point in the titration curve.

Measurements of sodium and potassium activities in solutions of the respective salts of PyP indicated possible association to form the complexes NaPyP and KPyP. In order to estimate the dissociation constants of such complexes from measurements of the cationic activities, it was assumed that all $PO_3{}^-$ units behave identically and independently. Since NaCl and KCl were added to the solutions of Na and K salts of PyP to investigate the region of high cation/PyP ratios, the activity coefficients assumed were those expected in solutions of the two alkali chlorides at the same activity. Also it was assumed that $\gamma_{Na^+} = \gamma_{a^-} = \gamma_{PO_3^-}$ and $\gamma_{K^+} = \gamma_{cl^-} = \gamma_{PO_3^-}$. From the usual formulation of the dissociation constant embracing these assumptions and from the relations

$$n_{MePyP} = M_{Me} - a_{Me^+}/\gamma_{Me^+} \tag{8}$$

and

$$n_{PyP^-} = N_{PyP} - M_{Me} + a_{Me^+}/\gamma_{Me^+} \tag{9}$$

where M_{Me} is the total molar concentration of Me^+, it follows that

$$pK = -\log \gamma_{Me^+} - \log a_{Me^+} - \log \left[\frac{N_{PyP}}{M_{Me} - a_{Me^+}/\gamma_{Me^+}} - 1 \right] \tag{10}$$

The data pertaining to the determination of the apparent pK's are given in Table 8. The differences in the pK's for the Na and K salts

TABLE 8

The Dissociation pK's of Sodium Polyphosphate

a_{Na_1}	E (mv.)	a_{Na_2}	M_{Na_2}	N_{PyP}	pH	pK	$\sqrt{m_{Na_1}'}$ *
0.0411	3.9	0.0354	0.0503	0.0093	10.38	2.23	0.206
0.0237	6.7	0.0183	0.0300	0.0105	9.93	2.56	0.145
0.0114	34.0	0.0030	0.0128	0.0116	10.61	3.21	0.057
0.0059	22.4	0.0025	0.0102	0.0093	10.36	3.30	0.051

The Dissociation pK's of Potassium Polyphosphate

a_{K_1}	E (mv.)	a_{K_2}	M_{K_2}	N_{PyP}	pH	pK	$\sqrt{m_{K_2}'}$ *
0.0410	3.1	0.0364	0.0501	0.0092	10.57	1.81	0.210
0.0220	3.9	0.0189	0.0300	0.0105	10.09	2.24	0.148
0.0115	28.2	0.0038	0.0129	0.0115	10.72	2.96	0.065
0.0059	16.6	0.0031	0.0103	0.0092	10.42	3.05	0.058

* m_{Na_2}' and m_{K_2}' refer to a_{Na_2}/γ and a_{K_2}/γ respectively.

are seen in the empirical plot of Fig. 5. The K salt dissociates to a greater extent than the Na salt in the concentration range considered. The pK's do not appear to be constants but are seen to vary nearly linearly as the square root of the unassociated ion concentration m'. It is clear that the assumption of the independence of the individual PO_3 units is not well founded.

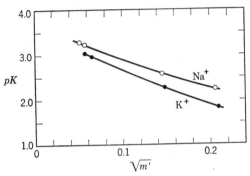

Fig. 5. Dissociation pK's of sodium and potassium polyphosphate plotted as a function of the free ion concentration m'.

DISCUSSION

It is evident from the study of the Na and K salts of the simple phosphoric acids presented above that, in the concentration range considered, the degree of ionic interaction may be largely accounted for in terms of the Debye-Hückel theory. There is no evidence that suggests that simple Na and K phosphates are not essentially completely ionized in aqueous solution. The experimental measurements presented do not indicate significant differences in the activity coefficients of Na^+ and K^+ in solutions with the same anion. This fact tends to refute the suggestion that the specificity of Na and K observed biologically depends upon their interaction with these anions, at least insofar as these interactions would occur in aqueous solution.

On the other hand, the findings in regard to the behavior of the Na and K salts of inorganic polyphosphoric acid indicate a possible association between the polyphosphate anion and the cations. It is not unreasonable to suppose this association in view of the findings with other polyelectrolytes.[28-31]

Van Wazer and Campanella [32] have reported pK values of 1.5 and 0.7 for the Na and K salts respectively of polyphosphoric acid. Although these values are different from those reported in the present study, the differences may be at least partially reconciled by the fact that the preparations were of a different average chain length and the methods of estimation were different. The analytic evidence of specific Na binding by the polyphosphates reported by Lamm and Malmgren [27] has no simple explanation.

Although considerable quantities of inorganic polyphosphate have been demonstrated to accumulate in yeast and other organisms during metabolism [33] it would appear that an explanation for the observed specificity of K accumulation should be sought elsewhere.

The alkali metals form salts that are, in general, completely dissociated in aqueous solution. In order to attain the degree of specificity of Na and K biologically evident, in all probability, chemical association is necessary. It would appear, then, that to reconcile the carrier hypothesis with these facts one must either seek exceptions to complete dissociation in aqueous solution or consider the membrane barrier as a region of low dielectric constant, wherein coulombic forces are of sufficient magnitude to lead to association. Exceptions to complete dissociation are found among certain of the chelating agents, some of which appear to exhibit marked differences in their affinity for sodium and potassium.[34-37] The natural occurrence of such substances has not, however, been demonstrated. Nerve and other cellular membranes are thought to consist largely of lipid and/or lipid-protein complexes. Such structures are quite probably regions of low dielectric constant, but little information on the behavior of ions in such phases exists; therefore, further speculation is unwarranted.

SUMMARY

The activity coefficients of sodium and potassium ions in salts of various organic esters of phosphoric acid, of inorganic pyrophosphoric acid (PP), and of inorganic polyphosphoric acid (PyP) have been investigated in aqueous solution. The phosphoric acid esters were glucose-1-phosphoric acid (G1P), glucose-6-phosphoric acid (G6P), glycerophosphoric acid (GP), fructose-1-6-diphosphoric acid (FDP), and adenosinetriphosphoric acid (ATP).

A potentiometric method employing a cell with liquid junction and incorporating a semipermeable collodion cation exchange membrane was used to estimate the activity coefficients at 25.4° C. No significant differences in the activity coefficients of Na and K were found. The slopes in plots of $- \log \gamma$ versus $\sqrt{I/2}$ approximate reasonably well that of the Debye-Hückel limiting law. In the case of inorganic polyphosphate, evidence interpreted as incomplete dissociation was found; only slight differences in behavior of Na and K are evident.

Acid-base titration curves were carried out with all the acids. The acid dissociation constants have been estimated.

The carrier hypothesis of ion transport across living cell membranes to account for the known concentration gradients of Na and K is briefly discussed. The data do not support the view that in aqueous solution the organic phosphates studied are directly involved in the mechanism responsible for maintaining these gradients.

Acknowledgment. The author is greatly indebted to Professor Francis O. Schmitt for his stimulation and advice in this investigation. He is also indebted to Professor George Scatchard for his many constructive criticisms.

NOTES AND REFERENCES

1. This chapter is based upon a thesis submitted in partial fulfillment of the requirements for the degree of Ph.D. at the Massachusetts Institute of Technology. The investigation was supported in part by a research grant from the Division of Research Grants and Fellowships of the National Institutes of Health, U. S. Public Health Service, and in part by a grant from the Trustees under the wills of Charles A. King and Marjorie King.
2. Formerly, Fellow in Cancer Research of the American Cancer Society. Fellow of the National Foundation for Infantile Paralysis.
3. R. Pulver and F. Verzar, *Helv. Chim. Acta., 23,* 1087 (1940).
4. A. Lasnitzki, *Nature, 146,* 99 (1940).
5. G. Schmidt, L. Hecht, and S. J. Thannhauser, *J. Biol. Chem., 178,* 733 (1949).
6. D. B. Cowie, R. B. Roberts, and I. Z. Roberts, *J. Cellular Comp. Physiol., 34,* 243 (1949).
7. R. B. Roberts, I. Z. Roberts, and D. B. Cowie, *J. Cellular Comp. Physiol., 34,* 259 (1949).
8. R. B. Roberts and I. Z. Roberts, *J. Cellular Comp. Physiol., 36,* 15 (1950).
9. A. K. Solomon, *J. Gen. Physiol., 36,* 57 (1952)
10. J. E. Harris, *J. Biol. Chem., 141,* 579 (1941).
11. C. W. Sheppard, *Science, 114,* 85 (1951).
12. G. Hevesy, K. Linderstrøm-Lang, and N. Nielsen, *Nature, 140,* 725 (1937).
13. J. Sachs and C. H. Altshule, *Am. J. Physiol., 137,* 750 (1942).
14. J. Sachs, *Cold Spring Harbor Symp. Quant. Biol., 13,* 180 (1948).
15. M. D. Kamen and S. Spiegelman, *Cold Spring Harbor Symp. Quant. Biol., 13,* 151 (1948).
16. S. W. Stanbury and G. H. Mudge, *Proc. Soc. Exper. Biol. and Med., 82,* 675 (1953).
17. E. T. Bolton, *Federation Proc., 9,* 153 (1950).
18. P. D. Boyer, H. A. Lardy, and P. H. Phillips, *J. Biol. Chem., 146,* 673 (1942).
19. P. D. Boyer, H. A. Lardy, and P. H. Phillips, *J. Biol. Chem., 149,* 529 (1943).
20. J. F. Kachmar and P. D. Boyer, *Federation Proc., 10,* 204 (1951).
21. J. A. Muntz, *J. Biol. Chem., 171,* 653 (1947).
22. H. A. Lardy, in: *Phosphorus Metabolism* (Editors, W. D. McElroy and B. Glass), Vol. 1, p. 477, Johns Hopkins Press, Baltimore, 1951.
23. F. M. Snell, *Biochim. et Biophys. Acta, 10,* 188 (1953).

24. D. A. MacInnes, *The Principles of Electrochemistry*, p. 167, Reinhold Publishing Corp., New York, 1939.
25. H. P. Gregor and K. Sollner, *J. Phys. Chem., 50,* 53 (1946).
26. J. P. Peters and D. D. van Slyke, *Quantitative Clinical Chemistry*, Vol. 2, p. 728, Williams & Wilkins Co., Baltimore, 1932.
27. O. Lamm and H. Malmgren, *Z. Anorg. Chem., 245,* 103 (1940).
28. W. Kern, *Makromol. Chem., 2,* 279 (1948).
29. D. Edelson and R. M. Fuoss, *J. Am. Chem. Soc., 72,* 306 (1950).
30. J. R. Huizenga, P. F. Grieger, and F. T. Wall, *J. Am. Chem. Soc., 72,* 2636 (1950).
31. I. M. Klotz, in: *Modern Trends in Physiology and Biochemistry* (Editor, E. S. G. Barron), p. 427, Academic Press, New York, 1952.
32 J. R. Van Wazer and D. A. Campanella, *J. Am. Chem. Soc., 72,* 655 (1950).
33. G. Schmidt, *Phosphorus Metabolism* (Editors, W. D. McElroy and B. Glass), Vol. 1, p. 443, Johns Hopkins Press, Baltimore, 1951.
34. G. Schwarzenbach, E. Kampitsch, and R. Steiner, *Helv. Chim. Acta, 28,* 828 (1945).
35. G. Schwarzenbach, E. Kampitsch, and R. Steiner, *Helv. Chim. Acta, 29,* 364 (1946).
36. G. Schwarzenbach, A. Willi, and R. O. Bach, *Helv. Chim. Acta, 30,* 1303 (1947).
37. G. Schwarzenbach and H. Ackermann, *Helv. Chim. Acta, 30,* 1798 (1947).

16·

Polarographic Behavior
of Various Plasma
Protein Fractions [1]

OTTO H. MÜLLER [*],[2]

INTRODUCTION

Among the many applications of the polarographic method in biology and medicine,[3] one type is particularly outstanding. It depends on a catalytic reaction of proteins and polypeptides at the dropping mercury electrode and thus differs fundamentally from the usual application based on diffusion currents that are proportional to the concentration of the reacting materials.[4] In contrast to the diffusion currents, the catalytic currents are still poorly understood and analyses based on them are largely empirical. Nevertheless these analyses have been most stimulating and have sometimes given information not obtainable by other means.

These catalytic reactions apparently require the presence of sulfhydryl groups in the protein and are best observed in an ammonia-ammonium chloride buffer solution containing cobalt. Compounds such as cysteine and cystine produce under these conditions a single wave in the shape of a rounded maximum, whereas many proteins and polypeptides yield a so-called "protein double-wave," which consists essentially of two such rounded maxima placed close enough together so that they may overlap. In neither case are the heights of the waves (or maxima) a linear function of the concentration of the reacting substance, but it is possible to find a small range of concentrations in which this condition is approximated to a sufficient degree to serve for analytical purposes.

[*] From the Department of Physiology, State University of New York, College of Medicine, Syracuse, N. Y.

301

PROTEIN DOUBLE-WAVES

Figure 1 will serve to illustrate such catalytic waves. The lowest curve, A, of this figure is for the buffer containing protein but no cobalt. The increase in current at -1.6 volts is produced by the protein, as can

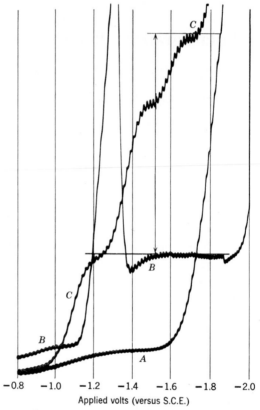

Applied volts (versus S.C.E.)

Fig. 1. Polarogram demonstrating the catalytic protein double-wave. (A) 1 ml. 1 M NH_4Cl + 8 ml. water + 1 ml. 1 M NH_4OH + 0.1 ml. human blood plasma, (B) 1 ml. 1 M NH_4Cl + 2 ml. 8×10^{-3} M $CoCl_2$ + 6 ml. water + 1 ml. 1 M NH_4OH, (C) 0.1 ml. human blood plasma added to solution B.

be seen by comparison with the corresponding curve of Fig. 2. It has been found that this protein reduction is catalytic in nature, and the corresponding wave has been called the "albumin-wave"[5] or "prenatrium-wave."[6] Our discussion will not be concerned with this reaction of proteins but rather with the one illustrated by the remaining curves of Fig. 1. Curve B, which is for the buffer containing cobalt but no protein, shows a sharp cobalt maximum, followed by the dif-

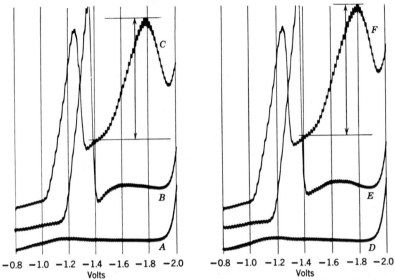

Fig. 2. Polarograms demonstrating the catalytic cysteine-wave. (A) 9 ml. cobalt-free buffer (1 ml. 1 M NH_4Cl + 9 ml. 1 M NH_4OH) + 1 ml. 10^{-4} M cysteine hydrochloride. (B) 9 ml. Co^{+++}-buffer (1 ml. 0.01 M $Co(NH_3)_6Cl_3$ + 1 ml. 1 M NH_4Cl + 8 ml. 1 M NH_4OH) + 1 ml. 10^{-4} M cysteine hydrochloride. (C) 9 ml. Co^{++}-buffer (2 ml. 8 × 10^{-3} M $CoCl_2$ + 1 ml. 1 M NH_4Cl + 6 ml. H_2O + 1 ml. 1 M NH_4OH) + 1 ml. 10^{-4} M cysteine hydrochloride. (D) 9.5 ml. cobalt-free buffer + 0.5 ml. approximately 10^{-4} M cystine. (E) 9.5 ml. Co^{+++}-buffer + 0.5 ml. approximately 10^{-4} M cystine. (F) 9.5 ml. Co^{++}-buffer + 0.5 ml. approximately 10^{-4} M cystine.

fusion current of cobalt. If protein is then added to the cobalt-containing buffer, as in curve C, the cobalt maximum is suppressed, the cobalt wave is shifted to more positive potentials, and the typical protein double-wave appears. Since in most instances the second peak is higher than the first, the height of the double-wave is usually measured, as indicated by the arrow in Fig. 1, from the inflection representing the diffusion current of cobalt to the peak of the second protein wave. If desired, a similar measurement to the peak of the first protein wave is also made (see Fig. 5). Whenever there is doubt about the true diffusion current of cobalt, because the cobalt maximum may not be sufficiently suppressed, its value must be determined by a blank experiment (see Fig. 7–8).

This catalytic reaction of proteins was discovered 20 years ago by R. Brdička when he tried to suppress the cobalt maximum by means of protein.[7] Brdička ascribed it to the sulfhydryl or disulfide groups of the proteins that form coordination compounds with cobalt and as such catalyze the reduction of hydrogen ions from the buffer. He based this conclusion on the fact that variations in the height of the protein double-waves could be correlated with the cystine content of the proteins and that of all the known amino acids only cystine and cysteine give waves similarly catalyzed by cobalt. However, as may be seen from Fig. 2, these two amino acids produce catalytic waves only in buffers containing divalent cobalt and the waves show but a single peak at a slightly different potential than either protein wave, whereas proteins produce a double-wave in either divalent or trivalent cobalt buffers.

This difference and the nature of the two peaks of the protein double-wave have not yet been satisfactorily explained. Brdička [8] assumes that the different shape of the protein waves is probably due to some special binding of the cystine or cysteine nuclei in the protein molecule and that the catalytic electrode process may then be modified by the influence of certain neighboring groups. To support this view, he cites the fact that the protein double-wave becomes transformed into a single wave with a rounded maximum (somewhat resembling that of cysteine) when ammonia is added in excess. [7]   On the other hand, Tropp, Jühling, and Geiger [9] believe that the second protein wave, because it has its maximum at about the same applied voltage as the cysteine wave, most likely represents the cystine or cysteine content of the protein, which reacts under the given conditions. These authors feel that the first wave is caused by some particular binding (possibly acid amide or diketopiperazine or still another type of binding) of the various amino acids in the protein molecule. Since we have been able to isolate the first polarographic wave (see Fig. 4), we favor the viewpoint that different structures in the protein molecule are responsible for the two waves and that the first wave does not necessarily involve sulfur-containing groups. This belief is strengthened by the observation (see Fig. 5) that the first protein wave grows at a rate markedly slower than the second protein wave during alkaline digestion.

Concerning Fig. 2, it should be mentioned that the waves of cystine and cysteine are identical if the concentration of the cystine is one-half of the concentration of the cysteine. This must be so because 1 molecule of cystine is reduced at the dropping electrode to 2 molecules of cysteine at a potential considerably more positive than the catalytic reaction, which is not visible on the polarograms reproduced here. Hence, at potentials more negative than -0.8 volt (versus the saturated calomel electrode) the electrode reaction is that of cysteine.

The catalytic protein reactions attained a special significance when Brdička found a difference between the behavior of normal blood plasma or serum and the behavior of serum from patients suffering from cancer and a number of other, mostly febrile, diseases.[10] This difference was small but could be magnified when the serum was sub-

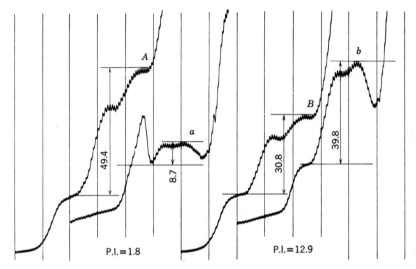

Fig. 3. Polarogram demonstrating digest and filtrate tests. (*A*) Digest test and (*a*) filtrate test obtained with normal human blood plasma, protein index 1.8. (*B*) Digest test and (*b*) filtrate test obtained with blood plasma from patient with choriocarcinoma, protein index 12.9. Digest and filtrate tests were recorded at $\frac{1}{300}$ and $\frac{1}{200}$ sensitivity of the galvanometer, respectively; each curve starts at −0.8 volt; interval between abscissas is 20 mv.

jected to partial denaturation by digestion for 30 min. at room temperature in a moderately alkaline solution, or in an acid medium in the presence of pepsin.[11] In general, the protein double-wave was found to be lower for the pathological than for the normal blood. The alkaline denaturation has been called the "digest test" and is illustrated by curves *A* and *B* of Fig. 3. Note that the double-wave of plasma from the patient with choriocarcinoma is lower than that obtained with plasma from the normal individual.

If now the digested solutions are deproteinated by precipitation with sulfosalicylic acid, a filtrate may be obtained that contains some split products from the protein, soluble in this medium. The exact nature of this material has not been established with certainty; it has been thought to be a relatively high molecular weight polypeptide, a proteose, a peptone, or a mucoprotein. Most probably it is not a single substance but a mixture of several. Waldschmidt-Leitz and Mayer[12] (see also Brdička[13]) were the first to find that the polarographic analysis of such filtrates produced a higher double-wave for the pathological samples than for the normal specimens. The possible interference of cysteine and cystine was eliminated by analyses in trivalent cobalt buffers where these amino acids do not give a wave. The two curves a and b of Fig. 3 may serve as examples of this so-called "filtrate test." These filtrate waves were obtained with the same plasma samples as the corresponding digest waves. Note that here the choriocarcinoma sample gives a much higher double-wave than the normal sample.

PROTEIN INDEX

Since everything about these procedures is highly arbitrary, our efforts were concentrated first on developing a technique that would provide results that could still be compared even though they were obtained with different dropping mercury electrodes and under different conditions. This technique would eliminate the continued need for a simultaneously analyzed "normal" control. We first developed a simple procedure in which the wave height obtained in the filtrate test is divided by the wave height found in the digest test at suitable galvanometer sensitivities. The ratio thus obtained was called the "protein index."[14] On the basis of numerous analyses,[15] the normal value of the protein index was found to be 2.4 ± 0.17 with a standard deviation of 0.95. Abnormal protein index values may go as high as 20. In the two cases shown in Fig. 3, the protein index for the "normal" was $8.7 \times 10/49.4 = 1.8$ and for the choriocarcinoma patient $39.8 \times 10/30.8 = 12.9$. Naturally, the protein index is still a highly artificial characterization of a given plasma since the two tests on which it is based are quite arbitrary. However, it is easily determined and is relatively independent of temperature and protein concentration and of the kind of capillary used for the dropping mercury electrode.

It was further found that these catalytic reactions are independent of the drop time of the dropping mercury electrode but proportional to the surface area of the drops.[15] Hence, by expressing results in terms of current density, we had a method for the direct comparison of data obtained with different dropping electrodes that had heretofore been lacking for these catalytic reactions. It is thus possible to make quantitative studies in this field that can be checked by others.

Numerous papers have been published concerning the applications of modifications of the filtrate and digest tests to the diagnosis and prognosis of malignancies, but so far all efforts have failed to make either one or a combination of the two tests specific for cancer. Furthermore, the tests have by no means been all positive in proved cancer cases. From a list published by Fořt, et al.,[16] one can conclude that out of 2358 cancer cases studied by different investigators who used several variations of the above tests only about 88% gave a positive reaction. None of the variations seemed to be particularly outstanding above the others. To this we might add our own results obtained on 129 patients studied in the tumor clinic. We assume that all those are abnormal whose protein index is in excess of 4.3, i.e., the mean protein index of normals plus 2 standard deviations.[15] On this basis we find the following: of 46 benign cases and cases without tumor, 28% were abnormal; of 29 cases with small or localized tumor, 24% were abnormal; of 48 cases with extensive local or metastatic tumor, 79% were abnormal.[17]

In view of these findings, it becomes of considerable importance that more be known about the nature of these clinical tests. However, relatively little has been accomplished so far in the solution of this problem.

SIGNIFICANCE OF DIGEST TEST

Brdička [13] assumed that in pathological blood a proteolytic degradation of protein takes place, which results in the diminished digest reaction and the increased filtrate reaction. He believes that during the alkaline denaturation (or during the acid digestion in the presence of pepsin) the serum proteins undergo structural changes that expose more disulfide groups and thus render the molecule more active, polarographically. Because of the proteolytic degradation of protein in pathological blood, many of the masked disulfide groups have already been exposed and split off and have in some way been removed from the blood stream so that there are fewer disulfide groups left that can be exposed during the digestion in vitro. One might expect that the structural changes of the proteins that give rise to the increased polarographic current would also cause an increase in the viscosity of the solution. That this actually occurs has been ascertained by Suolahti and Laine.[18] The possibility that changes in the protein concentrations would be responsible for the different behavior of pathological and normal blood was considered by Tropp,[19] who applied suitable corrections based on refractometric determinations of total protein. In spite of these corrections, differences still existed that indicate that the available protein in normal serum has more masked disulfide groups than that of pathological serum. However, this still leaves open the questions whether a diminution of relatively cystine-rich albumin and increase of cystine-poor globulin could be the cause of the low values in pathological blood or whether a decrease in the cystine content of any given protein fraction is involved.

Because of the known difference in cystine content of albumin and globulin, Brdička [20] and others have generally assumed without proof that the protein double-wave in the digest test is largely caused by albumin. Brdička [20, 21] also claims that after alkaline as well as peptic denaturation of crystalline serum albumin, filtrates were obtained that showed the double-wave typical of the cancer reaction. Thus Brdička implies that the albumin fraction of the plasma proteins is responsible for the digest test and the filtrate test as well. Some of these experiments and conclusions disagree with our own,[22] which will be discussed in more detail later on.

The existence of albumin fractions containing less than the normal cystine content has been reported on several occasions. For instance, the serum albumin in Bright's disease could be separated into a cystine-poor and a normal albumin fraction by Alving and Mirsky.[23] Similarly, Vassel, et al.,[24] found that the cystine content of the "albumins" (obtained by fractionation with sodium sulfate and ether) decreased during the acute phase of pneumonia infection in dogs and returned to normal during the recovery phase. These authors further noted that there was no change in the cystine content of the "globulins" during the infection. These findings had to be modified subsequently [25] because the "albumins" were found grossly contaminated with globulins (more so in the case of infected dogs than in normal dogs) when the fractionation was carried out with ammonium sulfate. However, even so, a definite though small decrease in the cystine content of "albumins" was still noted during the infection. To be convincing, such analyses would have to be repeated on fractions that had been prepared by other methods and had possibly been checked by electrophoresis. It would further be of value to show by corresponding polarographic analysis that the "cystine-poor" albumin fraction gives a lower polarographic double-wave than an equivalent amount of normal albumin. We have carried out a preliminary analysis of a similar nature on albumin (fraction V) fractionated by method 10 developed by Cohn, et al.,[26] from the blood of a choriocarcinoma patient with a high protein index (see Fig. 3) and compared it with a sample of "normal" albumin (pooled Red Cross blood) of similar concentration (determined by Kjeldahl nitrogen analysis). The polarographic curves of both were practically identical, indicating that differences in the composition of the albumin fraction (V) of human plasma proteins are not responsible for the different digest tests.[17]

Rusch, et al.,[27] who made acid digests of serum samples in the presence of pepsin, attributed the polarographic waves obtained wholly to albumin when they found a correlation between the albumin content and the digest waves. They were strengthened in this opinion when they further observed that the addition of globulins did not materially alter the shape of the albumin curve and that the globulin fraction did not yield the characteristic waves obtained with intact serum. However, we were not able to confirm [17] this observation when we analyzed similar peptic digests of various globulin fractions of plasma. It is also known that typical protein double-waves are obtained with undenatured serum globulins. For instance, Tropp, et al.,[9] who made one of the most extensive studies of individual protein fractions, found only minor differences in the behavior of albumin, globulin, and fibrinogen that had been isolated by salting-out procedures. We confirmed and extended this work with fractions obtained by the alcohol fractionation procedure used by Cohn, et al.,[28] and found, for instance, that, compared on a basis of molarity instead of per cent concentration, albumin and γ-globulin fractions, if undenatured, give practically identical curves.[17] (See also curves c of Fig. 5.)

SIGNIFICANCE OF THE FILTRATE TEST

There has been extensive work on the isolation and characterization of the material found in the sulfosalicylic acid filtrates. If Brdička's thesis is correct, this material must be eliminated from the body in some way, probably via the kidney. However, Vassel, et al.,[29] failed to find any proteinlike material in the urine of pneumonia-infected dogs, although there was a definite increase in the excretion of organic sulfur. Perhaps a species difference is responsible for this, since in human pneumonia one generally observes a definite albuminuria during the febrile stage of the disease. Tropp and Geiger [30] attempted to characterize the filtrate material by ultrafiltration but were unable to isolate or identify it. The polarograms of the ultrafiltrates were unfortunately made in divalent cobalt buffer so that the single catalytic wave obtained could hardly be distinguished from a cysteine curve and may very likely have been produced by cysteine. We have found that a collodion membrane permits passage of particles that give a unique polarographic curve in a trivalent cobalt buffer.[17] Since this kind of curve has never been published before, it is reproduced

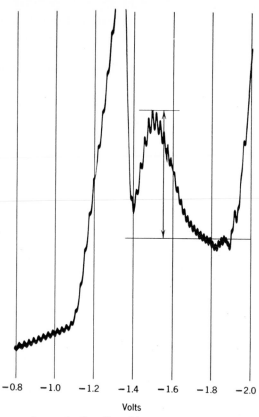

-0.8   -1.0   -1.2   -1.4   -1.6   -1.8   -2.0

Volts

Fig. 4. Polarogram demonstrating filterable material that produces only the first catalytic protein wave. 0.5 ml. 0.01 M $Co(NH_3)_6Cl_3$ + 0.5 ml. 1 M NH_4Cl + 4 ml. 1 M NH_4OH + 0.5 ml. ultrafiltrate obtained from pooled plasma (Wassermann samples) through parlodion-covered Giemsa ultrafilter. The cobalt diffusion current (bottom line) was obtained from a blank experiment. Note that the curve following the maximum at −1.5 volt returns to this diffusion current level and that there is no "pre-natrium wave" (see Fig. 1).

in Fig. 4. Note that there is only *one* wave following the partly suppressed cobalt maximum and that this wave has a peak at the same potential as the first protein wave. It cannot be due to cysteine or cystine because these amino acids do not give a wave in trivalent cobalt buffer, except in very high concentrations. Other free amino acids, likewise, produce no waves under these conditions. On the basis of experiments with *tryptic digests* of protein fractions, we believe that either *arginine* or *lysine* or both, as part of the protein or polypeptide, give rise to the first protein wave. The exact nature of this wave is still being investigated.

As far as the writer is aware, Brdička still maintains his thesis that the polarographic filtrate wave is produced by cystine-containing material. This material is supposed to have been split off from proteins by enzymatic action in the pathological blood, since polarographically identical material can be split off enzymatically (or by alkaline digestion) from normal blood in vitro. Also the cystine content of hydrolysates from normal and pathological sera paralleled the magnitude of their filtrate waves. However, Mayer [31] isolated, from the sulfosalicylic acid filtrate of heat-denatured human serum, a material that after alcohol fractionation again gave the polarographic wave. It was found to contain considerable quantities of total sulfur but none of it in the form of cysteine and only a little in the form of cystine, whether it was from normal or from cancer blood. Since it also contained carbohydrate and glucosamine, Mayer believes that it is a mucoid-like substance which causes the filtrate wave. Winzler, et al.,[32] isolated from perchloric acid filtrates of undenatured plasma a mixture of three mucoproteins that contained even less total sulfur than Mayer's preparation and still gave the polarographic double-wave. The concentration of these mucoproteins is increased over normal levels in a large percentage of patients with cancer.[33] Although the most important of these mucoproteins moves with the α_1-globulin fraction [34] during electrophoresis at pH 8.4, it is most likely left unprecipitated in fraction VI during Cohn's alcohol fractionation procedure.[26] The latest report from Cohn's laboratory, by Schmid,[35] seems to confirm this viewpoint; the acid glycoprotein isolated from fraction VI seems to be identical with the mucoprotein.

However, it is doubtful that this is the only material responsible for the filtrate wave, since it exists before digestion in the plasma and, as will be shown, additional material is liberated from certain protein fractions during digestion.

EXPERIMENTAL PROCEDURES

It seemed worthwhile to us to study the denaturation in mild alkaline medium of relatively pure protein fractions in order to get some insight into the results obtained under similar conditions with whole plasma or serum. Obviously, such a denaturation seems far removed from any real physiological process, but it should aid in clearing up some of the uncertainties of the two clinical tests described earlier. Peptic and tryptic digests have been started in this laboratory and have shown definite and consistent differences from the alkaline digests, but, for the present, only the alkaline denaturation experiments will be reported.

PROTEIN FRACTIONS AVAILABLE

We were fortunate in our studies in getting carefully prepared protein fractions given to us. Dr. Mulford, then of the Division of Biological Laboratories of the Massachusetts Department of Public Health, kindly furnished us with dried samples of human plasma fractions that had been prepared by Cohn's procedure.[28] Since they were prepared from pooled blood collected by the American Red Cross, we may consider them typical normal samples. According to Dr. Mulford, fractions II (γ-globulin) and V (albumin) were 99% pure, as determined by electrophoresis. The composition of the other fractions was as stated in the literature: fraction I, predominantly fibrinogen; [28] fraction III, predominantly β-globulin; [36] fraction IV-1, predominantly α-globulin with less than 25% albumin; [28] and fraction IV-4, 41% α-globulin, 29% β-globulin, and 30% albumin.[37] One must realize, of course, that these fractions, even when electrophoretically pure, are by no means single pure substances. However, since they behave similarly during fractionation and electrophoresis, they may be expected to show some other uniformity of behavior. As will be seen, our polarographic studies seem to bear out this conclusion.

PROCEDURE

The proteins were dissolved in 0.9% sodium chloride to yield an approximately 5% solution. The exact concentration was determined by Kjeldahl nitrogen determination. In every case, aliquots were used for the digest and filtrate tests, and the progress of the digestion was followed against time. Otherwise, the solutions used and the procedure followed were the same as in earlier publications [15, 38] except that a Sargent Model XII Polarograph was used in addition to the Nejedly instrument.

EFFECT OF TIME OF DIGESTION ON THE DIGEST TEST

Some typical digestion experiments are illustrated in Fig. 5. The lower part (b) shows the progress of the digestion of human albumin (fraction V). Of the 5% solution of albumin, 0.5 ml. is mixed with 0.5 ml. of water and 0.25 ml. of KOH (1 N). This yields a solution of 2% albumin in 0.2 N KOH. From this solution, 0.05 ml. samples are pipetted into 10 ml. of a divalent cobalt buffer after given intervals of time. Thus, every curve on the polarogram represents 1 mg. of protein in 10 ml. of final solution. The control is obtained with material to which water has been added in place of the KOH. Note how in the control curve C the protein double-wave consists of two peaks which in this instance are approximately equal in height. During the first 10 min. of digestion the first wave increases slightly while the second wave shows a marked increase with time. This rapid rise is followed by a much more gradual decrease of both waves with time. For convenience, we shall use the term *activation reaction* for the early rise in wave height, during which somehow the molecule has become polarographically more active. The subsequent diminution of the wave height may be called the *decay reaction*. Here the protein molecule undergoes changes that diminish the number of polarographically active groups.

ACTIVATION REACTION

In contrast to the behavior of albumin, notice the behavior of γ-globulin (fraction II) in part a of Fig. 5. Here no activation re-

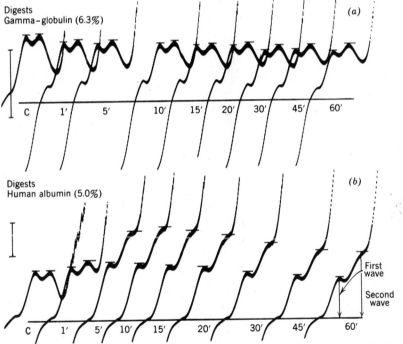

Fig. 5. Polarograms showing the effect of time on the digest test. (a) Carried out with γ-globulin (fraction II). (b) Carried out with albumin (fraction V). The horizontal line represents the diffusion current of cobalt (obtained during a blank experiment). The vertical lines at the left indicate 10 μa. in this and the other polarograms.

action is noticeable; but there is apparent a gradual decrease in wave height with time, indicating a progressive decay reaction. We have obtained a series of similar polarograms with all the different protein

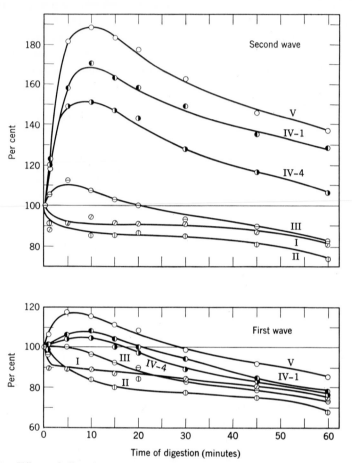

Fig. 6. Effect of digestion on the polarographic waves of six protein fractions of human plasma, expressed as per cent of the undigested control values. The solutions used were: fraction I, 5%; fraction II, 5%; fraction III, 5.2%; fraction IV-1, 4.9%; fraction IV-4, 4.3%; and fraction V, 5%.

fractions and present a summary of our findings in Fig. 6. For simplicity, the results are expressed in per cent of the control values. Thus, starting with 100%, we find, for instance, that the second wave of the human albumin fraction increases some 80–90% over the starting value. The changes in the first wave are markedly smaller, but they are in the same direction as those of the second wave. Of greatest interest to us is the increase observed in protein fractions V, IV-1, and IV-4, as contrasted to the absence of the activation reaction in fractions I, II, and III. Since both fractions IV-1 and IV-4 contain some albumin, one may suspect that this impurity is responsible for the reaction. Although we shall be uncertain about this point until we get samples that are albumin-free, we believe that the effect cannot be entirely due to albumin and that the α- and β-globulins present in both these fractions contribute also, to a small extent, to the activation reaction. However, their contribution is unquestionably so much less than that of albumin that the activation reaction of all the globulins will become negligible compared to that of albumin not only in normal plasma where albumin is in excess but even in pathological plasma where there is more globulin than albumin. This means that plasma will usually exhibit the same activation reaction as the albumin contained in it. We have tested this conclusion in several rather extreme cases (cancer and nephrosis) in which we have isolated fraction V, and we have so far found no exceptions. This may then serve as proof of the assumptions of Brdička and others that the albumin fraction of serum proteins is responsible for the digest test. From preliminary experiments with acid digests of similar fractions in the presence of pepsin, we conclude that essentially the same situation holds there too, in confirmation of the findings of Rusch, et al.,[27] mentioned earlier.

DECAY REACTION

Concerning the decay reaction, we wish to mention here only the bare essentials in order to conserve space. As may be noted from Figs. 5 and 6, every protein fraction studied eventually shows a progressive decrease in wave height as the alkaline digestion continues. It is further found that this decrease is about the same for the first and the second protein waves. This means that in all the proteins the number of polarographically active groups present per molecule decreases with time or, more likely, that the protein molecule itself disintegrates and forms polarographically inactive or at least less active products. Under certain conditions, this decay reaction appears to be of the first order for the first hour of digestion; therefore, it is possible to calculate half-lives for a given protein. This method of characterization has proved to be very convenient, because it has allowed not only certain distinctions between the different plasma protein fractions, but also rather marked distinctions between the albumin fractions of different species.[39] Details of this study will be published elsewhere.

EFFECT OF TIME OF DIGESTION ON THE FILTRATE TEST

Considerable differences in the behavior of the different protein fractions were found when they were subjected to the filtrate test. In this test, as used by us, 1 ml. of water and 0.1 ml. of 1 N KOH were added to 0.5 ml. of the 5% protein solution. Identical mixtures were left to digest for different known intervals of time, and then 1 ml. of a 20% solution of sulfosalicylic acid was added to the digest. After standing 10 min. the resulting precipitate was filtered through Whatman No. 5 filter paper. The filtrate then contained unprecipitated material from a 1% protein solution that had been digested for a given

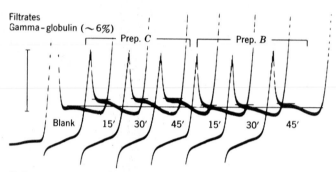

Fig. 7.   Polarogram showing the effect of time of digestion on the filtrate waves of γ-globulin (fraction II).

length of time in 0.06 N KOH. Of the clear filtrate 0.5 ml. was added to 5 ml. of a trivalent cobalt buffer and polarographed immediately. In the controls water was substituted for the KOH.

Some typical results are shown in Figs. 7 and 8. An essentially negative reaction is illustrated in Fig. 7, which shows the results of tests with two different preparations of γ-globulin, both of which gave hardly any reaction. In neither case was there any evidence that the small wave grows with time of digestion. The albumin fraction behaves similarly; it shows even less of a response. These findings may be contrasted with those shown in Figure 8a, which shows the effect of time on the filtrates from fraction III. Notice a definite increase in the double-waves as the digestion is proceeding, followed by a gradual decrease with time. This decrease seems to be characteristic of fraction III, since fraction IV-1 shows a continuously growing double-wave, at least for the first hour of digestion (see Figure 8b), whereas fraction IV-4 seems to approach a limiting value of the double-wave after 30 min. of digestion, which then remains relatively constant. These results are best compared on the basis of the graph shown in Fig. 9, which includes the data obtained with all six human protein

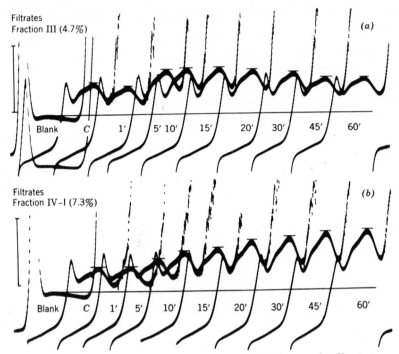

Fig. 8. Polarograms showing the effect of time of digestion on the filtrate waves of (a) fraction III, and (b) fraction IV-1 of human plasma.

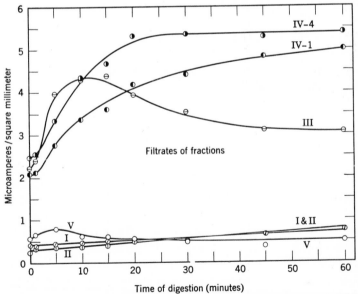

Fig. 9. Effect of time of digestion on the filtrate values from six protein fractions of human plasma. The solutions used were: fraction I, 4%; fraction II, 6.7%; fraction III, 4.7%; fraction IV-1, 7.3%; fraction IV-4, 4.3%; and fraction V, 5%.

fractions available to us. It is obvious that the behavior of fractions III and IV is markedly different from that of fractions I, II, and V. This was a surprise to us; we expected fraction II, which is known to contain antibodies, to contribute something to this reaction that becomes so marked in disease. However, it is apparent that neither fraction II nor V can be involved in the filtrate reaction, and we have to look for fractions III and IV, i.e., probably α- and β-globulins, to furnish the filterable material. Of course, some material existing preformed in fraction VI, such as the mucoproteins mentioned earlier, would also contribute to the filtrate waves. However, it is clear from Fig. 9 that in every instance the undigested filtrate values were smaller than those obtained after digestion. Hence, additional material responsible for the test must be liberated from the proteins by mild alkaline digestion. Since filtrate values of plasma show a similar rise with time of digestion as fractions III and IV, we believe that the α- and β-globulins contained in these fractions *must* contribute to the filtrate test.

It should be mentioned here that we have carried out additional studies, using Cohn's method,[26] on protein fractions prepared in our own laboratory from the plasma of various patients. However, we have not found the above distinctions between fractions III and IV. This is not surprising since in disease the composition of these fractions probably changes the most. On the other hand, we have consistently found negative filtrate tests with fractions II and V, so that all the filtrate test material that is liberated with time of digestion had to come from fractions III and IV. (Fraction I was not tested.) We also found filtrate test material in fraction VI, in which it seemed to be readily available and did not have to be liberated by digestion.

CONCLUSIONS

We can state with considerable certainty that the digest test is largely determined by the albumin content of the blood and that the filtrate test probably reflects on the content of α- and β-globulins, plus the presence of an abnormal amount of mucoproteins. γ-globulin seems to contribute to the digest test only to a minor degree and not at all to the filtrate test. Since the two tests are determined by two essentially different protein fractions, Brdička's suggestion concerning the formation and subsequent loss of filterable material must be rejected. In general, one can conclude that the protein index represents the inverse of the well-known albumin/globulin ratio, a relationship that had been appreciated but never analyzed in this fashion.

In our experience, the albumin fraction never contributes to the filtrate test. This is in direct contradiction with Brdička's findings,[20, 21] according to which crystalline serum albumin produces filtrate waves, after either alkaline or peptic digestion, that are indistinguishable from those obtained with carcinomatous sera. Attempts to duplicate Brdička's results have been handicapped by inadequate description of his experiments.[20, 21] However, we did find a definite filtrate reaction when we made an acid (peptic) digest of albumin, which consistently showed a negative filtrate reaction during alkaline denaturation. Here we have a definite difference in the polarographic behavior of proteins, depending on the denaturing agent. It may be that this and other differences that will be reported elsewhere may contribute to a refinement of the polarographic techniques used in diagnosis.

Acknowledgment. It is a pleasure to acknowledge our indebtedness to Dr. Mulford for furnishing us the protein fractions and to Dr. Cohn and co-workers who kindly instructed us in the latest fractionation technique.

REFERENCES AND NOTES

1. This work was aided in part by a grant from the Division of Research Grants and Fellowships of the National Institutes of Health, U. S. Public Health Service, and in part by a grant from the Hendricks Research Fund of the State University of New York College of Medicine.
2. With the technical assistance of Mary Jane Elwood and Patricia Folse.
3. For a recent compilation see M. Březina and P. Zuman, *Polarography in Medicine, Biochemistry, and Pharmacy* (in Czech), 529 pp., Zdravotnické Nakladatelstvi, Prague, 1952.
4. For a short introduction to the polarographic method, see Otto H. Müller, *The Polarographic Method of Analysis,* 2nd Ed., Chemical Education Publishing Co., Easton, Pa., 1951; for a comprehensive treatise, see I. M. Kolthoff and James J. Lingane, *Polarography,* 2nd Ed., Vols. I and II, Interscience Publishers, New York, 1952.
5. J. Babička and J. Heyrovský, *Collection Czechoslov. Chem. Communs., 2,* 370 (1930).
6. R. Brdička, *Collection Czechoslov. Chem. Communs., 8,* 366 (1936).
7. R. Brdička, *Collection Czechoslov. Chem. Communs., 5,* 112 (1933).
8. R. Brdička, *Research (London), 1,* 25 (1947).
9. C. Tropp, L. Jühling, and F. Geiger, *Hoppe-Seyler's Z. physiol. Chem., 262,* 225 (1939).
10. R. Brdička, *Nature, 139,* 330 (1937).
11. R. Brdička, *Nature, 139,* 1020 (1937).
12. E. Waldschmidt-Leitz and K. Mayer, *Hoppe-Seyler's Z. physiol. Chem., 261,* 1 (1939).
13. R. Brdička, *Acta Unio Intern. contra Cancrum, 3,* 13 (1938).
14. O. H. Müller and J. S. Davis, Jr., *J. Biol. Chem., 159,* 667 (1945).
15. O. H. Müller and J. S. Davis, Jr., *Arch. Biochem., 15,* 39 (1947).

16. M. Fořt, R. Brdička, K. Ott, and M. Voříšková, *Časopis Lékářů Českých, 81,* 1181 (1942).
17. Unpublished results from this laboratory.
18. O. Suolahti and T. Laine, *Biochem. Z., 308,* 216 (1941).
19. C. Tropp, *Klin. Wochschr., 17,* 1141 (1938).
20. R. Brdička, *Klin. Wochschr., 18,* 305 (1939).
21. R. Brdička, *Nature, 142,* 617 (1938).
22. O. H. Müller, *Federation Proc., 10,* 95 (1951).
23. A. S. Alving and A. E. Mirsky, *J. Clin. Invest., 15,* 215 (1936).
24. B. Vassel, R. Partridge, and M. L. Crossley, *Arch. Biochem., 1,* 403 (1943).
25. B. Vassel, R. Partridge, and M. L. Crossley, *Arch. Biochem., 14,* 451 (1947).
26. E. J. Cohn, F. R. N. Gurd, D. M. Surgenor, B. A. Barnes, R. K. Brown, G. Derouaux, J. M. Gillespie, F. W. Kahnt, W. F. Lever, C. H. Liu, D. Mittelman, R. F. Mouton, K. Schmid, and E. Uroma, *J. Am. Chem. Soc., 72,* 465 (1950).
27. H. P. Rusch, T. Klatt, V. W. Meloche, and A. J. Dirksen, *Proc. Soc. Exptl. Biol. Med., 44,* 362 (1940).
28. E. J. Cohn, L. E. Strong, W. L. Hughes, Jr., D. J. Mulford, J. N. Ashworth, M. Melin, and H. L. Taylor, *J. Am. Chem. Soc., 68,* 459 (1946).
29. B. Vassel, R. Partridge, and M. L. Crossley, *Arch. Biochem., 4,* 59 (1944).
30. C. Tropp and F. Geiger, *Hoppe-Seyler's Z. physiol. Chem., 272,* 134 (1942).
31. K. Mayer, *Hoppe-Seyler's Z. physiol. Chem., 275,* 16 (1942).
32. R. J. Winzler, A. W. Devor, J. W. Mehl, and I. M. Smyth, *J. Clin. Invest., 27,* 609 (1948).
33. R. J. Winzler and I. M. Smyth, *J. Clin. Invest., 27,* 617 (1948).
34. J. W. Mehl, J. Humphrey, and R. J. Winzler, *Proc. Soc. Exptl. Biol. Med., 72,* 106 (1949).
35. K. Schmid, *J. Am. Chem. Soc., 75,* 60 (1953).
36. J. L. Oncley, M. Melin, D. A. Richert, J. W. Cameron, and P. M. Gross, Jr., *J. Am. Chem. Soc., 71,* 541 (1949).
37. D. M. Surgenor, L. E. Strong, H. L. Taylor, R. S. Gordon, Jr., and D. M. Gibson, *J. Am. Chem. Soc., 71,* 1223 (1949).
38. O. H. Müller and J. S. Davis, Jr., *Am. J. Med. Sci., 220,* 298 (1950).
39. O. H. Müller, L. H. Gershenfeld, and M. J. Elwood, *Federation Proc., 11,* 110 (1952).

17.

Some Observations on Electrocardiographs and Electrocardiographic Leads *

FRANKLIN D. JOHNSTON † AND JEROME F. CORDES ‡

Although electrocardiographs capable of recording ordinary electrocardiograms with reasonable accuracy have been available since Einthoven devised the string galvanometer 50 years ago, many of the instruments in use today employ vacuum tube amplifiers and could not have been developed without the great advances in electronics of the past 20 years. The voltages produced by the heart are quite large compared with those arising from many other structures in the body and vary considerably with the type of lead employed. When electrodes are placed on parts of the body remote from the heart, as in the usual limb leads, voltages ranging from a small fraction of a millivolt (0.001 volt) up to a few (2–3) millivolts must be recorded. If an electrode is placed on the surface of the ventricle, voltages approximately twenty times as large as those mentioned above exist between this terminal and another electrode located some distance from the heart.

Figure 1 shows an actual electrocardiogram with the coordinates that are used to measure the voltage of different waves and the important intervals in the records. It is clear that the heart produces alternating voltages with a fairly complicated wave form. The *QRS* complex consists of relatively rapid changes in voltage, whereas the *P* and, especially, the *T* waves are waves of much lower frequency. To record voltages of this kind accurately, the electrocardiograph must respond faithfully to the low- as well as the high-frequency components of the tracings. The string galvanometer, of course, has a d-c. re-

* Some of the material included in this article was obtained with the help of a grant given to the late Dr. Frank N. Wilson by the S. S. Kresge Foundation.

† Professor of Internal Medicine, University of Michigan Medical School, Ann Arbor, Mich.

‡ Formerly Instructor and Research Associate in Internal Medicine, Heart Station, University Hospital, Ann Arbor, Mich.

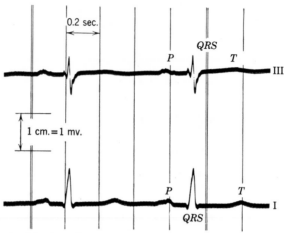

Fig. 1. Standard leads I (below) and III (above) taken simultaneously with a two-channel electrocardiograph employing a resistance-condenser coupled amplifier and mirror galvanometers. This instrument has an excellent response to high frequencies (nearly flat to 400 cycles per second) and the low frequency response shown in Fig. 2a.

sponse, and, with proper design of the amplifier, other electrocardiographs will record the low-frequency components without distortion. Figure 2a shows the decay curve when a millivolt is introduced into (and remains impressed on) the circuit of a well-designed electrocardiograph that employs a resistance-condenser coupled amplifier and has a mirror galvanometer as the recording element. It will be observed that the time constant is close to 2 sec. and that there is a short, nearly horizontal initial segment before the exponential part of the decay curve appears. It has been shown that any instrument with a low-frequency response of this kind will record the T waves without distortion.

Problems relating to the registration of the higher-frequency components of the electrocardiogram are more complicated, and their solution is more difficult. It is usually stated that the fundamental frequency of the QRS complex is around 15 cycles per sec. on which small voltages with frequencies up to 70 cycles per sec., or more, are superimposed. These small voltages are responsible for the notching and slurring so frequently seen on the major waves of QRS deflections. These statements refer primarily to tracings taken with limb or precordial leads where electrodes are not close to the heart. When an electrode is in contact with the heart, sizable voltages of high frequency, invisible or appearing only as notches in tracings taken with

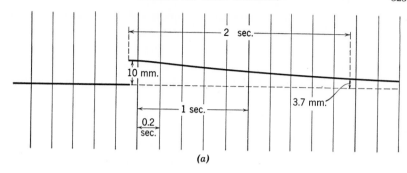

(a)

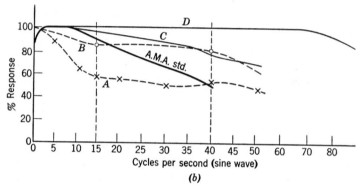

(b)

Fig. 2. (a) Illustrates the response of a well-designed electrocardiograph employing a resistance-condenser coupled amplifier and mirror galvanometers (see text).
(b) The heavy line illustrates the minimum requirements for high-frequency response of electrocardiographs accepted by the Council on Physical Medicine and
Rehabilitation of the American Medical Association. Curves A and B indicate
the response of two direct-writing electrocardiographs, and C and D the behavior
of a string galvanometer instrument with different string tensions (see text).

the conventional leads, may be recorded, if the instrument employed
has a sufficiently good high-frequency response.

These comments raise the question about the ability of electrocardiographs in common use to record the high-frequency waves in the electrocardiogram with sufficient accuracy. This question cannot be
answered with certainty at this time, largely because there is considerable doubt whether high-frequency voltages in ordinary limb and
chest leads have enough clinical significance to justify the use of the
more complicated and expensive instruments needed for their accurate
registration.

Langner, in a series of papers,[1,2,3] has described an electrocardiograph that records, with high fidelity, voltages arising in the heart and

has pointed out details of the QRS complex that may be of clinical importance not seen in tracings taken with conventional instruments. These studies were done with routine limb and precordial leads and, if supported by further work, may indicate that electrocardiographs must have a better response for high frequencies than is now true of many in daily use.

Several years ago, largely as a result of the development of direct-writing electrocardiographs, it was decided that standards for the performance of all electrocardiographs for routine clinical use should be established. A group of prominent cardiologists and physicists studied the many aspects of this problem and, in 1947, made recommendations that were accepted by the Council of Physical Medicine and Rehabilitation of the American Medical Association.[4] Among a number of other things, standards for the high-frequency response of the instruments were set up. These standards are shown in graphic form in Fig. 2b. In this figure the heavy curve represents the A.M.A. standard for high-frequency response and the other lines give the performance of two direct-writing instruments (curves A and B) and an electrocardiograph employing a string galvanometer as the recording unit (curves C and D). It will be observed that one of the direct writers is definitely poorer in performance than the other and does not meet the A.M.A. standard. This means it is inferior as an electronic or mechanical instrument but does not, for reasons outlined above, necessarily mean that it records electrocardiograms that are unsatisfactory for ordinary clinical work. It is astonishing that a mechanical writing element can be designed and built to move as quickly and to record the details of the QRS deflections as well as those employed in direct-writing electrocardiographs actually do. It seems unlikely that instruments of this type can be greatly improved as far as their response to high frequencies is concerned, and, should future developments make it clear that tracings taken with conventional leads contain high-frequency components of clinical importance, it may be necessary to employ mirror galvanometers, string galvanometers of special design, or even cathode ray oscillographs, for the recording elements in all electrocardiographs. This would, of course, imply the use of photographic registration of the records. The writer does not believe that this situation is likely to arise. Direct-writing instruments are already being employed by a great many physicians, probably by the majority of them, using electrocardiographic equipment, and, for ordinary clinical work, the records seem to be satisfactory.

A word should be said about the high-frequency response of the electrocardiograph employing a string galvanometer. Curves C and D

in Fig. 2*b* illustrate the behavior of a commonly used instrument of this type. Curve *C* indicates behavior of the string when its tension has the value used in the registration of the average electrocardiogram at normal sensitivity § with an interelectrode resistance of about 2000 ohms, whereas curve *D* shows the response of the string when its tension is increased to lower the sensitivity to one-half of normal, without any change in the resistance of the entire circuit.

These two curves illustrate how greatly the high-frequency response of the string galvanometer depends on the string tension and emphasizes that the ordinary electrocardiograph of the string type may not be any better than a direct-writing instrument in its performance at voltages of high frequency. As a matter of fact, if the resistance of the galvanometer circuit is very high, owing to high inter-electrode resistance, the high-frequency response of the string may be much poorer than that of any other type of electrocardiograph.

It has been suggested above that, when leads are employed with one electrode located on or very close to the heart, an electrocardiograph of special design should be used to be sure that voltages of unusually high frequency and amplitude are faithfully recorded. It may seem strange that the frequency, as well as the magnitude, of the electrocardiogram increases as an electrode approaches the heart. This is not the place to discuss this statement in detail, but, very briefly, it is true because voltages recorded from electrodes remote from the heart represent the resultant of e.m.f.'s existing at the same time and oriented in different directions in many regions of the heart. Under these circumstances rapid changes in voltage occurring in any local area in the heart are likely to be balanced more or less completely by opposed e.m.f.'s elsewhere in the heart or may be too small to be recorded. On the other hand, when an exploring electrode touches, or is very close to, the heart, electrical effects produced in nearby muscle are greatly exaggerated and very rapid changes in voltage of considerable magnitude may exist between this electrode and one remote from the heart. This does not mean that e.m.f.'s arising in more distant parts of the heart fail to influence the potential differences between the exploring electrode in question and an indifferent electrode.

A number of special clinical and experimental studies have been made in the course of which ordinary electrocardiographs, which were quite unsuitable in their high-frequency response for the work under investigation, were employed. Publications based on data of this kind

§ Normal sensitivity means that 1 mv. introduced in the galvanometer circuit will cause a deflection of 1 cm. in the tracing.

are likely to contain grossly incorrect statements and conclusions and help to swell an already over-voluminous medical literature.

Einthoven suggested the use of electrodes on the right arm, left arm, and left leg nearly 45 years ago and appreciated the unique character of leads employing electrodes on the extremities. He also understood the relationship between e.m.f.'s produced by heart and those existing between the extremities and recorded in the conventional bipolar limb leads. The equilateral-triangle scheme of Einthoven expresses this relationship, and no facet of electrocardiography has been subject to more misunderstanding and controversy. In spite of all the arguments about the validity of the Einthoven triangle concept, it continues to serve a useful place in clinical electrocardiography.

During the periods of electrical activity of the heart, voltages produced by this organ cause currents to flow through the heart itself and the tissues of the torso. The current density is naturally greatest in and near the heart, and it can be shown that currents do not flow for any appreciable distance into the extremities. The latter fact means that all regions of a single arm or leg have the same potential with respect to a reference point elsewhere on the body and this in turn is the reason why an electrode can be placed at any convenient place on an extremity without any alteration in the character of the tracing recorded. Einthoven appreciated this advantage of extremity leads, and it was one of the reasons for his selection of these leads for routine electrocardiographic work. When electrocardiograms are recorded from the precordium or when an exploring electrode is located close to the heart with leads of any kind, the precise location of this electrode becomes a matter of great importance. Even slight shifts of its position may alter significantly the character of the electrocardiogram that is recorded.

The Einthoven triangle scheme assumes that the human body is a large homogeneous volume conductor with a centrally placed heart having negligible size compared with the dimensions of the surrounding medium and that the points of attachment of the right arm, left arm, and the left leg to the trunk are equidistant from the heart and can be considered the apexes of an equilateral triangle. Figure 3a shows a somewhat fanciful representation of the equilateral triangle and how poorly it fits the human body. The heart is centrally placed in this diagram, whereas its center is actually definitely to the left of the midline in the human body. The construction within the triangle and on its sides illustrates the effect an e.m.f. in the heart, represented by *OE*, would have in the three standard leads I, II and III, if the

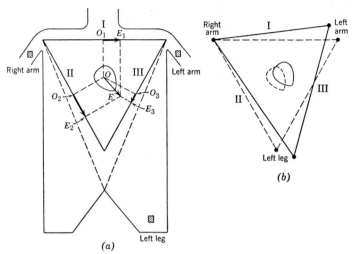

Fig. 3. (a) Diagram of the Einthoven equilateral triangle with the construction employed to relate an e.m.f. in the heart (OE) to those recorded in the standard limb leads I, II, and III. (b) The equilateral and oblique (Burger) triangles (see text).

assumptions underlying the Einthoven equilateral triangle concept were strictly true. Experimental studies by Burger and vanMilaan,[5] Wilson, Bryant, and Johnston [6] and others, however, indicate that an oblique triangle similar to that shown in Fig. 3b represents the actual situation in the human body much more closely than does the equilateral triangle. There are several reasons for this, most important of which is the eccentricity of the heart, specifically the fact that the heart is closer to the region of the left shoulder than it is to the right shoulder or to the attachment of the left leg with the trunk. Since the left ventricle, under many circumstances, contributes more than the right to the electrocardiogram, the effect of eccentricity is accentuated and the equilateral triangle is correspondingly inaccurate. On the other hand, when the right ventricle is hypertrophied and may therefore shift the effective electrical center of the heart toward the midline, calculations involving the use of the equilateral-triangle scheme are probably not so greatly in error.

Clinical electrocardiography is a curious mixture of rule-of-thumb reading by patterns and more intelligent interpretation based on knowledge of the electrical phenomena involved. The late Doctor Frank N. Wilson did a great deal to make electrocardiography a logical science by clarifying a number of fundamental electrical problems relating to the heart and by carrying out experiments that have made the records obtained in many cardiac abnormalities understandable even by the average practicing physician. In spite of over 30 years of intensive study, many basic and important things in connection with e.m.f.'s arising in the heart remain to be clarified. For example, the manner by which e.m.f.'s spread over the ventricles during excitation of these chambers is not clearly known even in the normal heart. It has been generally believed that activation occurs from the inside (endocardial) surface in a roughly radial fashion to the outside (epicardial) aspect of the ventricles, but even in subjects with normal hearts doubts have been raised about whether the process of excitation is not actually more variable and complex.

The situation relating to leading systems of different kinds has been even more confused and poorly understood. This has been particularly true in connection with leads used to take spatial vectorcardiograms. There has been great interest in the last years in the registration, by means of the cathode ray oscillograph, of loops that are supposed to represent the projection of e.m.f.'s existing in the heart on the frontal, transverse and sagittal planes through the center of the heart. Much has been written by some workers in this field suggesting that the use of this complicated method for displaying electrocardiograms is a new and powerful tool for the study of the voltages existing in the heart. Actually this is very far from being true, since vectorcardiograms must be recorded from electrodes (usually) on the surface of the body and tracings of the conventional type taken from the same electrodes (or from ones with better placement) have been familiar to experienced workers for a long time. It is true that vectorcardiograms provide figures that show clearly the effects of phase differences existing between the two voltages that give rise to them and may, at a glance, give some idea of the orientation of e.m.f.'s within the heart.

The concepts of the lead vector of Burger and vanMilaan,[5] the tubes of influence of Lepeschkin[7] and particularly the lead field recently described by McFee and Johnston[8] give us for the first time a rational method for the determination of the behavior of any type of lead and the knowledge necessary to design leads that may be far better, for certain applications, than those in common use. The idea of the lead field is beautiful in its simplicity. In Fig. 4a it is assumed that several small electrodes are applied to the precordium overlying the heart and a similar grid of electrodes is placed on the left posterior chest behind the heart. Each of the electrodes of the anterior and posterior grids are connected through large equal resistances to two terminals, A and B. If a battery is connected to these terminals, it is clear that currents will flow in approximately uniformly spaced parallel lines in an an-

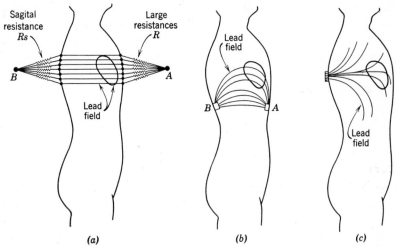

Fig. 4. (a) Ideal electrode system for obtaining the sagittal component of the mean cardiac e.m.f.'s. Note the character of the lead field. (b) Electrodes employed and lead field obtained with the cube system for recording the sagittal component of mean cardiac e.m.f.'s. (c) Electrode behind the heart with ones on the right arm, left arm, and left leg (central terminal) are used to obtain the sagittal component of cardiac e.m.f.'s when the tetrahedron system is used. Note how different the lead fields in (b) and (c) are from the desired field shown in (a) (see text).

terior-posterior direction through the heart. These lines represent the lead field of the lead in question. If this system of electrodes produces such a field within the heart then, by the reciprocity theorem, e.m.f.'s that are produced by the heart and are oriented in the anterior-posterior direction will be recorded most effectively by the same arrangement of electrodes. In other words, the grid system illustrated in Fig. 4a is the best available lead to obtain the anterior-posterior (sagittal) component of the mean cardiac e.m.f. In Fig. 4b and 4c the leads and lead fields in the commonly used cube and tetrahedron arrangements for obtaining the sagittal component of the mean cardiac e.m.f. are shown. It will be observed that the lead field associated with the electrodes used with the cube system (Fig. 4b) has marked curvature as it passes through the heart. This means that this lead is also sensitive to vertical (and probably transverse) components of cardiac voltages and is a poor arrangement to obtain the desired sagittal component. From the standpoint of their lead fields the electrodes of the cube arrangement to record the transverse and vertical components of cardiac e.m.f.'s are nearly as unsuitable as those for the sagittal component.

Nevertheless, the system has been extensively used by a number of workers.

The scheme involving the use of the tetrahedron is far superior to the cube setup, especially for registration of the transverse and vertical components, but, as will be seen from Fig. 4c, the lead field for the sagittal component leaves a good deal to be desired.

SUMMARY

Modern electrocardiographs are, in general, well-designed machines probably capable of recording ordinary routine tracings accurately enough for clinical purposes. This statement includes instruments of the direct-writing type. Under some circumstances, the high-frequency response of an electrocardiograph employing a string galvanometer may be poorer than that of a direct writer.

Special electrocardiographic studies in which one electrode is on or close to the heart should always be done with instruments that employ a mirror galvanometer with an excellent high-frequency response, a cathode ray oscillograph, or a specially designed string galvanometer as the recording element.

Although it has become clear that the equilateral triangle of Einthoven is a rather crude approximation to the situation existing in the human body, nevertheless, it has been and continues to be of value in clinical work. Studies by Burger and vanMilaan, Lepeschkin, and the related but simpler concept of the lead field suggested and elaborated by McFee have given us for the first time the tools we need to understand the behavior of leads of any kind and to design better ones.

REFERENCES

1. P. H. Langner, Jr., *Circulation, 5*, 249 (1952).
2. P. H. Langner, Jr., *Am. Heart J., 45*, 683 (1953).
3. P. H. Langner, Jr., *Circulation, 8*, 905 (1953).
4. Council on Physical Med., *J. Am. Med. Assoc., 134*, 455 (1947).
5. H. C. Burger and J. B. vanMilaan, *Brit. Heart J., 8*, 157 (1946) ; *9*, 154 (1947) ; *10*, 229 (1948).
6. F. N. Wilson, J. M. Bryant, and F. D. Johnston, *Am. Heart J., 37*, 493 (1949).
7. E. Lepeschkin, *Modern Electrocardiography*, p. 56, Williams & Wilkins Co., Baltimore, 1951.
8. R. McFee and F. D. Johnston, *Circulation, 8*, 554 (1953).

18·

Preoperative Electroencephalographic
Localization of Brain Tumors

B. K. Bagchi *

INTRODUCTION

The contrast between spontaneous pulsating electrical activity of
the living brain tissue and lack of such spontaneous activity in a theoretically equal mass of living but resting peripheral nerve fibers and
muscle tissues is something of a mystery to the physiologist, physical
chemist, and anatomist as well as to the electroencephalographer. Differential morphology and metabolism, though important, can explain
only in part the difference between these two masses. The ionic
changes in individual brain cells, ionic exchanges between the cells
and their immediate environment, and the nerve impulses that arise
in them of course depend upon chemical elements and complex processes of metabolism. But additional mechanisms are required if a
·living brain is to function properly. The mechanisms of almost instantaneous reception, selection, rejection, or collation of countless signals that come to or arise in the brain, of storing these signals subject
to immediate use, and of their massive integration and consequent
maintenance of dynamic equilibrium and purposeful directioning of
the entire system—these are only a few of the concepts that may be
postulated in connection with the brain. Chemically mediated, all
these processes would involve in addition intricate and elaborate "electrical" circuitry with constants and constituent parts. Although resembling in some respects an electronic automatic digital computor
with storage and controlling feedback properties,[63] a living brain is
obviously infinitely more complex than that remarkable automaton,
which is its handiwork.

* From The Neuropsychiatric Institute, University Hospital, University of
Michigan, Ann Arbor, Mich. This work was financed in part by the Horace H.
Rackham Fund.

The field of electroencephalography (EEG) cannot reveal all the electrical processes that go on in the brain. It deals only with summated expression of electrical discharges of individual nerve cells. Electrodynamics of each brain cell or of the entire brain is unknown and cannot certainly be equated with what is delivered by an electroencephalograph. Concepts of the nature, origin, controlling factors, and physicochemical significance of potentials of single brain cells or their aggregates are slowly evolving on the basis of many experiments. They have been dealt with by many authors.[1, 15, 17, 20, 33, 61, 62] Narrowly conceived, EEG is the art and science of recording brain potentials and interpreting these potentials in terms of cerebral physiology or clinical syndromes. Teamwork between the physiologist, anatomist, electronic engineer, biochemist, neuropathologist, and neurological surgeon will lead to much advance in the knowledge of this subject. At present we know more about the clinical correlation of brain potentials than about brain potentials themselves. Numerous studies or historical accounts are available on this subject of clinical correlation.[22, 29, 36, 37, 55, 57, 61]

This paper deals only with a small part of this correlation, namely, the correlation between brain waves and brain tumors. In particular, it seeks to point out electroencephalographic signs that are helpful in preoperative localization of intracranial tumors. Electroencephalography is an entirely non-traumatic diagnostic procedure and should always be used before such radical diagnostic x-ray contrast studies as arteriography, ventriculography and pneumonencephalography, which involve some amount of risk and morbidity. In some centers there has grown a very intimate cooperation between the electroencephalographers on the one hand and neurologists and neurosurgeons on the other to the benefit of both groups. In many places this rapport is lacking or is physically impossible. Although human brain waves were first recorded by Berger, a German neuropsychiatrist, in 1929, and although the possibility of localizing brain tumors was suggested by Berger and clearly indicated later by Walter, an Englishman, in 1936, it is only in the last decade or so that some of the large neurosurgical centers have adopted EEG as a routine procedure for localizing brain tumors.

Before elaborating upon the electrical signs found associated with brain tumors we may point out that alternating potentials in the form of alpha waves (8.5–12 per sec.) and beta waves (13–30 per sec.) are present in all normal brains or in normal areas (Fig. 1a: strips 1, 3, 5, 6; 1b: strips 5, 6, 7). The voltage varies between 5–120 and 5–25 millionths of a volt respectively. Modern researches indicate that the diffuse projection system of the thalamus (intralaminar nuclei and

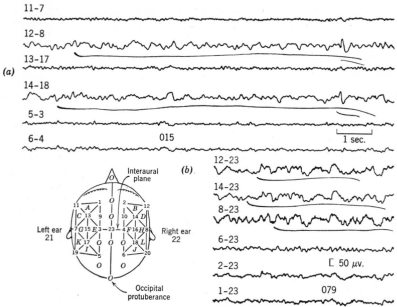

Fig. 1. Preoperative EEG of a 34-year-old patient, who was operated on for a large tumor (astrocytoma occupying right anterior and midtemporal and parietal regions and extending down into basal ganglia). No clinical localization. History of grand mal and psychomotor seizures without Jacksonian component. No headache, no papilledema. Attention was first directed to the presence of the focal lesion by EEG. Later studies: Cerebro-spinal fluid pressure was 150 to 180 mm. of mercury. Arteriogram and pneumoencephalogram were positive. Six-channel machine was used (*a*). Underlined strips 2 and 4 show in bipolar recording irregular mixed delta and theta 3–6 per sec. waves and rare spikes from the right temporal and neighboring regions but not from the corresponding regions of the left (strips 1 and 3). Parieto-occipital-motor bipolar recordings of left and right hemispheres are relatively clear (strips 5 and 6). (*b*) With vertex lead (23) as reference right anterior (12), "sylvian notch" (14), and midtemporal (8) leads show high-voltage irregular focal delta 2.5–4 per sec. waves (strips 1, 2, and 3). Right parieto-occipital (6), right and left frontal regions (2 and 1) are clear (strips 4, 5, and 6). Calibration of 1 sec. and voltage calibration of 50 μv. are given in this and succeeding figures.

reticular formation) and the core of the brain stem reticular formation in addition to hypothalamus have a determining influence on the normal electrical activity of the entire brain.[24, 25, 35, 38, 39, 47, 48, 51] This activity is presumably the result of a two-way influence, that is, a reverberation between the cortex and lower centers.[16, 27] However any aggregate of nerve cells of the brain insulated and isolated from the above-mentioned structures (thalamus, hypothalamus, brain stem) also have their own electrical rhythms if their blood circulation is kept intact.[28, 31, 42] The autorhythmicity of cell aggregates of different parts of the nervous system is a recognized fact.[2, 16, 18, 20, 44, 45, 47, 49, 50, 53, 56]

Individual brain cells may be conceived of as relaxation oscillators [32] producing beats or electrical pulsations, the character and rate depending upon the internal chemistry and geometry of the cells in relation to their environment. Each of the cells takes a finite time to build up an electrical charge in it like a condenser that it immediately discharges. This process repeating over and over again gives the rate of pulsations per second. This rate is also influenced by delay in conduction time across the synapses [61] and the characteristics of the network and the axons over which the impulses travel. The concept of scanning has also been related to some brain rhythms.[62] Much of this aspect of EEG is speculative or only an approximation to truth.

FOCAL EEG SIGNS

There are four types of waves that arise from the neighborhood of brain tumors. The brain tumors themselves are electrically silent or non-pulsating, though conductive. These focal waves originate from adjacent pathophysiologically disturbed, pulsating gray matter suffering from the effects of pressure, circulatory deficit, or irritation because of the presence of the tumor. These focal waves spread in different directions through the brain by neuronal propagation, volume conduction, or induction and can be picked up by leads placed on the scalp.

The first type of focal wave is the delta of 0.5–4 per sec. frequency, and of irregular voltage (Fig. 1b). The second type, theta wave, has a frequency of 4.5–7.5 per sec. (Fig. 1a). Near tumors of the upper convexity of the brain, the thetas, by themselves, are much less common than the deltas and should be considered as definitely atypical. The focal waves may occur frequently or only occasionally, may be medium or high in voltage, or may be simple or complicated in form or pattern. The exact mechanism of their production is unknown. They may be conceived of as due to summation of intrinsic slow beats of disturbed neurons or summation of normal but temporally dispersed beats of such neurons. The biochemical changes of these disturbed neurons need to be investigated by the chemists using appropriate techniques.

The third type of focal wave (an atypical pattern) has high-voltage spikes or fast activity of 10–20 per sec., occurring as single or multiple formation. These waves are, by themselves, found in not more than

1 or 2% of supratentorial tumors; but they may be seen mixed with slow delta or theta waves or slow undulations (Fig. 1a). The fourth type of spotting focal pattern is episodic- or consistent-voltage (or amplitude) increase of normal alpha waves of 8.5–12 per sec. to the

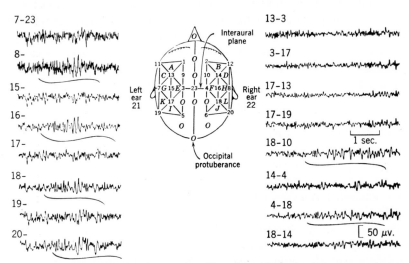

Fig. 2. Preoperative EEG of a 46-year-old patient who had a large tumor (astrocytoma) occupying the right lateral ventricle extending up under the motor strip. Progressive paralysis of left arm and leg over a period of 2 years, sensory anesthesia bilaterally in the distribution of T_{12}. No other neurological signs. The focus was suggested by EEG, but its nature was not correctly interpreted before operation. Eight-channel machine was used. Underlined strips (strips 2, 4, 6, and 8) on the left-hand side occasionally show increased voltage of alpha, beta, and some theta waves without deltas in the lateral aspect of the posterior quadrant of the right hemisphere compared to the corresponding regions of the left hemisphere (strips not underlined). The same increase of alpha or beta voltage is seen in underlined strips on the right-hand side (strips 5 and 7) but not in the corresponding areas of the left hemisphere (strips 4 and 2). This record had a predominant medium- to high-voltage beta (15 to 17 per sec.) background. Focal waves were seen occasionally in different runs. The appearance of alpha in a region against a predominant background of betas or increase of voltage of alpha against a background of alphas of lower voltage is a definite focal sign.

extent of 40–100% or more over the voltage of the corresponding unaffected region of the uninvolved hemisphere (Fig. 2). These hypersynchronous alpha waves without any associated deltas may be seen at the scalp within 5–15 cm. of the structurally involved area of the brain. Normally, homologous areas of the brain are supposed to function in a homologous fashion, hence amplitude asymmetry of alpha waves between homologous areas is a focal sign requiring elaborate technical work-up for accurate localization. Focal increase of alpha waves may be the only sign or the first sign of a growing brain tumor. If there are associated slow or delta waves in or near the region where there is unilaterally high alpha, that site is pathologically important. This does not mean that the low-voltage site is always unimportant, because it may at times be the site of "atrophy" where most nerve cells are dead and the remaining intact ones cannot together produce enough voltage, or it may be the site where subdural hematoma or a discrete superficial plaque-like tumor is present causing interference with conduction.

TECHNIQUE

Small solder pellet electrodes or other electrodes are placed on symmetrical points of the scalp and fastened with collodion, bentonite, or plastic electrode holders. Interelectrode distances should be the same in the corresponding regions of the two hemispheres. The electrodes are connected to a six-channel or eight-channel machine, which records pulsating voltage from as many places of the brain simultaneously. The electroencephalograph is a push-pull amplifying device capable of faithfully recording at least 0.5–70 per sec. waves and amplifying them to the extent of a million times. As brain waves are slow and feeble, a slow-period, high-amplification machine with high discrimination is an absolute necessity. Observations are sometimes made on a dual beam cathode ray oscilloscope.

Many techniques have been devised to localize brain tumors.[21, 22, 29, 30, 34, 55, 57, 58, 59, 61, 64] Bizarre techniques are sometimes encountered. Some techniques are adequate, some are not. Our technique has been mentioned elsewhere.[5, 7, 11, 12] A proper technique must concern itself with the following points (see also Table 1).

1. An adequate coverage of the scalp with leads (12–26), overlying not only each important lobe of the brain but different portions of each lobe, longest distance between two adjacent electrodes preferably not exceeding 8 cm., if an accurate localization (not simply lateralization) is desired.

2. An adequate electrode patterning (or array). This means recording voltages between different scalp leads and "indifferent" leads, such as ears (monopolar), or between different scalp leads themselves (bipolar), so that each particular area (or lead) is viewed some time or other, as it were, from different perspectives. In our scheme, each lead is recorded together with at least 6 or 7 reference leads. This is done for several purposes: to include or correct for, as the case may be, the effects of equipotentiality of two regions as recorded by push-pull amplifiers that cancel out synchronous common elements of signals be-

Table 1. Routine and Localizing Runs

(Actual recording time, a minimum of 60–90 min.; each run is for 2 to 4 min.)

8-channel 12-23 system

Routine runs: Routine monopolar

1. G_1: 1, 2, 3, 4, 5, 6, 7, 8
   G_2: 22 (both ears) *. . .
2. G_1: 1, 2, 3, 4, 5, 6, 7, 8
   G_2: 22 (right ear) †. . .
3. G_1: 1, 2, 3, 4, 5, 6, 7, 8
   G_2: 21 (left ear) ‡. . .

Routine bipolar

4. G_1: 1, 2, 3, 4, 7, 8, 7, 8
   G_2: 3, 4, 5, 6, 3, 4, 5, 6
5. G_1: 1, 2, 3, 4, 7, 8, 7, 8
   G_2: 3, 4, 11, 12, 3, 4, 5, 6

Photic stimulation

6. Repeat (4) or other setups.

Interaural coronal bipolar, posterior coronal, bipolar and monopolar

7. G_1: 7, 3, 4, 7, 8, 7, 5, 6
   G_2: 3, 4, 8, 22,* 22,* 5, 6, 8

Localizing runs: Anterior quadrants, bipolar and monopolar

8. G_1: 1, 2, 9, 10, 11, 12, 13, 14
   G_2: 23 (vertex) . . .
9. G_1: 1, 2, 9, 10, 11, 12, 13, 14
   G_2: 22 *. . .

23 electrodes for 23 positions. For additional positions unimportant electrodes are re-used.

10. G_1: 1, 2, 9, 10, 11, 12, 13, 14
    G_2: 22 †. . .
11. G_1: 1, 2, 9, 10, 11, 12, 13, 14
    G_2: 21 ‡. . .

Lateral aspect of posterior quadrants, bipolar and monopolar

12. G_1: 7, 8, 15, 16, 17, 18, 19, 20
    G_2: 23 (vertex) . . .
13. G_1: 7, 8, 15, 16, 17, 18, 19, 20
    G_2: 22 * . . .
14. G_1: 7, 8, 15, 16, 17, 18, 19, 20
    G_2: 22 † . . .
15. G_1: 7, 8, 15, 16, 17, 18, 19, 20
    G_2: 21 ‡. . .

Anterior-posterior bipolar

16. G_1: 11, 12, 13, 14, 1, 2, 9, 10
    G_2: 19, 20, 17, 18, 5, 6, 5, 6

Anterior triangles and other bipolars

17. Triangle A   Triangle B
    G_1: 11, 1, 13, 13, 14, 12, 2, 14
    G_2: 1, 13, 11, 9, 10, 2, 14, 12

Anterior lateral triangles and other bipolars

18. Triangle C   Triangle D
    G_1: 11, 7, 13, 7, 8, 12, 8, 14
    G_2: 7, 13, 11, 9, 10, 8, 14, 12

* Ground electrode setting: 21 and 22.
† Ground electrode setting: 22 (right ear).
‡ Ground electrode setting: 21 (left ear).

Interaural lateral triangles and other bipolars

19. Triangle G   Triangle H
    G_1: 13, 7, 17, 15, 16, 14, 8, 18
    G_2: 7, 17, 13, 9, 10, 8, 18, 14

Interaural parasagittal triangles and other bipolars

20. Triangle E   Triangle F
    G_1: 13, 3, 17, 17, 18, 14, 4, 18
    G_2: 3, 17, 13, 9, 10, 4, 18, 14

Posterior triangles and other bipolars

21. Triangle I   Triangle J
    G_1: 19, 5, 17, 3, 4, 20, 6, 18
    G_2: 5, 17, 19, 5, 6, 6, 18, 20

Posterior lateral triangles and other bipolars

22. Triangle K   Triangle L
    G_1: 19, 7, 17, 19, 20, 20, 8, 18
    G_2: 7, 17, 19, 15, 16, 8, 18, 20

23. Active leads with vertex reference, special triangles, multiple reference leads recording the same area simultaneously, are used, if needed.

24. Anterior triangle versus posterior triangle, if needed.

25. Special coronal bipolar setups, if needed—e.g.,
    G_1: 11, 1, 2, 19, 5, 6 (and two other bipolar setups)
    G_2: 1, 2, 12, 5, 6, 20

26. In parasagittal premotor or parietal or other localization, additional bipolar setup, if needed—e.g.,
    G_1: 9, 10, 3, 23, 4, left and right upper parietal and midparietal
    G_2: say 20 . . .
    (common reference lead)

27. Special extracranial reference lead (mid-cervical, neck, etc.) if needed. Also all areas of one hemisphere to contralateral ear, if needed.

28. Long-distance reverse polarity setup is used when needed to correct for possible equi-potentiality factor in previously mentioned short triangulations—e.g.,
    G_1: 5, 13, 5, 14, 5, 9, 5, 10
    G_2: 13, 6, 14, 6, 9, 6, 10, 6, etc., if lesion is suspected near 9 and 5 and 6 are clear.

29. So-called "posterior fossa work-up" for deep lesions, if needed. All monopolar. To check variability between anterior-posterior parasagittal regions, and parasagittal-lateral regions.
    G_1: 1, 2, 9, 10, 5, 6, 7, 8
    G_2: 22 *. . . or neck or midcervical reference lead. Keeping 1, 2, 9, 10, 5, and 6 constant, substitute 11, 12, for 7, 8, etc., until all leads have been used in pairs including left and right lower occipitals.

30. Hyperventilation with appropriate leads, if not contraindicated.

tween two such regions; to determine the anteroposterior extension and the over-all pattern of the delta waves; to cause 180° reversal of delta waves by placing the affected lead in opposite poles of two channels of the machine; to correct the findings from short contaminated triangles by the findings from large triangles, from long-distance bipolar recording with a common reference such as vertex, from long-distance phase reversal system; to compare the effect of a diffuse reference lead like an ear lead on a scalp lead with the effect on that scalp lead of another scalp lead used as reference; to correct for the effect of homolateral ear-lead reference contaminated by an adjacent lesion (e.g., in temporal lobe) by employing the uncontaminated contralateral ear lead as reference; to give enough time for a lead to show up its abnormal episodic wave; to include or correct for, as the case may be, the interelectrode distance effect on an area, etc.† The use of alternate ear lead as ground was first introduced in 1947,[7] then later adopted by others,[29] and facilitated by the incorporation of a device in the Grass Machine by the Grass Instrument Company. This method has now become standard in many laboratories.

On an eight-channel machine with two grids (G_1 and G_2) on each, numbered electrodes corresponding to locations on the scalp are employed. Combined routine and localizing work-ups are shown in Table 1, which are to be studied in reference to the electrode diagram, Figs. 1 and 2. They have been fully illustrated elsewhere.[5] A semilocalizing work-up omits such leads as posterior temporals (19 and 20) and lower motors (15 and 16) and premotors (9 and 10) and related triangles and linkages. Those who do not possess a 23-point electrode board and have only an 18-point one can re-use some of the unimportant leads for the full localizing work-up and omit altogether two areas represented by leads 15 and 16. The elaborate technique mentioned here does not preclude the exercise of the art, which develops with experience, of using other special electrode combinations for graphically bringing out an elusive focal pattern in an area.

3. Adequate sampling time (25–90 min. or more) in actual recording. It should be emphasized that a limited recording (a 20-min. work-up with 10 or 12 leads, scalp to ear or scalp to scalp recording) may be adequate in so-called idiopathic epilepsy or where sampling of general electrical functioning of the brain is desired but such a recording may be entirely inadequate when a brain tumor is to be ruled in or ruled out. Although this distinction is not absolute, failure to keep this fact in mind may lead one to underestimate the difficulty of

† As a rule, disregarding lobar specificity, voltage is a function of interelectrode distance until a plateau is reached at about 12–13 cm.[5,11]

preoperative localization of some brain tumors and the capacity of EEG to localize them if sufficient care is taken. Although it is true that many tumors (temporal and prefrontal) are easy to localize within a very short time (20 min.), if an ordinary technique is used, about 20–30% of tumors, especially in deeper parts of the cerebrum and parasagittal parietal regions, are not so easily localizable. They may show atypical focal signs or delayed typical focal signs that may be brought forth by the above-mentioned techniques. Most of the other supratentorial tumors fall between these two extremes. The value of an adequate EEG technique is impressed upon us by its use in over 4000 cases of verified or suspected focal intracranial lesions of one type or another. Also an adequate EEG work-up is essential for the purpose of gathering data that may be eventually useful in making a differential diagnosis of intracranial lesions on the basis of EEG alone. The art and science of EEG cannot advance without such a work-up.

A neurosurgeon may not operate only on the strength of EEG focal findings lest they prove to be non-surgical in significance. But it would be not only frustrating but almost disastrous for him to operate on the brain on minimal or questionable arteriographic, ventriculographic, or clinical focal evidence and not to find a tumor. Before a brain is opened by him for exploration, he should first order a non-traumatic diagnostic procedure such as a full-localizing EEG. If the EEG focal evidence supports in full or in part the clinical impression, then and then only should follow other radical diagnostic x-ray contrast studies, which are not always free from risk. Craniotomy is also attended with much coincidental danger. If an adequate localizing EEG fails to support the clinical impression of a focal lesion, a reassessment of all the findings should be in order for a final decision. This refers to cases suspected of having tumors particularly near the upper convexity of the cerebral hemispheres. Conversely, if EEG gives strongly positive focal evidence in absence of dependable clinical signs or other laboratory evidence of a brain tumor, the clinician should reevaluate the case, for example, of a candidate for air study or wait for further development and thus not relegate the case to limbo. EEG may furnish the first clue to the presence of a brain tumor when symptoms without signs are non-localizing in character. This has been our experience many times. In quite a few cases EEG suggested the localization of tumors 2 months to 4 years before they were verified by operation or at autopsy. In many cases EEG strongly influenced the adoption of other diagnostic studies. The report is often heard that in some places EEG has been of no particular value to neurosurgery. If that is true, it is not the EEG that is at fault but the technique and the interpretation employed by the electroencephalographer.

INTERPRETATION

In evaluating focal EEG signs corresponding regions of the two hemispheres should be compared. As a general proposition, it can be stated that if delta, theta, or other abnormal waves, mentioned before,

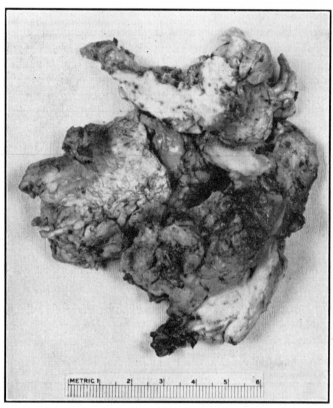

Fig. 3. Same case as in Fig. 2. Photograph of the tumor that was removed.

are present in one or two regions of one hemisphere and not in the corresponding region or regions of the other hemisphere, the focal condition is in the first hemisphere (Fig. 1a, b, Fig. 2). Findings of not one run or epoch but all runs or epochs of recording should be integrated for a total evaluation. As mentioned before, interelectrode distance, relative equipotentiality of neighboring focal regions and so-called diffuse "field effect" [5,7] introduce changes that may be different in different electrode settings, hence the evaluation of focal EEG waves depends upon a proper assessment of all findings from all electrode settings. This integrated evaluation is sometimes unnecessary, when the focal pattern is very outstanding, or is impossible, when the focal pattern is widely fluctuant or cannot be sharply distinguished from the general pattern. One of the ways to bring the focal pattern [58] into prominence is to put the focal or offending lead in opposite poles of any two channels to make the focal pattern appear 180° out of phase. This reversal of the phase of delta or other abnormal waves in a lead indicates that the "focal" area is under that lead. But one must remember that in all cases the electrically "focal" area may not be where the tumor is, because delta or other abnormal waves may spread through the brain and may be made to reverse in phase in other regions to which deltas have spread but where the focal lesion is not present. Delta waves due to edema may not be immediately subjacent to the lead where the reversal of deltas is taking place.[5] "Projected" waves from a deep posterior fossa tumor can also be reversed 180° by the reverse polarity arrangement, but the tumor is certainly not subjacent to the scalp leads. These limitations of the phase reversal system introduced by Walter [58] must be borne in mind lest misleading information about a focus be given.

When there are many slow or other abnormal waves in different areas of one hemisphere it is possible by using a number of methods (see Table 1) to identify the areas where they occur most frequently and on that basis to suggest whether the tumor is present anteriorly or posteriorly, laterally or parasagittally, in that hemisphere. Rarely is there false anterior or posterior displacement of a unilateral EEG focus. This is probably due to the factor of pressure, conduction, or edema giving EEG lateralization rather than localization of tumor. If idiopathic epilepsy, epilepsy due to brain damage or a vascular lesion, encephalitis, or pronounced generalized degeneration is clinically ruled out and if delta waves are bifrontal, bipremotor, or occasionally bitemporal in occurrence, a deep tumor on the midline, or a relatively superficial tumor with deep extension, is likely. The tumor may be in the deep anterior quadrant or in the posterior fossal region. More often than not under such a circumstance, there is a shift of such waves or theta waves or voltage increase between homologous regions of two hemispheres. That is, these waves are noticed in an area of one hemisphere at one time, then in the corresponding area of the other hemisphere at another time and vice versa, in the same or succeeding run. There may be over-all one-sided emphasis of such waves when the tumor is deep on the midline with unilateral extension. However, if there is no shift phenomenon but only biprefrontality of the bursts with some differences between two frontals, the tumor is usually on or near the surface anteriorly and sagittally. The shift phenomenon relative to delta, theta, and even alpha bursts is a very important clue because it suggests (1) a deep growing neoplasm or (2) a non-neoplastic deep pathophysiological trigger. Electrophysiological explanation of the shift is not forthcoming. True shifts of abnormal waves should not be confused with pseudoshift of abnormal waves arising particularly in lateral leads when an alternate ear ground is used for reference. When bilateral slowing is not present even with the use of one ear-lead reference contaminated by a homolateral lesion, pseudoshift of slow waves may occur episodically in the uninvolved hemisphere. This pseudoshift is due to (1) contamination of contralateral uninvolved hemisphere by contaminated reference ear lead and (2) pushpull cancellation of abnormal waves of the involved hemisphere by the same contaminated reference ear lead.[5]

Instead of uniform and simultaneous appearance of focal waves in one or two areas in a hemisphere, there may occur a fluctuation of focal waves between several areas (that is, one area fires while the other area does not, and vice versa) in the same quadrant or between areas of anterior and posterior quadrants of the same hemisphere. This phenomenon is termed "interareal variability" or "temporal dispersion." If this phenomenon is found in addition to a great many focal slow waves, much spread of these waves, some bilaterality of bursts and background slowing, coupled with clinical signs of increased intracranial pressure, a malignant or a deep cerebral tumor on one side is likely to be present. But, if only a few of the above-mentioned signs were seen, that prediction could not be made with as much confidence. Sometimes a non-neoplastic degenerative condition, due to thrombosis, hemorrhage, etc., or some other type of lesion, may also reveal the above-mentioned combination of signs. These statements about differential diagnosis of lesions of the brain on the basis of EEG alone should be taken as only tentative because often the same type and distribution of focal waves may be seen in different types of lesions.[5] There have been attempts at differential diagnosis, but the opinions are quite divergent.[41,57,64] However, if any one region exclusively [8] shows abortive 2–3 per sec. spike-and-waves or only sharply triangular deltas with positivity or negativity [40] and never any deltas of irregular form or voltage, chances are better than even that they do not represent a supratentorial tumor. As a group, discrete non-malignant tumors such as meningioma show less delta-wave spread over different areas and less interareal variability of deltas than infiltrating malignant tumors like glioma. These two broad tumor groups can often be differentiated from each other on this basis in a particular case if it is known on other grounds that the choice lies between them.[5] However, a sarcomatous meningioma, a very large meningioma, or a meningioma near the sagittal region blocking the venous return to the sagittal sinus and causing edema may behave like a malignant glioma. Rarely, some malignant tumors behave like meningiomas. It is not possible to distinguish between different types of malignant tumors on the basis of EEG findings.

ACCURACY OF LOCALIZATION

Seventy-three to ninety per cent of correct EEG localization of brain tumors has been reported.[21, 26, 30, 34, 57, 64] In many laboratories the figure is as low as 50–60%. Our over-all accuracy of preoperative localization (to the quadrant and/or to the lobe) and lateralization of 333 supratentorial tumors has been 83.7% (Table 2). If forty-two deep cerebral tumors (intraventricular and parachiasmatic) are ex-

TABLE 2. EEG LOCALIZATION OF SUPRATENTORIAL TUMORS

	No.	%	Correct No.	Correct %	Lateralized No.	Lateralized %	Equivocal No.	Equivocal %	Negative or False No.	Negative or False %
Meningioma	65	19.5	60	92.3	2	3.1	1	1.5	2	3.1
Astrocytoma	43	12.9	39	90.7	1	2.3			3	7.0
Ganglioglioma	9	2.7	8	88.8	1	11.1				
Metastatic carcinoma	20	6.0	17	85.0	1	5.0	1	5.0	1	5.0
Glioblastoma multiforme	93	27.9	79	84.9	7	7.5	2	2.1	5	5.4
Glioma, unclassified	20	6.0	16	75.0	4	25.0				
Oligodendroglioma	17	5.1	14	82.3			2	11.8	1	5.8
Sarcoma	6	1.8	4	66.6					2	33.3
Hemangioma	6	1.8	3	50.0			1	16.7	2	33.3
Craniopharyngioma	11	3.3	2	18.1	1	9.1	4	36.3	4	36.3
Pituitary adenoma	10	3.0	2	20.0			4	40.0	4	40.0
Spongioblastoma polare	7	2.1			2	28.5	2	28.5	3	42.7
Miscellaneous:										
Astroblastoma	3				2				1	
Melanoma	4		2				1		1	
Tuberculoma	3		2						1	
Neuroepithelioma	2		2							
Ependymoma	2		2							
Lipoma	1						1			
Metastatic sarcoma	1		1							
Colloidal cyst	1		1							
Papilloma	2				1				1	
Osteochondroma	1						1			
III Vent., unspecified	1								1	
Neuroblastoma	3		2						1	
Lymphosarcoma	1								1	
Pinealoma	1		1							
	333		257	77.1	22	6.6	20	6.0	34	10.2

279 or 83.7%

cluded from this group, the over-all accuracy of localization and lateralization increases to 91.6%. Olfactory-groove and sphenoid-ridge meningiomas are not included in the deep cerebral group. Unclassified gliomas have been localized or lateralized 100% of the time. Of the forty-two deep tumors only 33.4% have been localized or lateralized. Localization has been most accurate (92.3%) in cases of meningioma but poorest (18–20%) in such deep tumors as craniopharyngiomas, pituitary adenomas, or other parachiasmatic tumors. This failure is not due to technical deficiencies but probably due to the fact that, unless there is encroachment upon the inferior surface of the frontal lobe or the hypothalamus, pathological waves are either not produced or not projected to the scalp in these tumors. Secondary involvement of the basal ganglia does not cause any additional EEG change. Thalamic tumors which are lateralizable and sometimes localizable are different from the above mentioned tumors inasmuch as in the former cortical-petal-fibers may project slow waves to the homolateral side. They also produce shift phenomenon in the contralateral side but not as much as in posterior fossa tumor (see later). In our depth localization by EEG we rule out superficial involvement and suggest depth of the tumor on the midline or on one side without definitely indicating the actual structures involved. There is much more work to be done concerning deep tumors.

The tumors that are mentioned in Table 2 occupy different locations, the most common being in frontal and temporal regions. These tumors are easily localized. Sagittal bifrontal deltas can be technically reversed to the side of a superficial unilateral sagittal frontal tumor by reverse polarity frontal coronal setup (Table 1, run 25) or emphasized by alternate ear ground reference. Atypical theta signs [5] or delayed typical signs are often seen in parasagittal parietal tumors, which are usually difficult to localize unless much technical effort is made. (See Table 1.)

SUBTENTORIAL TUMORS

No clue to the preoperative EEG localization of subtentorial or posterior fossa tumors has been available in the literature dealing with EEG and these tumors.[14, 21, 43, 54] Indirect or "projected" EEG changes that are found associated with them are caused evidently by one or more of the following factors: disturbance of the thalamus and upper brain stem by ventricular dilatation, upward compression of the tentorium against occipital or temporal lobes, vascular congestion and functional aberration of cerebello-cerebral conducting system and brain stem reticular formation. The EEG changes are not only diffuse but varied and are difficult to interpret. The tentative EEG criteria that we proposed [9,10,11] sometime ago are helpful in suggesting preoperatively the existence of deep lesions including those that are in the posterior fossa. But these criteria are not as definitive as those that are available for the localization of cerebral tumors. These criteria have been established after checking them against the EEG findings on control subjects and thousands of epileptics and other patients. If the following clinical conditions are absent (clinical reservations) and the following EEG findings are present in a case, the possibility of a deep focal lesion such as one in subtentorial structures should be definitely considered.

Clinical reservations, the reasons for which are explained elsewhere,[11] are: absence of convulsive disorder, "temporal lobe" seizure, generalized cerebral "degeneration" with or without hypertension, absence of an acute condition such as encephalitis, trauma, or intracranial hemorrhage.

Electroencephalographic criteria are: (1) bilaterally synchronous alpha, theta, or delta bursts in anterior and/or posterior areas (Figs. 4 and 5); (2) anterior or posterior parasagittal concentration of these bursts (Figs. 4 and 5); (3) over-all unihemispheric emphasis of them in voltage, wavelength or incidence (Figs. 4 and 5); (4) occasional shift of bursts to the non-emphasized hemisphere irrespective of areas (Fig. 4); (5) anteroposterior or parasagittal-lateral variability of bursts (Fig. 5) including anterior displacement of the voltage of alpha.

The EEG work-up in these cases should be elaborate and should particularly include routine bipolar and so-called monopolar posterior fossa runs (Table 1). Exclusive anteroposterior bipolar recordings as done in some laboratories are not adequate because for one thing they are likely to cancel out some parasagittal bursts that are common in posterior fossa tumors.

Sixty-eight per cent of lateralized posterior fossa tumors with or without midline involvement showed over-all contralateral emphasis of bursts in the scalp leads. This may be considered as giving a slight clue to their lateralization preoperatively, although to a neurosurgeon this is not too important when he turns the suboccipital flap. Crossed cerebello-rubro-thalamo-cortical connection may in part explain the contralateralization. Unfortunately unilateral over-all emphasis was present in some midline posterior fossa tumors as well. Parenchymatous tumors and tumors in children often show more slowing than extraparenchymatous tumors such as cerebello-pontine-angle tumors. Parachiasmatic and anterior or posterior III ventricle tumors cannot

(a)
LF. Low cervical

(b)

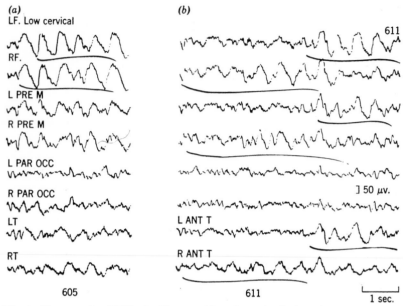

RF.

L PRE M

R PRE M

L PAR OCC

R PAR OCC

LT

RT

605

611

L ANT T

R ANT T

] 50 μv.

611

⌊___⌋ 1 sec.

Fig. 4. Preoperative EEG of a 51-year-old patient who had a subtentorial tumor (spongioblastoma polare in the IV ventricle extending into the left side). Patient was left handed. Six-month history of frontal headache, impaired memory, disorientation (organic brain syndrome), nystagmus, the right pupil larger than the left and reacting sluggishly to light, blurring of disc margins with hemorrhage at the right eye, slight weakness of right arm and leg, slight decrease of both corneal reflexes. The initial clinical diagnosis was a frontal tumor. Ventriculogram that demonstrated symmetrical enlargement of the lateral and third ventricles and displacement of the fourth ventricle to the right disproved the initial clinical impression and confirmed the interpretation of preoperative EEG findings. See below. EEG can often be of much help when the choice lies between a frontal and a subtentorial tumor. Eight-channel machine. (a) One-and-one-half to 2.5-per-sec. bursts are seen bilaterally with some emphasis in anterior parasagittal regions (strips 1 through 4). (b) In about a minute, overlapping shift of the bursts is noticed with an over-all emphasis on the right side (strips 2, 4, and 8). Complete shift of the bursts to the left hemisphere, which does occur, is not shown here. Variability between posterior parasagittal regions (strips 5 and 6) and anterior parasagittal regions (strips 1 through 4) are shown here. These and other findings not shown here were interpreted preoperatively as suggesting a deep focal condition probably in posterior fossa on the midline with a left-sided emphasis (contralateralization). No focal cerebral lesion near the surface could be suspected on the basis of EEG. See posterior-fossa criteria. LF, RF = left and right frontal (leads 1 and 2 in electrode diagram in Figs. 1 and 2), L and R PRE M = left and right premotor (leads 9 and 10), L and R PAR OCC = left and right parieto-occipital (leads 5 and 6), L and RT = left and right temporal (leads 7 and 8). Low cervical is reference lead.

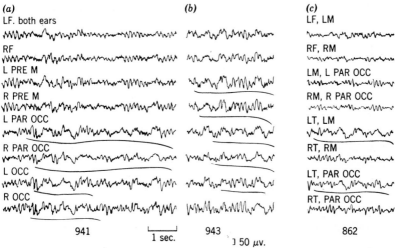

Fig. 5. Preoperative EEG of a 63-year-old patient who had a metastatic carcinoma occuping subtentorial structures (vermis, IV ventricle extending to the right cerebellum). After respiratory infection 2 months before first admission there was an onset of dizzy spells, bilateral tinnitus, falling to right, occipital headache, but no eye sign. Two weeks later at second admission neurological examination revealed papilledema, confusion, positive Romberg on right, weakness of left. The diagnosis of labyrinthitis was raised at first admission. EEG done at first admission directed attention to the possibility of a posterior-fossa lesion. Ventriculogram was negative. Eight-channel machine was used. (a) Posterior parasagittal areas of both sides (underlined strips 5 through 8) show many 1.5–2-per-sec. waves. (b) In 20 sec. both premotor areas (strips 3 and 4) share those waves with the above-mentioned areas (interareal variability). Frontals (strips 1 and 2) show less-slow waves. (c) In routine bipolar recordings (scalp leads linked with one another, ungrounded, Table 1, run 4) left side shows emphasis in delta waves (strips 5 and 7). Shift phenomenon is not shown here. These and other findings not shown here were interpreted preoperatively as suggesting a deep focal lesion probably in posterior fossa with right-sided emphasis (contralateralization). See posterior-fossa criteria. L and R OCC = left and right true occipitals (unnumbered empty circles, posterior to leads 5 and 6 in electrode diagram in Figs. 1 and 2). Both grounded ear leads (21 and 22) are tied for reference in (a) and (b).

be distinguished from posterior fossa tumors by these criteria. However, if, in addition to the above-mentioned EEG signs, there is associated convulsive disorder, a deep cerebral tumor such as a parachiasmatic tumor rather than a posterior fossa tumor is likely. Further, if the shift phenomenon is present between the areas of the anterior quadrants only, a parachiasmatic tumor rather than a posterior fossa tumor is probable, although most of the former type of tumors do not show any important EEG signs. Failure to obtain a definite clinical reservation would often disturb the EEG diagnosis of posterior fossa tumor.

In the case of 47 subtentorial lesions (not including 21 criteria cases) it was possible on the basis of the criteria to indicate correctly to the neurosurgeon before operation that in 34 of them (1) there was no superficial cerebral lesion and (2) there was a deep focal lesion, which was probably in the posterior fossa. In the remaining 13 cases EEG diagnosis was equivocal, negative, or false. As mentioned before, in about 68% of the cases, EEG lateralization corresponded with surgical lateralization. It is obvious from the above data that, although some progress has been made in an area in which EEG was previously considered as of no value to neurosurgeons, much work is needed to give more definitive information. Clinical findings should be correlated with EEG findings before posterior fossa diagnosis is considered.

CONCLUSION

It has been demonstrated that when used with care and thoroughness electroencephalography, in spite of its limitations, can be of much aid in the preoperative diagnosis of brain tumors. It is reasonable to suppose that further EEG data on patients and on experimental animals may in the future not only remove some of these limitations but reveal fundamental facts about the function of the normal brain.

Acknowledgment is due to Misses Hazel Calhoun and Mary Vogel for their valuable assistance in tabulation, recording and carrying out other details.

REFERENCES

1. E. D. Adrian, "The Physical Background of Perception," 95 pp., *Clarendon Press,* Oxford, 1947.
2. E. D. Adrian and F. J. J. Buytendijk, "Potential Changes in the Isolated Brain Stem of Goldfish," *J. Physiol., 71,* 121–135 (1931).
3. R. B. Aird and J. E. Adams, "The Localizing Value and Significance of Minor Differences of Homologous Tracings as Shown by Serial Electroencephalographic Studies," *EEG Clin. Neurophysiol., 4,* 45–60 (1952).

4. R. B. Aird and S. Bowditch, "Cortical Localization by EEG," *J. Neurosurg.,* *3,* 407–420 (1946).

5. B. K. Bagchi, "Electroencephalographic Localization of Intracranial Tumors," Chapter 3, in: *Correlative Neurosurgery* by E. A. Kahn, E. C. Crosby, R. C. Bassett, and R. C. Schneider, Charles C Thomas, Springfield, Illinois (1955).

6. B. K. Bagchi and R. C. Bassett, "The Localization of Intracranial Lesions by EEG," *Univ. Mich. Med. Bull., 9,* 86–87 (1943).

7. B. K. Bagchi and R. C. Bassett, "Some Additional Electroencephalographic Techniques for the Localization of Intracranial Lesions," *J. Neurosurg., 4,* 348–369 (1947).

8. B. K. Bagchi and R. C. Bassett, "The Problem of Electroencephalographic Contribution to the Differential Diagnosis of Localized Intracranial Lesions," *Trans. Am. Neurol. Assoc., 73,* 187–190 (1948).

9. B. K. Bagchi and R. C. Bassett, "Further Experience with EEG Localization of Posterior Fossa Lesions," *EEG Clin. Neurophysiol., 4,* 117 (1952).

10. B. K. Bagchi, R. L. Lam, and K. A. Kooi, "Examination of the Validity of New Empirical Criteria for the Localization of Posterior Fossa Lesions," *EEG Clin. Neurophysiol., 3,* 383 (1951).

11. B. K. Bagchi, R. L. Lam, K. A. Kooi, and R. C. Bassett, "EEG Findings in Posterior Fossa Tumors," *EEG Clin. Neurophysiol., 4,* 23–40 (1952).

12. R. C. Bassett and B. K. Bagchi, "Intracranial Neoplasm Localized Electro-encephalographically by the Use of a Three-Dimensional Scheme," *J. Neurosurg., 5,* 298–306 (1948).

13. H. Berger, "Über das Elektrenkephalogramm des Menschen," *Arch. Psychiat. Nervenkrankh., 87,* 527–570 (1929).

14. R. G. Bickford and E. J. Baldes, "The EEG in Tumors of the Posterior Fossa," *Proc. Cen. Soc. Clin. Research, 20,* 87–88 (1947).

15. G. H. Bishop, "Interpretation of Cortical Potentials," *Cold Spring Harbor Symposia Quant. Biol., 4,* 305–317 (1936).

16. G. H. Bishop, "Potential Phenomena in Thalamus and Cortex," *EEG Clin. Neurophysiol., 1,* 421–436 (1949).

17. M. A. B. Brazier, *The Electrical Activity of the Nervous System,* The Macmillan Co., New York, 1951.

18. F. Bremer, "Effets de la déafférentation complète d'une région de l'écorce cérébrale sur son activité électrique spontanée," *Compt. rend. Soc. Biol.,* Paris: *127*:355–359 (1938).

19. F. Bremer, "L'activité électrique spontanée des centres nerveux et l'électro-encéphalogramme: Essai d'interprétation," *J. belge neurol. psychiat., 47,* 9–28 (1947).

20. F. Bremer, "Considérations sur l'origine et la nature des "ondes" cérébrales," *EEG Clin. Neurophysiol., 1,* 177–193 (1949).

21. W. A. Cobb, "Intercranial tumors," in: *Electroencephalography,* Eds., D. Hill and G. Parr, 438 pp. (see pp. 273–301), Macdonald, Great Britain, 1950.

22. R. Cohn, *Clinical Electroencephalography,* McGraw-Hill Book Co., New York, 1949.

23. E. W. Dempsey and R. S. Morison, "Some Afferent Diencephalic Pathways Related to Cortical Potentials in the Cat," *Am. J. Physiol., 131,* 718–731 (1941).

24. E. W. Dempsey and R. S. Morison, "The Production of Rhythmically Recurrent Cortical Potentials After Localized Thalamic Stimulation," *Am. J. Physiol., 135,* 293–300 (1942).

25. E. W. Dempsey and R. S. Morison, "The Interaction of Certain Spontaneous and Induced Cortical Potentials," *Am. J. Physiol.*, *135*, 301–308 (1942).

26. R. S. Dow and Ray Grewe, "An Analysis of Failures in Electroencephalographic Localization in Expanding Intracranial Lesions," *Western J. Surg. Obstet. and Gynecol.*, *58*, 279–283 (1950).

27. J. G. Dusser de Barenne and W. S. McCulloch, "Functional Interdependence of Sensory Cortex and Thalamus," *J. Neurophysiol.*, *4*, 304–310 (1941).

28. F. Echlin, V. Arnett, and J. Zoll, "Paroxysmal High Voltage Discharges from Isolated and Partially Isolated Human and Animal Cerebral Cortex," *EEG Clin. Neurophysiol.*, *4*, 147–164 (1952).

29. F. A. Gibbs and E. L. Gibbs, *Atlas of Electroencephalography*, 1st ed., Vol. 1, 221 pp., Lew A. Cummings Co., 1941; 2nd ed., Vol. 1, 324 pp.; Vol. 2, 422 pp., Addison-Wesley Press, 1950.

30. F. A. Gibbs, D. Munro, and W. R. Wegner, "A Standard Electroencephalographic Technique for the Localization of Gross Intracranial Lesions," *New Engl. J. Med.*, *225*, 279–282 (1941).

31. C. E. Henry and W. B. Scoville, "Suppression-Burst Activity from Isolated Cerebral Cortex in Man," *EEG Clin. Neurophysiol.*, *4*, 1–22 (1952).

32. A. V. Hill, "Wave Transmission as the Basis of Nerve Activity," *Cold Spring Harbor Symposia Quant. Biol.*, *1*, 146–151 (1933).

33. H. Hoagland, "Rhythmic Behavior of the Nervous System," in: collected papers presented at *Centennial of American Assoc. for the Advancement of Science*, Washington, D. C., 1950, pp. 299–307.

34. P. F. A. Hoefer, E. B. Schlesinger, and H. H. Pennes, "Clinical and Electroencephalographic Findings in a Large Series of Verified Brain Tumors," *Trans. Am. Neurol. Assoc.*, *71*, 52–57 (1946).

35. J. Hunter and H. H. Jasper, "Effects of Thalamic Stimulation in Unanaesthetised Animals," *EEG Clin. Neurophysiol.*, *1*, 305–324 (1949).

36. H. H. Jasper, "Electrical Signs of Cortical Activity," *Psychol. Bull.*, *34*, 411–481 (1937).

37. H. H. Jasper, "Electroencephalography," in: *Epilepsy and Cerebral Localization*, W. Penfield and T. C. Erickson, x, 623 pp. (see pp. 380–454). Charles C Thomas, Springfield, Ill., 1941.

38. H. H. Jasper, "Diffuse Projection Systems: The Integrative Action of the Thalamic Reticular System," *EEG Clin. Neurophysiol.*, *1*, 405–420 (1949).

39. H. H. Jasper and J. Droogleever-Fortuyn, "Experimental Studies on the Functional Anatomy of Petit Mal Epilepsy," *Research Publs. Assoc. Research Nervous Mental Disease*, *26*, 272–298 (1947).

40. E. V. Jones and B. K. Bagchi, "Electroencephalographic Findings in Verified Thrombosis of Major Cerebral Arteries (14 cases)," *Univ. Mich. Med. Bull.*, *17*, 295–310 (1951).

41. J. Kershman, A. Conde, and W. C. Gibson, "Electroencephalography in Differential Diagnosis of Supratentorial Tumors," *Arch. Neurol. Psychiat.*, *62*, 255–268 (1949).

42. K. Kristiansen and G. Courtois, "Rhythmic Electrical Activity from Isolated Cerebral Cortex," *EEG Clin. Neurophysiol.*, *1*, 265–272 (1949).

43. G. C. Lairy-Bounes and H. Fischgold, "L'electroencéphalographie dans une série de trente-huit tumerus de la fossa postérieure," *Sem. Hop. Paris*, *26*, 2633–2635 (1950).

44. B. Libet and R. W. Gerard, "Automaticity of Central Neurones after Nicotine Block of Synapses," *Proc. Soc. Exptl. Biol. Med., 38,* 886–888 (1938).
45. B. Libet and R. W. Gerard, "Control of the Potential Rhythm of Isolated Frog Brain," *J. Neurophysiol., 2,* 153–169 (1939).
46. D. B. Lindsley, J. W. Bowden, and H. W. Magoun, "Effect upon the EEG of Acute Injury to the Brain Stem Activating System," *EEG Clin. Neurophysiol., 1,* 475–486 (1949).
47. R. S. Morison and D. L. Bassett, "Electrical Activity of Thalamus and Basal Ganglia in Decorticate Cats," *J. Neurophysiol., 8,* 309–314 (1945).
48. R. S. Morison and E. W. Dempsey, "A Study of Thalamo-cortical Relations," *Am. J. Physiol., 135,* 281–292 (1942).
49. R. S. Morison and E. W. Dempsey, "Mechanism of Thalamo-cortical Augmentation and Repetition," *Am. J. Physiol., 138,* 297–308 (1943).
50. R. S. Morison, K. H. Finley, and G. N. Lothrop, "Spontaneous Electrical Activity of Thalamus and Other Forebrain Structures," *J. Neurophysiol., 6,* 243–254 (1943).
51. G. Moruzzi and H. W. Magoun, "Brain Stem Reticular Formation and Activation of the EEG," *EEG Clin. Neurophysiol., 1,* 455–473 (1949).
52. S. A. Obrador, "Effect of Hypothalamic Lesions on Electrical Activity of Cerebral Cortex," *J. Neurophysiol., 6,* 81–84 (1943).
53. C. L. Prosser, "Rhythmic Activity in Isolated Nerve Centers," *Cold Spring Harbor Symposia Quant. Biol., 4,* 339–346 (1936).
54. M. B. Rheinberger and L. M. Davidoff, "Posterior Fossa Tumors and EEG," *J. Mt. Sinai Hosp., N. Y., 9,* 734–754 (1942).
55. R. S. Schwab, *EEG in Clinical Practice,* W. B. Saunders Co., Philadelphia, 1951.
56. E. A. Spiegel, "The Electrothalamogram: Comparison of the Thalamic, Cortical, and Cerebellar Potentials," *Trans. Am. Neurol. Assoc., 62,* 53–55 (1936).
57. H. Strauss, M. Ostow, and L. Greenstein, *Diagnostic EEG,* Grüne and Stratton, New York, 1952.
58. W. G. Walter, "The Location of Cerebral Tumors by EEG," *Lancet, 2,* 305–308 (1936).
59. W. G. Walter, "EEG in Cases of Cerebral Tumor," *Proc. Roy. Soc. Med., 30,* 579–598 (1937).
60. W. G. Walter, "Discussion of the EEG in Organic Cerebral Disease," *Proc. Roy. Soc. Med., 41,* 237–250 (1948).
61. W. G. Walter, "Introduction, Technique, and Interpretation," in: *Electroencephalography,* Eds., D. Hill and G. Parr, 438 pp. (see pp. 1–91), Macdonald & Co., London, 1950.
62. W. G. Walter and Vivian J. Walter, "The Electrical Activity of the Brain," *Ann. Rev. Physiol., 11,* 199–230 (1949).
63. N. Wiener, *Cybernetics or Control and Communication in the Animal and the Machine,* John Wiley, New York, 1948.
64. C. L. Yeager and S. Luse, "EEG Localization and Differentiation of Lesions of Frontal Lobes; Pathological Confirmation," *Arch. Neurol. Psychiat., 54,* 197–201 (1945).

19.

Electrical Signs of Epileptic Discharge

HERBERT H. JASPER *

It seems very appropriate that the Electrochemical Society should sponsor a symposium on bioelectric phenomena. The electrical activity of the nervous system has been under observation with steadily improving apparatus for over 50 years. The electrical activity of the brain has been under intensive investigation for about 25 years. Countless nerve impulses, synaptic potentials, brain waves, and muscle action potentials have been accurately recorded with precise electronic devices. All agree that they are electrochemical events. During recent years discoveries of considerable importance have begun to suggest their fundamental nature.

In the nerve fiber the movement of Na and K ions across the nerve membrane by means of an unknown molecular transport system, which requires oxidative metabolism for its maintenance, gives us the best account to date of the generation and conduction of the nerve impulse.[1] Conduction across synapse or from nerve to muscle seems to require special chemical transmitter substances such as acetylcholine. But much remains to be explained.

The nerve membrane, at rest, is maintained in a more or less stable electrochemical equilibrium. When this equilibrium is momentarily upset, excitation results, but within a few milliseconds equilibrium is normally reestablished. The process of excitation is being constantly opposed by the process of accommodation. When accommodation is defective, such as in a nerve treated with decalcifying agents, the nerve may undergo spontaneous discharge and we have the condition known as tetany. This phenomenon has received no satisfactory electrochemical explanation.

---

* From Department of Neurology and Neurosurgery, McGill University and the Montreal Neurological Institute.

CLINICAL AND ELECTRICAL PATTERNS OF EPILEPTIC SEIZURES [2]

Uncontrolled hyperexcitability and spontaneous repetitive discharge of nerve cells within the central nervous system are at the basis of epileptiform disorders of the brain. Convulsive seizures are the most dramatic manifestation of the massive excessive discharge of brain cells that takes place during an epileptic attack. This result occurs only when those parts of the brain connected with motor pathways are involved.

Discharges in sensory areas cause the patient to experience various forms of sensation: tingling of the fingers, a buzzing noise in the ears, spots of light before the eyes, a bad smell or a strange feeling in the pit of the stomach may also result from local epileptic discharge in specific areas of the brain. Or, there may be only a brief lapse of consciousness such as in the so-called petit mal attack.

Peculiar illusions of perception may also occur; things may appear smaller and farther away, or larger, or one may have the strange feeling of having seen or heard all of this before. These are caused by discharges occurring in the temporal lobe where many other complex epileptic phenomena also occur, such as dreamlike hallucinations, and episodes of inappropriate automatic behavior with amnesia, the so-called *psychomotor* attack.

These are only a few of the many forms of epileptic seizure that may occur depending upon functions subserved by the various centers and circuits in the brain whose neuronal aggregates become involved in epileptic discharge. It is likely that the epileptic process is essentially the same in all types of seizure, i.e., the basic electrochemistry is probably the same. In many, the electrical signs of epileptic discharge are also the same, except for localization. Differences in form and frequency of electrical discharge do occur, however. It is thought that these differences are largely due to the functional properties and connections or circuits over which the epileptic discharge is propagated rather than to any fundamental difference in the nature of the epileptic process itself in individual neurons.

The electrical signs of epileptic discharge, as seen in the electroencephalogram recorded from the surface of the scalp in epileptic patients, or in the direct cortical electrogram taken from electrodes placed on the exposed cortex at operation, shows a rather wide variety of patterns. In general, most epileptic seizures begin by a gradual or sudden increase in the voltage of the electrical activity of the cortex, which may reach five to ten to even twenty times the voltage of the resting rhythmic activity that was present before the attack.

There are, however, certain types of seizure whose onset is marked not by an increase in voltage but rather by a decrease in voltage of activity as recorded on the surface of the cortex. In these cases even

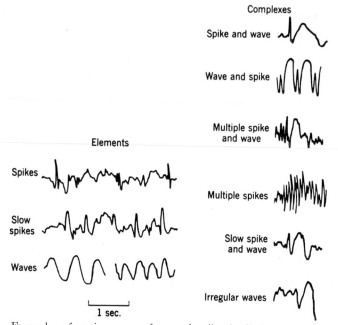

Fig. 1.   Examples of various wave forms of epileptic discharge as seen in the electroencephalogram taken from patients with epilepsy.

though there may be sporadic epileptic discharge without a clinical attack, the onset of the clinical attack itself is marked by a disappearance of epileptic activity and a flattening of the electrical record rather than an increase in voltage of the abnormal waves recorded from the surface of the cortex. These have been called "electrically silent seizures," but they are far from silent when recorded with microelectrodes in the depths of the cortex, as will be described later.

The abnormal waves themselves may take various forms. Some of these forms have been given names such as spikes, sharp waves or slow spikes, spike and wave complexes, rhythmic slow waves, and so forth, and are illustrated in Fig. 1. It has been proposed by some investigators that the form of epileptic seizure bears a close relationship to the form of the electrical pattern of discharge during the attack.[3] Thus, a most characteristic pattern, the 3-per-sec. rhythmic spike and wave sequence, is thought to be identified with a petit mal seizure that clinically is characterized by an impairment or lapse of consciousness (Fig. 2). The rapid repeated spikes or rapid waves are thought to be characteristic of the grand mal seizure or the major convulsion (Fig. 2). Seizures that are marked by rhythmic slow waves

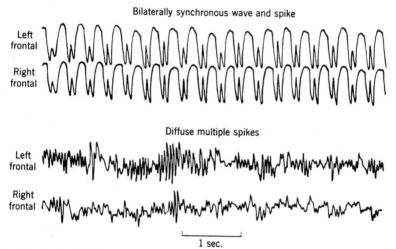

Fig. 2. Typical EEG tracing from left and right frontal regions (ear reference) of patient with petit mal seizures, upper two lines, and from a patient with generalized grand mal attacks, lower two lines.

at 2 to 4 or 6 per sec. have been called psychomotor because it is commonly observed that this pattern occurs during an attack in which the patient exhibits various mental disturbances with automatic behavior and amnesia (Fig. 3).

These relationships of electrical wave form to the pattern of the clinical attack are true only when related to the localization of these discharges in the brain. The spike and wave sequence is consistently associated with a petit mal seizure only when it appears synchronously from left and right hemispheres and of maximum voltage in frontal or frontal and parietal areas of the brain on both sides. When it occurs from a local area, such as in the motor area, it may be of a similar form, but it is not associated with a clinical attack which might be called petit mal but rather with a Jacksonian motor seizure. Likewise, the rapid discharges, as observed in major convulsive seizures or grand mal, may be also recorded from a local area of the cortex

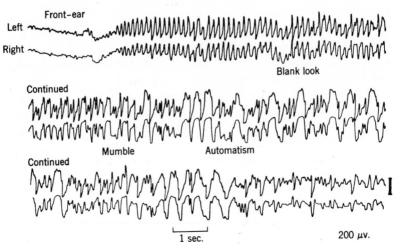

Fig. 3.   EEG tracing from left and right frontal regions (ear reference) during a psychomotor attack.

during a focal cortical seizure, which may or may not spread over the surface of the cortex to become a generalized attack. Seizures arising in the temporal lobe have most peculiar electrographic forms since they frequently begin by a depression in electrical activity which may be followed by rhythmic slow waves during the attack itself.

Do these various patterns of electrical activity represent different neurophysiological or even possibly electrochemical events in the brain, or are they due only to the organization of electrical discharge in the various neuronal aggregates and circuits that make up the complicated network of neurons contained in the cortex and their relationship with subcortical structures? We cannot give a final answer to this question, but it seems most likely, from present evidence, that both the biochemical environment of brain cells and their functional interrelationships are important in determining the over-all pattern of gross electrical activity seen in the usual electroencephalogram or electrocorticogram.

It has been said that the clinical manifestation of the attack depends upon the functions subserved by that particular portion of the brain primarily activated or engulfed by the epileptic discharge. It must be added, however, that it depends also upon the physiological effect of this discharge and the subsequent fatigue or depression in activity that follows it. The active phase of the discharge may produce three different kinds of effect upon neuronal aggregates subserving a specific or generalized brain function: (1) activation, (2) interference or functional blockage by occlusion, and (3) inhibition. Postictal effects, when present, are usually of a paralytic nature.

The positive effects of activation have been discussed above. No such positive effect may result, however, from the same form of epileptic discharge in the anterior frontal region, or in the parietal areas, or with local epileptic discharge in the speech areas of the left hemisphere. This discharge causes aphasia, not speech. Interference with complex intellectual functions may be the only result of epileptic discharge in anterior frontal areas, and loss of sensory discrimination ability may be the only effect of local discharge in the parietal region. These symptoms are apparently due to the epileptic blocking of neuronal circuits necessary for complex mental functions.

The presence of epileptic discharge in definitely inhibitory systems of the brain is less certain, particularly since so little is known of the neurophysiology of central inhibition. There is growing evidence, however, that some "brain waves" do have an inhibitory rather than an excitatory effect upon cortical cell discharge. Jung and Tönnies [4] have described these as "Bremswelle." It has been suggested that the slow wave that follows the spike in the spike-end-wave complex of petit mal epilepsy may have an inhibitory or blocking action, preventing the development of a convulsive seizure. Some support is given for this conception in recent microelectrode studies being carried out with Dr. Li in the laboratories of the Montreal Neurological Institute.

MICROELECTRODE STUDIES OF EPILEPTIC DISCHARGE

During recent years there has been a renewed interest in the unit analysis of the activity of the brain by the use of microelectrodes capable of recording the activity from single nerve cells. This method applied to the cerebral cortex has yielded quite a different picture of the electrical activity of the brain than was apparent from the records obtained with gross electrodes on the cortical surface.[5,6] It is clear that one cannot detect the discharge of single cortical cells by gross surface electrography. Many of the electrical waves recorded on the surface are not associated with cortical cell discharge. Furthermore, there may be very active asynchronous cell discharge in the absence of electrical signs on the surface. We cannot enter into the details of such studies, but we will mention briefly only a few of the results bearing upon the interpretation of the electrical activity of the brain during epileptic discharge.

The electrical waves making up the usual electroencephalogram or electrocorticogram are a minimum of 10 to 20 msec. in duration. The brief spikes recording with an intracortical microelectrode from single neurons are less than 1 msec. in duration. The so-called "epileptic spikes" seen in the electroencephalogram are usually at least 20–40 msec. in duration. On the negative peak of an "epileptic spike" such as that produced by local application of strychnine to the surface

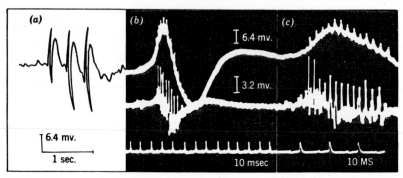

Fig. 4. Unitary cortical cell discharge recorded with microelectrodes in the depths of the cat's cortex, which had previously been treated locally with a 1% strychnine solution. (*a*) At the left is shown the ink-writing oscillographic tracing of a spike and wave sequence recorded from the cortical surface. (*b*) Here two microelectrode tracings are shown, the upper one with a longer-time-constant amplifier to show the slow waves and the lower one with a shorter-time-constant amplifier at twice the gain to show the unitary spikes on the negative peak of the strychnine wave. (*c*) Another strychnine spike taken at higher sweep speed. Note that unit discharge occurs at about 500 per sec.

of the cortex there may appear a burst of high-frequency unit-cell discharges, as shown in Fig. 4. Repetitive firing of single units may reach over 800 per sec. in the brief burst occurring on the peak of a strychnine "spike." Normally, cortical cells do not fire repetitively at frequencies over about 50–60 per sec., and more commonly they fire at the rate of only 10–20 per sec. Thus, it is clear that excessive rapid repetitive discharge of single cortical cells is a feature of the epileptic process. However, the slow wave that sometimes follows the strychnine "spike" may not be associated with any firing of cortical cells; in fact they may be inhibited as shown in Fig. 4*b*.

During epileptiform after-discharge that follows electrical stimulation of the cerebral cortex there may also be excessive discharge of cortical cells, even when the surface record shows no high-voltage electrical activity. In fact, the development of rhythmic high-voltage slow waves may be associated with a diminution of unit-cell discharge, each slow wave apparently interrupting what would otherwise be a more continuous unit discharge.

Such observations as those described above have led us to the conclusion that there are at least two forms of electrical activity of the cortex; one is associated with some form of membrane polarization phenomena in the synaptic network of the cortex, and the other represents the actual firing of cortical cells. The former we have tentatively called "synaptic potentials" or electrical field potentials. They regulate cortical excitability in a complex manner, but they cannot be identified with the actual discharge of cortical neurons. We believe that an analysis of the biochemical and neurophysiological mechanisms of epileptic discharge will have to take into account both of these factors, i.e., the excitability and discharge of nerve cells and the alterations in membrane polarization in the synaptic networks of the cortex, before much progress can be made in our understanding of the basic mechanisms of epileptic discharge.

In closing, I would like to emphasize that epileptic disorders are only disturbances in the mechanisms controlling the activity of ganglion cells and the transmission of impulses in synaptic centers under normal conditions. Acetylcholine and similar transmitter substances in the central nervous system may also play an important role in epileptic discharge. Likewise disturbances in ionic balance and metabolic factors affecting nerve membranes under normal conditions must be sought for in the investigation of the biochemical bases of epileptic processes.

REFERENCES

1. J. C. Eccles, *The Neurophysiological Basis of Mind,* The Clarendon Press, Oxford, 1953.
2. W. G. Penfield and H. H. Jasper, *Epilepsy and the Functional Anatomy of the Human Brain,* Little, Brown & Co., Boston, 1954.
3. F. A. Gibbs, and E. L. Gibbs, *Atlas of Electroencephalography,* Addison-Wesley Press, Cambridge, Mass., 1952.
4. R. Jung and J. F. Tönnies, "Hirnelektrische Untersuchungen über Entstehung und Erhaltung von Krampfentladungen: Die Vorgänge am Reizort und die Bremsfahigkeit des Gehirns," *Arch. Psychiat. Nervenkrankh., 185,* 701–735 (1950).
5. C. Li, H. McLennan, and H. H. Jasper, "Brain Waves and Unit Discharge in Cerebral Cortex," *Science, 116,* 656–657 (1952).
6. C. Li and H. H. Jasper, "Microelectrode Studies of the Electrical Activity of the Cerebral Cortex in the Cat," *J. Physiol., 121,* 117–140 (1953).

INDEX